THE
TIMELESS LOVE
OF
TWIN SOULS

JANET KAY DARLING
&
PHILLIP GEORGE

THE TIMELESS LOVE OF TWIN SOULS

www.thornepublishing.com

Editing & Book Design : Thorne Media & Art
Artwork & Cover Design: Thorne Media & Art
Photo : Jentz Photography, Lansing, MI USA
Paperback edition   : ISBN 978-0-9926094-0-5
Audio Book edition : ISBN 978-0-9926094-2-9
eBook edition (Kindle) : ISBN 978-0-9926094-1-2
eBook edition (EPUB) : ISBN 978-0-9926094-3-6

This book is dedicated to my husband
Beloved Ron Ascended

- Foreword -

You may ask - what exactly is a Twin Soul and, who are Twin Souls or even 'why' are there Twin Souls at all? It's also reasonable to ask, as I did, where the idea of Twin Souls came from in the first place and why don't we know more about them than we do now? These are all important questions and ones where the answers will lead you to places that you never expected to go. I know this because I've been there and it's changed my life in the most incredibly wonderful way as a result. In the past there have been many attempts to adequately define this illusive and mysterious aspect of our existence but due to the very nature of the subject itself it has been difficult to put into words in any meaningful way. Until now that is.

There are very few guidelines which can be applied to something which appears almost as though it exists solely in the angelic realms, although this is actually not the case at all. Throughout our history there have been many references to this subtly compelling dynamic of our individual existence, where various terms have been applied to this state of being which implies that we are somehow separate from an unspecified 'something'. A state of existing outside of a spiritual law which appears to assert that you are an important part of something else; a completeness. An eternal Oneness that you are an integral half of or an essential element of; a 'total loving being' which is much more than the sum of who you already are while just being you.

A certain uniquely indefinable something which you have an inexplicable longing to be re-united with but which is unknown or unknowable to you; until that moment when you blissfully discover its long forgotten magic. A state which speaks to you in hushed tones of a deeply intimate togetherness where a part of you listens with interest, although not fully understanding why. That part of you which has deliberately chosen not to remember in order that you can live out certain stages of the life, which you have elected to experience, so that you are able to evolve in the most beneficial spiritual way possible. But, what is this 'something' which is missing? It surely is a paradox which has remained hidden from the forefront of mankind's collective consciousness for a very long time.

Some people refer to it as 'my other half', 'my soul mate', 'my one true love' or 'my twin flame' where even as far back as the times of Plato he made references in his writings to a 'split apart'. You may say, but what does this mean in terms that I can understand? What was he referring to and who was I before I became less than that which I had been or who I am now?

Plato was a philosopher who had always been deeply interested in the origins of humanity and the mysteries of the universe, so there must have been a good reason for him to refer to the individual as being split apart from a certain something; a previous state of some other preferred way to exist. Maybe he knew what that certain state of 'being' had been before the 'dividing' by whatever it was that split it apart. Unfortunately, mankind has had to stumble blindly on through the ages without any true understanding of just exactly what Plato had gained an insightful awareness of; until now that is.

In this respect it's quite natural to ask ... Am I a 'split apart' and do I have a Twin Soul and, if so, how do I go about finding him or her if he or she exists? Is it important for me to go looking for my twin soul if she or he is present in this world right now? Or maybe more importantly ... what am I missing through being without my 'Other Half' and how do I know when or if I've actually found him or her?

These are all questions which have answers but which have had very little in the way of information published on the subject or even hinting at the concept for that matter. Until recently, precious little was known about this most fascinating aspect of our humanity as there were only very few to tell their stories or to even give advice and guidance in any meaningful way.

There has been a reason for this, so I have discovered, in that the consciousness of mankind in general has been such that it has not been receptive to the finer vibrations of what constitutes the energy of a twin soul. Now, the world is experiencing a new energy transformation in which all of our vibrations are being raised and so, at this point on our journey, we can begin to discern in a much more self aware manner the truly Divine nature of ourselves.

Through understanding twin souls then you will find your way much closer to a deeper appreciation of this aspect of yourself. What you are about to read will not only address the captivating issue of twin souls but it will also help you to get a much better and more complete insight into many aspects of your life which you may not have been aware of before now. More than this, you will hopefully gain a greater awareness of matters which extend far beyond this life that you are leading. In so doing you will be gently guided to a new and exciting appreciation of a life without limitations. It will hopefully be a very freeing experience for you and one which I am certain that you will find quite compelling.

My amazing journey through this life, and what I have discovered through living it, has given me a deep and abiding appreciation for so many things; but the most magical of all was to discover my twin soul. How I achieved this resulted in my also learning about how to follow my heart and then trusting to what I felt intuitively guided by; even in the face of a social environment which didn't fully support what I instinctively believed. There were many challenging twists and turns along my journey but I persevered in order to find my true love. In so doing I found a heavenly happiness which exceeded even my most heartfelt wishes in the process. What happened to me, what I did and what I discovered along the way is what I want to share with you now.

This is the story of Janet and Ron who found each other not only in this life but across time as well. We were to learn that time is no barrier to love and that eternity is not long enough to erase or even undermine this most enduring of life-giving energies. Ron is no longer with me on this physical plane as he has gone ahead to prepare for things that he can only attend to from a different dimension. He is my protector and my guide while surrounding me with his amazing love which I feel so acutely present each and every moment that I draw breath. I would like to share with you one of the many uplifting messages that I have received from him. These words of wisdom are his way of leading me on towards the time when I make yet another transformational change on my journey. A gentle transition back to the place where I will know a Oneness which transcends the limits of any humanly imagined state of being. When it eventually arrives then I will be 'home' once more with my love and I will be complete yet again.

Ron speaks from the other side of the veil:

Loving anchors must be placed around the world. Love is the only answer. I know that to be so from being over here. People need to be told so they can find that love within themselves and then search out and find their twin soul, because that's the only thing that makes sense.

The energy of the twin soul is very high and sometimes the beings disagree and the energy can become explosive. They even fight but through it all they know they are inseparable. Those types of twins need to calm down and use that power to change the world.

This is a powerful time that we are living through. It is important that the energy that is put forth is of the light and full of love. That will bring heaven on earth for everyone and even the most tortured soul will heal. God truly is love.

On this planet at this time, if you are thinking or hearing about twin souls at lectures, or such, then your twin soul is out there. If that is not the case then you would have been shielded from ever hearing the message.

If you are thinking about twin souls then you are at the level of evolvement or work where you can handle issues which this would bring up. In fourth dimensional consciousness your true mate, your other half can be drawn to you magnetically as surely as a compass turns toward the north.

He is saying that, simply because you are reading these words then this means that you are already able to appreciate at the level you need to, the twin soul vibration which is calling to you from your twin flame. You may actually have already found your 'other half' and not fully appreciated it, or you may have recognised that feeling in your heart which is leading you forward on your search. Whatever your situation is, then as Ron says, let love guide your footsteps to a greater understanding and awareness. Encourage your mind take a back seat while you journey to a place which can be as close as the other side of the bed, where your loved one sleeps, or to another part of the world where you feel drawn to go. Any other state in between will be brought to your attention if only you set the firm intent to let the process to unfold.

Whatever else you do then be sure to allow love to be the paramount force which influences your journey. The distracting energies of fear will only result in your continued confusion which is a state that you have suffered over many incarnations. Now is the time to set yourself free and so, if you are looking for clues about where to start, then read our inspiring story and see what strikes a chord in your wonderful heart. Listen to the melody of this Divine chord and then let it carry you to that sublime place of bliss which it has been encouraging you to remember for more lifetimes than you can possibly imagine.

Table of Contents

THE
TIMELESS LOVE
OF
TWIN SOULS

A Spectacular Journey into the Innate Memory of a
Deeper Understanding that Love Truly is Eternal

- Chapter 1 -

My Sense of Incompleteness

Long before I became aware of what the true meaning of love really is, I was absolutely certain that it existed. From the very moment of my somewhat dramatic entrance into this world I needed to look no further than my family for unequivocal proof of love's enduring presence in my life. In fact, for quite some time it was actually pretty difficult for me to fully recognise something which had always been such a completely natural part of my growing up. In those early times of exploring the world around me I gladly accepted the happiness of a home that had always been overflowing with tender-heartedness and a gently nurturing atmosphere. While still being very young and filled with an enthusiastic fascination for so many things which captured my imagination, I assumed that everyone else was part of a similarly loving family as well.

I knew no different at that time and couldn't imagine life as being any other way than I experienced it to be in those blissful days of my childhood innocence. To me it seemed perfectly normal that I should be so happy and contented within the idyllically affectionate bond of our familial 'togetherness'. From the somewhat limited perspective of my early upbringing it also felt completely okay to me that I should view everyone else as being very much as we were.

It wasn't until I started to become more aware of the world around me that I began to really appreciate how I had lived my life in comparison to that of others. Even before my age approached double figures, I was somehow able to get a sense of something very special about the circumstances of my home environment. Of course, I could have no idea at that time of my upbringing of just how important an impact it was to have on me. It would take very many years until the wisdom of age allowed me to look back on those times with an appreciation for just exactly what my parents had created and how it would shape my life. Their wonderful gift to me lives long within the depths of my very grateful heart and it was this which enabled me to travel the pathway of all my amazing experiences. It proved to be a journey which would inevitably take me to an understanding of the truly mysterious nature and power of that most compelling of all universal forces; the one which we call love.

From how I see things now, it's easy for me to appreciate that I must have come into this life with a certain degree of sensitivity which made it possible for me to be keenly aware of my feelings. I clearly recall that my view of life was a very happy one and that I had never been in any doubt whatsoever about how my parents felt about me. In this respect I can see why I assumed that it was the same for everyone else; but I'm not sure if it could have been because I wished for things to be this way or whether I had been trying to shut out what I didn't want to see. My sensitivity may well have been confusing to me and so it was easier to take the view from the high ground where everything in the valley always looked rosy. However, I do acknowledge that there were occasions when I could appreciate that it certainly did appear as though other people around me might not have been quite as happy as I was.

For some reason, whenever these moments of youthful insight occurred, I seemed to be drawn to observe their circumstances while feeling quite unsettled by what I saw at the time. Apparently there existed in me a certain need to understand more fully what was wrong, as I saw it, while also having a sense of a compelling desire to somehow put it right. This caused me even more consternation in not having a clue as to how I would go about doing it; as well as feeling powerless through being so young. All the while these emotions were present in me at those times, I remember how it would very often cause me to experience a kind of inexplicable fear; but I had absolutely no idea as to why.

What I did know was that I didn't like it at all in the respect that this feeling ran so contrary to how I experienced my life as being, but despite my misgivings something kept urging me to pay attention to it. This was all very puzzling and difficult for me to understand. Although, it seems to me now that my budding sense of 'self', or my identity, must have been trying to establish itself from very early on in my childhood. Through my perceptiveness I began seeing myself partly as a reflection of how I viewed my world and what felt right in it. Whenever I noticed something that upset me then I became more aware of what attracted my attention while making me wonder just why it was that I felt as I did about it. I didn't appreciate, while being so young, that I needed the contrast in my life so as to enable me to find my way towards a true 'completeness' of being. Neither did I have any kind of understanding for the fact of just how keen my perceptiveness actually was; or, more importantly, what an impact this aspect of my personality would have on my life through the awareness which it gave me.

I'm sure that what came to me as a result of being this way proved to be largely responsible for setting me off on the pathway of thinking about the whole subject of love; even though my views were still very much in their formative stage. Love wasn't even a word to me at that age. It was more like a strong feeling which represented a sense of security and a refuge from within which to explore and retreat to whenever it proved necessary. To me, love was tangible and while it touched my heart I could touch it back where it would almost speak to me in a language that I understood. It was 'known' to me and it had a certain 'form' which I somehow recognised the absolute truth of; although I had no explanation of how I had come to appreciate this. I just knew what love should be, but again, how I came by this knowledge I had no idea.

Later in life, whenever I attempted to wrestle with this most elusive concept in having taken it so much for granted from such a young age, I would have to ask myself how I really viewed it in the respect of what it actually meant to me. Being raised in such a supportive family environment, and to have been afforded such a wonderful start in life, it allowed me to experience first hand one very important and sustaining aspect of 'love in action'. To feel myself as being so much a cherished part of the loving 'nest', which my parents' Lee and Helen Parks had created for my brother Leonard Dean (LD) and I, was such an enduring gift that I am eternally grateful for.

Not only was it so beneficially nurturing for me in my formative years but it also provided me with a kind of enduring 'standard' which greatly helped to reassure and support my own feelings about how I viewed things. My family gave me a kind of validation for who I felt myself to be; even though I wasn't conscious of having any need to trust the guidance which was coming from some sort of inner 'knowing'. As a result of what they had created for me I always had a point of reference or an idealised expectation from which to view other areas of my life; as well as something to aspire to in whatever I did. Their example not only provided me with an inspirational constancy on which to build my own life but it also proved to contain an enigmatic dimension that touched something buried deep inside me. Whenever it did then I found myself being presented with an emotional dilemma that took me many years to resolve.

During those times when I would look back from within the clarity of having the degree of wisdom that a lifetime of experience has provided me with, I could appreciate why I felt as I did. On the one hand I had a certain awareness that my home life was something that I could never imagine being without; but on the other hand there seemed to be another part of me that, as I grew up, began to appreciate that all was not as perfect as I assumed it to be. I can see now that the 'future' kept making its presence felt in my consciousness. So, as I became increasingly more concerned about the message that it seemed to be bringing me then it didn't appear to be anywhere near as comforting a prospect as how my life had been up to that point in time.

My view of life beyond my home environment seemed to be fraught with increasing apprehensions about what my emotions were giving me an insight into. Unfortunately I was too naive to appreciate what this could be. Certainty began to show signs of fracturing despite my best efforts to convince myself otherwise. This growing doubt then began to cast a small shadow onto the peaceful meadow of my otherwise idyllic existence where, surely but slowly, the clouds of a gathering storm came ever closer. In so doing they infused the horizon of my anticipated future with their anxious energies.

It seems to me now that I already possessed an intuitive awareness of the fact that there was undoubtedly a certain 'more' to an aspect of my life and myself that I knew precious little about. From quite early on in my childhood I can remember catching fleeting glimpses of the inexplicable feeling that something was missing; but I couldn't even really guess at what it might possibly be. At that age it didn't seem to make any sense to me at all, but no matter what I did I just couldn't do anything to put the thought out of my mind. This unresolved awareness began to puzzle me more and more as time went on and so, despite my experiences of being surrounded by such a lovingly protective family, my mind and my feelings began to create the increasing sense of a highly mysterious 'longing' within me. This I found incrementally confusingly and progressively more unsettling as the years went by.

What proved to be especially disconcerting for me, when pondering all this, was the fact that my parents' left no doubt in my mind whatsoever about how much they constantly cherished and cared for me. In being able to easily appreciate this fact then I couldn't help but wonder what it was that I could consider as being 'wrong' while in the midst of such apparently perfect 'rightness'. All that happened when I tried to figure it out was that I ended up feeling somewhat guilty at even considering the possibility that something, anything, could perhaps be missing from my life. It made me seem so ungrateful, but I just couldn't deny this questioning part of me which, as I got older, contributed more and more to my sense of incompleteness.

I found myself encountering occasions of quite intense reflection which would often result in my entering a state of acute unease that felt incredibly uncomfortable and very threatening. Whenever this happened then it seemed to urge me to pose a recurring question that appeared to have no straightforward answer. This was quite a scary prospect in itself as I had been completely unaccustomed to feeling insecure about my family life or myself in any way whatsoever. Not only that, but I realised at some level that it was a question which I didn't even know how to ask or who to ask it of as I had no understanding of the language in which it had been proposed. This I regarded as being an unwanted ripple on the surface of the otherwise tranquil and idyllic lagoon of my young existence.

However much I tried to ignore these thoughts and feelings I just couldn't seem to find a place of peace at the level which I felt the need to. It wasn't until much later in my life that I was to discover just what these anxious feelings were and where they had come from, but most importantly of all I got to appreciate why they were there at all. This revelation proved to be a very important discovery for me and one which would lead me in a direction that I'd never dreamed of.

Early Perspectives of USA Post War Life

My childhood days were filled with all sorts of magic which gave me a lasting fascination for the world that I grew up in. My attitudes and beliefs were very much influenced by the post war era of the 1940s and early 1950s North American cultural society which I inhabited. The atmosphere of the city, and what it had to offer, appealed to me very much although a good deal of it seemed to be beyond my ability to comprehend in any meaningful way. I could see that there was a lot that I wanted to do, but I somehow lacked the key to open those all important doors which would allow me access into the depths of its tantalisingly hidden mysteries.

From very early on I had a feeling that there was much more to 'grown up' life, and the world in general, than I could possibly appreciate at that time. Unfortunately I had absolutely no idea how to go about discovering what I felt the need to know. I was, however, smart enough to realise that the horizons for a girl in those days were quite limited where we were taught that only boys got to have adventures; while delving into the 'unknown' and doing 'man' stuff. Girls just didn't do those kinds of things unless they were invited along for the ride. Even then they were always expected to look feminine. I wanted to do both!

In those days there was little in the way of influence from TV and movies in contrast to how our modern-day, twenty-first century society is inundated with information and iconic imagery coming at us from just about every direction imaginable. All we had to judge our world by at that time essentially came from whatever we saw on advertising billboards and in magazines; where things were much less than lifelike and dull by comparison. Even so, they still looked pretty good to me and so there existed an increasing longing in me to experience more; but again I had no idea where this feeling came from or even what it was that I wanted to find out about.

I could see how my father played his part as the head of our family where my elder brother, my mother and I would follow his lead when it came to taking trips to new places, attending special occasions or doing anything important. He showed me that I was growing up in a man's world where women only got to do things when they had a man who took them places that they were not supposed to go on their own. Even my brother got to do more than me but in being more than nine years older I guessed that age had something to do with freedom as well.

My awareness allowed me to appreciate that my mother had her 'man' but through observing how her life had turned out as a result then I became more and more conscious of the need to have one of my own when I got to be old enough. More importantly, however, was the aspect of my getting to realise through studying her relationship with my father that a great deal of her happiness came from having the 'right' man. This only served to cause me even more consternation as I didn't have a clue as to how I would go about finding the necessary right one for me.

All I knew for sure was that if I wanted to achieve the same level of happily married life as she obviously had then I would have to find love outside of my family. This seemed to excite me in one way but it also filled me with a kind of petrifying dread and anxiety in another. It proved to be frustrating in the sense that I could so clearly see marital love in action and I could also feel love being given to me as a daughter but I really didn't know, in the way that I felt a strong need to, just exactly what love was. I just had to find out; but how?

That presented me with another question altogether. My young inexperienced mind tried in vain to apply its lamentably limited logic to unravelling the greatest mystery of all time. Unfortunately for me, all that came from my deliberations were more seemingly unanswerable questions the most perplexing of which was ... how could I possibly find what it was that I wanted when I obviously needed a man to take me to the places where I might discover it? My reasoning told me that when I found it then I would surely have been led to my man, my 'Mr Right', but in order to get to him then I needed a man first. It was all so confusing while leaving me feeling as though I had been given a huge ball of mental fog to untangle.

It was also quite scary to appreciate how limited my options were while wondering how I would ever be able to survive later in life without someone to protect me. A strong and loving man just like my father, but how would I ever be able to find someone like him? I dared not even contemplate never finding this Mr 'must-be-absolutely-perfect-just-like-my-dad' who surely had to exist. He had to! He absolutely must! But what if he didn't? Or, even worse, what if he was living in some distant land that I could never get to? Somehow I just wouldn't accept this as being so, but very often the dark cloud of this most unthinkable prospect came to cast its shadow over my otherwise very happy little existence.

Whatever else that may have plagued the highly fertile corners of my youthful mind, I knew for certain that I was truly and unconditionally loved. This surely was the sustaining aspect of my life which allowed me to probe the rather fragile areas of my personality which, in the process, could prove to be more than a little uncomfortable. However, it wasn't until I got to be old enough to appreciate just how much I was loved, and why, that I got to see the Divine hand at work in my life. In time I began to realise that so much of what had happened to me, in the respect of how my home environment served to support me, was to prove so meaningful in how my life turned out. Through this awareness I came to a true appreciation of the wisdom which states that everything has its place in how the gloriously rich tapestry of any journey is constructed.

My own amazingly colourful 'adventure' unfolded in ways that go far beyond the limits of imagination which taught me to take particular notice of many other factors outside of my immediate experience. There were many examples to illustrate this. One of the more memorable involved my mother when, at an early point in her childhood and being only four years of age, she almost came to an abrupt end of her own journey. At this highly impressionable stage of her life she became traumatised through being involved in an unfortunate incident when she was run over by a horse and buggy.

I can only guess at how close she came to complete disaster in a tragedy which could so easily have ended her life while never giving me a chance to experience mine. She had been badly hurt while suffering injuries to her pelvic bone and abdominal area which, at that young age, were still in their formative stages of development. Through compassionate care and a long period of recuperation she did manage to make a remarkable recovery but the consequences of her misfortune were to follow her for the remainder of her days. There was only so much that her young frame could completely heal from and which nearly prevented me from being born at all.

When my mother got to childbearing age she was told that as a result of her injuries, and the subsequent lasting damage, then it would probably prove very difficult for her to become pregnant and to bear children in a natural way. This must have come as a shock to her but my mother had tremendous faith in a power much greater than herself which sustained her through many years of doubt. She had an irrepressible determination that absolutely nothing would be allowed to prevent her from having her own children, even if it meant going through yet more pain and discomfort in the process.

I can't begin to imagine how she must have felt in those days of the early twentieth century when medical science was still in its infancy. Living in a remotely situated small township where there were virtually no emergency facilities for miles around must have been incredibly scary for such a young girl. In that year of 1916 the world was still gripped in the equally painful throes of war where basic drugs, even if they were available, were probably in short supply. I don't even want to think of how she suffered as a result of her injuries while being deprived of proper medication. You certainly had to be tough in those days.

There is a saying which asserts that *'what doesn't kill you makes you stronger'* and this, to my way of thinking, must have definitely applied to my mother. To have survived all that she did only to be told later on that there were doubts about her being able to have children was something that I have no idea how I would have coped with. Fortunately for her, my mother had an indomitable spirit which gave her the most remarkable faith in her life's purpose as well as her own abilities. I say fortunately for her, but of course, it was obviously very fortunate for my brother and me as well. We are both eternally grateful to her for her courage, her determination and her amazing gift of love.

Despite all of her many trials and in the face of gloomy warnings from her medical advisors she did eventually become pregnant with my brother who was born in the spring of 1931 and delivered by Caesarean section. His arrival had undoubtedly been viewed by my mother as being something over and above the ordinary 'miracle' of bringing a new life into this world. To her it had been a complete vindication of what love-in-action could produce when presented with even the most daunting of hurdles. Here was her proof and, having demonstrated herself capable of doing what she most wanted to do, it wasn't long before the thought of having a second child became foremost in her mind. But there was yet another problem to be taken into account.

Having already gone through one Caesarean delivery then this left her with only one more chance to successfully bear a child. This limitation had been imposed on having babies born in this manner at that time. My mother was absolutely set on giving another soul the opportunity to come into this world so as to share in all the love which my parents had to offer and so they tried again; but their efforts were to be tested for the depths of their sincerity and commitment. Time held its breath for what must have seemed to them like an eternity.

Finally, the moment did arrive where the result of my mother and my father's determination, I'm very pleased to say, was my appearance in their life. However, they had to wait over nine anxiety-filled years after my brother was born for me to finally make my joyful entrance as the newest, and last, member of the family. I can only guess at how apprehensive all this must have made my father as well as what my mother must have gone through in order to bring me into this world. Is it any wonder that I love my parents so much as well as being so grateful to my mother for being as determined and brave as she was? What an amazing woman and what an inspiration she has been to me.

To be born into this world while knowing for certain just how very much wanted and cherished you are is a feeling that absolutely everyone should know in at least one lifetime. It really is the most incredible experience. I was delivered in the same manner as my elder brother but I had been the one who closed the door to the possibility of anyone ever following me. So it came to be that I found myself being especially treasured by my mother and father in the poignant knowledge of their gift. They considered me to be their little miracle of life in miniature, as was my brother when he first appeared, and so he and I grew up being showered with the love from two eternally grateful parents.

It proved to be the most wonderful start to my life and, from living through the incredible magic of its gently nurturing introduction into my social environment, I learned the true value of raising children in this way. From the time I realised that I wished to have a family of my own I was in no doubt about how I wanted to bring them up and in what kind of atmosphere.

Again this caused me confusion and anxiety because I appreciated that in order to do so then I would need someone just like my father. A really special man who would love me in the way of being my true companion and partner, but who would also love and treasure our children to the same degree.

I knew exactly what I wanted but just how to go about getting it seemed to be an overwhelming task given my dilemma with feeling as I did about myself in this respect. What gave me the determination to follow my dream was the example set by the two people who I loved most dear in all the world. I figured that if they could do it then, somehow, so could I.

The Big City and Me

Growing up in the relatively modest metropolitan areas of Lansing, the state capital city of Michigan, I began to see and interact with a world of people who were generally friendly and kind. The city had been built around government institutions, education establishments and manufacturing industries where the making of cars played a big part in our heritage as well as the city's economy. Lansing also had a diverse cultural basis which actively encouraged the performing arts, so I got exposed to music and dancing from very early on. To this day it still plays an important role in my life; I just love to dance. This aspect was also instrumental, in every sense of the word, in bringing me to a place on my journey which would ultimately change my life forever.

Fashions of that time were something that I also had access to where I could readily express and indulge my outgoing and flirtatious nature; especially in those years of finding my way towards maturing into the kind of woman that I imagined myself to be. The commercial areas of the city and its many stores, filled with all manner of things I couldn't imagine living without, offered me lots of opportunities to go shopping. I loved to buy the things which made me feel special while also being accepted into my social world of friends.

Much of what I bought also helped me to express my identity as I began to gain a certain level of confidence in who I was becoming but, again, it somehow didn't bring me the kind of satisfaction which I felt that it ought to. This proved to be yet another frustrating puzzle that I couldn't figure out at the time and one which probably accounted for my fears over feeling that I didn't really fit in; or that somehow I wasn't accepted for being who I truly considered myself to be. This, I discovered later, was all connected with my enduring sense of not being whole. That indescribable state of being less than the person I saw looking back at me each day in my make-up mirror. I wanted to 'paint' her into existence but I just didn't seem to know how. Where was this 'me' that I appeared to be on a never ending quest to find and why wasn't I this illusive 'her'? Questions, so many questions but there didn't appear to be anyone in my world at that time who could give me answers of the kind which would in any way satisfy my innate curiosity or my unrelenting neediness.

My parents were wonderful role models for me as they represented just about everything which I felt that life had to offer in the way of an ideal 'togetherness'. They so obviously enjoyed a loving relationship with each other as well as sharing a journey through life where it seemed as though one would never be complete without the other. I knew that I wanted the same as what they had when I grew up as it had become impossible for me to imagine living any other way, but in truth I had little or no concept of parents being in any way unlike how mine were. I was so happy to be able to receive so much love and encouragement from them, in the respect of how they raised me, although I didn't fully appreciate their extraordinary gift to me until I had progressed well into experiencing the joys of being a parent myself.

From all that I saw around me as I grew up then I figured that my elder brother and I were part of the 'perfect' family; the dream that I saw advertised in the magazines and shown on TV. Even so, I just couldn't shake the 'knowing' that there was something missing. Something truly special but evidently completely illusive to the degree that finding it seemed to be almost an impossibility. Unfortunately, this feeling would haunt me for a long while until I eventually did find what I had been searching for.

For all of the time of my growing up through those early years of my teens and beyond, I really had no way of knowing what it was that I sensed to be missing from my life. Through this lack of understanding, I had precious little to guide me when it came to judging whether or not I enjoyed a truly happy existence. Everything I did, when it came to the subject of relationships and affairs of the heart, was always compared to how things were between my mother and my father. It almost seems now, when I look back, as though I chose my parents so that they would be a constant reminder to me of what it was that I wanted and which kept me searching for it until I eventually found it. They were such an inspiration for me and I am so grateful for their wonderful presence in my life. I miss them both very much but I draw comfort from the fact that I know without doubt that they watch over me and, when my time comes to make the transition, I will once more be with them in a place where I will be able to fully share all the love that I have for them.

Living under the quite compelling influences of a progressive and vibrant city suited me well in certain respects in that I got to see life as being an adventure much like Alice in Wonderland. There had always been so much to do and to see where I could explore what it was that I felt attracted to. I liked to discover things and to see how other people did what they did and then learn how to do it myself; if I couldn't get anyone to show me. I particularly enjoyed doing anything which made me feel special and that would get me attention. Looking back, I can see that growing up in a big city taught me that if you wanted to get noticed then you had to stand out in a crowd. Although, it certainly had been a lesson which had come with mixed blessings.

Like most every other young girl of my era I always knew that I was expected to get married and then raise a family by the time I'd reached a certain age. I didn't mind at all as I felt this to be exactly what I wanted to do, as well as what I hoped for, although I seemed to have little or no idea what my heart was telling me when it came to the subject of men and romance. This caused me a lot of problems from early on where I had doubts about many things. Even when I first married it was with a certain degree of hesitation on my part although I knew that love did play an important role in our relationship.

My parents had come from a small township many miles north of Lansing where it had been easy for me to see how they could have met while finding that special someone which each of them had probably longed for just as I did. By comparison, the city that I lived in was huge and filled with a great many people which left me wondering, on many occasions, just how I would go about achieving what my parents had. It seemed a daunting prospect to find my Mr Right in among a veritable sea of cosmopolitan humanity and so when Bob came along, when I was fourteen and in high school, then I kind of grabbed onto him.

I did this while naively anticipating that it would work out the same for me as it had done for my parents. After all, what more did I have to go on? As did any other girl of my age in those days. There had been precious little in the way of information on the subject where romance novels of the time really didn't help much. So it was to be a journey towards the altar filled with hope and expectation which led me to believe that all my doubts and fears would be dispelled while I got to recreate all that my parents had; and more.

The city, however, had planted yet another doubt in my mind when it came to figuring out just what love is. Lansing presented me with so many attractions not the least of which was the aspect of there being a lot of boys that got my attention. Quite a few looked really cute and so it made me wonder if my mother had found my father just as cute when he was a teenager and whether or not it had anything to do with the love that they shared. I found myself wondering if love and attraction were one and the same thing as it seemed reasonable to me, at that impressionable age, to assume that they were. It all felt very much like an unfathomable mystery but I had found Bob and he seemed to fit into my ideal of what romance and life as a couple ought be, so I guessed that I had found love just like my mother had.

So many influences of city life conspired to convince me that I had made the right choice and that my destiny seemed assured in that I would enjoy the kind of family life that I had experienced at home; only this time it would be of my own creating instead. For a while I did enjoy a certain level of happiness but as time went on I kept feeling more uncertain about how my life was turning out as the emotion of incompleteness made itself more evident. I just couldn't shake it off, the result of which was that I became increasingly unhappy in my marriage. My awareness that there was still something wanting in my life just seemed to keep getting stronger, but the problem remained that I had no idea of what exactly I wanted. Thankfully, all of that changed on the arrival of one joyously memorable day. This was the day when I met the man who would answer not only the calling of my heart but who would also provide me with the answer to my 'big question' as well.

Ron proved to be my knight in shining armour who, in true 'Prince Charming' fashion, came to rescue me from a life which up to that point had felt very much as though it had remained unfulfilled; despite my having three wonderful children. Until his appearance I had no idea as to the true depths of my sense of 'loss'. However, I was soon to learn much more about not only the unfathomable healing capabilities of true love but also the eternal qualities of something that few get to experience in countless lifetimes. Ron would lead me into a highly eventful journey the like of which nothing or no one could have ever prepared me for.

With my twin soul by my side I encountered a great deal that I found thrilling as much as I found challenging, but that 'ride' took me to places that I most surely would never have gone without him. The whole amazing experience allowed me to travel to the most far reaching point in my personal universe. That truly sacred place, the one which we are all in the process of searching for, where the Divine essence of our true self resides. It has been, and is, a journey which I am extremely happy to have made and one which I would be so grateful to share with you in the hope that you too will benefit in a most uplifting way.

- Chapter 2 -

Parallels in Time and Heartspace

To me, the name Pennsylvania Avenue conjures up a completely different image to that which it does for very many others in my country. My own Michigan based 'Pennsylvania Avenue' is not quite as wide or as ostentatious as its illustrious counterpart, but its presence in my life is nonetheless important to me. The place where it led me still holds a lot of precious memories due to the influences which it exerted over me. However, these were not altogether dissimilar from what our iconic symbol of classic American tradition holds for so many in my country.

The famous mini-highway in Washington DC, part of which spans the long mile that separates the US capitol and the White House, carries more than just traffic. To a significant percentage of our population it represents the union of trusted authority with the meeting of educated minds where the evolutionary determination and cultural direction for the future of our society is debated and decided. More than this, the wide tree-lined route also serves to symbolise the direct link between two aspects of our nation's soul. That essential aspect which resides in the heart of a metropolis where its design has been intentionally crafted to inspire by its example.

This crucible core of our society blends together all aspects of human endeavour in its often faltering attempts to make each of us better than we were yesterday while striving to visualise where we are heading tomorrow. The 'highway of many emotions' which links the two major buildings of high office, shows us that our journey is to walk the enlightened course of true intent, the straight and narrow causeway of purposeful self-realisation. To tread our current pathway with unimpeded vision in our constant search for wisdom. This we do while recognising that we can choose to see the route created by our footsteps as one of celebration or that of remorse; or anywhere in between.

The famous avenue in DC has witnessed every human emotion which we are capable of expressing since its inception in the mid 1800s. It has a great deal to say to those who would take the time to listen to its enduring story; and is a constant reminder of the very spirit which underpins our existence. Celebrations and tragedies come and go while the avenue continues confidently on while offering its dispassionate service to all who are transported by its material presence. No one is the greater or the lesser for having been taken to a different place of awareness by virtue of its design where it treats all as equal while echoing the basic tenet of our constitution.

The road to freedom is as short or as long as we wish to make it. We as individuals make that choice even though many others may help to illuminate the signposts which guide us to our destination.

Alongside another Pennsylvania Avenue, in Lansing Michigan, is the stately old building of Eastern High School. It's nowhere near as grand as those two famous buildings in DC. However, in its own way it represents the same principles and aspires to the same goals as does the two hallmarks which constitute the seat of our democratic government. Eastern High is the oldest senior school in Lansing and one which had been built, no doubt, with the same aims in mind; in respect of helping shape the future of our country through influencing the generations who will contribute to its growth. I became one of their number in my freshman year of 1954 and it was with a certain degree of trepidation that I entered into its somewhat hallowed halls.

Eastern had been my initiation into the world of adulthood where, for the first time, I felt as though a new era of my life had truly begun. Even the somewhat classy neighbourhood in which the building was located made it seem as though I had moved into an atmosphere where I could really explore myself in the way that I felt the need to. Just like the historic halls of power in Washington DC, Eastern had its own imposing structure which, to me at that impressionable age, led me to imagine myself moving in the midst of the grandiose cultural aspirations from a different time.

In 1928, when it had been built just before the onset of the great depression, the architectural influences of large imposing structures were still in full flow; so Eastern High had been constructed to reflect this. Like a fledgling adult, who is oftentimes over-enthusiastic about asserting its new found confidence, the style of its creation spoke of a pretention which suggested an intimate knowledge of perfection. A regal 'rightness' which didn't invite any kind of contradiction or inquiry as to its reason for existence. It simply 'was' and needed no one to defend its imposing personality or that of anyone who chose to become a subject of its influence. It had been designed to mould and shape through being the instrument of its creator's intent and so I became a willing student in a world which stimulated not only my imagination but my innate sensitivity as well.

I remember when I first saw the quite amazing, large auditorium and the beautiful wood of the lavish foyer which appeared to be something straight out of a novel that I'd once read. It just didn't seem real but there I was standing in the midst of its imposing presence, along with many others who I'm sure were affected to one degree or another by the impressive spectacle of their new surroundings. I could feel that this was indeed a building which surely wanted to make its mark on everyone that it touched but I had no idea just how much it would influence my life in the years that followed.

Just as my parents' had been my anchor into a past which allowed me to find my way towards the future, so Eastern would provide me with a similar experience. As I journeyed along the somewhat uncertain path which would lead me to my independence, I was once again surrounded by the reassurance of an environment which had absolute confidence in its purpose. It was similarly protective and nurturing while allowing me to discover more about myself. However, this time there were many more chances of finding the answers that I had been searching for. The diversity of opportunity which it offered me to explore the uncharted regions of my personality and my identity also helped me to continue my implacable quest to understand love. One of the more memorable opportunities came in a way that I had least expected.

The Perils of Rampant Religion

My best friend Susie also went to Eastern and it was through my close relationship with her that I got to attend the Sunday school where her mother taught. It had a wonderfully friendly atmosphere and somewhere that I really liked to go. It also gave me the opportunity to gently find my way back into religion after the quite off-putting encounters that I had come across before that time. Susie's mother was always very kind and would often ask us to help out. This got me even more involved in the atmosphere of the place while also helping me to overcome my apprehensions.

This proved to be a very healing experience for me as my first exposure to organised religion had left me quite emotionally scarred. In those uninformed times of the late forties and early fifties, there existed the culture of bible thumping religion which was all too commonplace. Unfortunately, to a sensitive and impressionable soul such as myself, this had a big impact on me; where one particular encounter nearly ended my desire to attend church ever again.

I grew up thinking, like so many others, that God was some white bearded old man who lived above the clouds while looking down on us all as he pulled the strings of our lives. The religious teachings that I had heard up to that point in time encouraged me to believe that this almighty old man had to be kept continually happy; otherwise unimaginable things would happen to those who upset him. The vision I got from all that I heard was that we were like helpless puppets where he got to pull the strings while we mindlessly danced our lives out for him.

This resulted in my becoming somewhat superstitious through not really understanding just exactly what I found myself being asked to believe. To add to my confusion I had to reconcile the fact that, as much as a part of me felt this way, another part of me didn't. Something within me existed which seemed to have a strong sense of some powerful force that would protect me from anything really bad. Looking back from my current perspective I can see that I really did have a highly sustaining concept of what God truly meant to me. Unfortunately, at that time of my life, I was still too easily intimidated by those who I considered were in authority to voice my opinions. Somehow I sensed that the love which my parents' showed me had something to do with a Divine presence. Of course, I had no idea how I knew this. But with so much else that people were trying to convince me of, it created a kind of conflict in me which no doubt resulted in my superstition. It was probably my way of hedging my bets at that age.

I remember on the many occasions that whenever I would walk along a rail then I would be wary of falling off. I tried my best to balance all the way along it and a lot of times I was successful, but if ever I did fall then I convinced myself that I would flunk a grade in school; or something else of that nature would go wrong for me. It seems crazy to have thought this way now, but those were very different times when our society was ruled much more by gossip than by television; or other forms of mass media information. It's amazing to look back at those days and then think about how far we have come in such a relatively short space of time.

Even though in one way it kind of scared me to know what other people perceived this Divine presence or 'God' to be, there was a part of me which absolutely would not accept the misleading 'truth' of this popularised notion. Unfortunately for me, the society in which I lived at the time didn't give me any help in understanding my feelings when it came to questioning the words of others. At that time there was no one around in my life like Susie's mother who would listen to my point of view or even take the time to explain things more clearly to me. My parents were always very encouraging, but I felt the need to have someone outside of my family environment to talk to so as to bring a balance to what I felt others were trying to get me to believe.

Throughout that era of my life the Second World War was still fresh in everyone's memories and had left many people in a fearful state as my country attempted to get back on its feet once more; in the hopes of a better life to come. In this energy of fear, along with times of great uncertainty, many people naturally turned to religion for guidance and reassurance. It was an ideal opportunity for those in power, or any sphere of influence, to assert their authority and to drive the message home; in whatever way they saw fit. Religious leaders were often given to asserting their own liberal interpretations of the scriptures in their attempts to ensure their places in society. I was to remember one of these more dramatic and fear-inducing instances for the rest of my life.

My parents were not churchgoers in the traditional sense so I found myself joining in with the neighbourhood kids and just following along while they went to their local church. At that time I had no idea which kind of church it was because in my state of innocence I believed that every church was the same. After all, there was only one 'God' so why did you need more than one type of church to go see Him in? This was my youthful reasoning anyway. My companions didn't seem to have any different ideas on the subject either and so I felt safe in their company. It always gave me a lot of pleasure to hang out with them. They made it fun and I really liked the singing as well as the prayers, but I wasn't at all keen on some of the sermons; particularly when the message turned out to be a scary one. I especially didn't like the occasions which appeared to challenge my limited views of a Divine presence or 'God' by reinforcing beliefs which I found myself being an unwilling subscriber to.

I did, however, love riding on the bus with my neighbourhood friends which always felt like some kind of magical adventure that I was setting out on. I liked to imagine that our destination was a very special one where some mystical power had been acting to draw me irresistibly towards it. The bus would be the special carriage which took me to see someone grand who lived in a huge, beautifully decorated house. A fabulous place where lots of people came to visit because he was the one who looked after them. I felt so excited to be one of the ones who got to be invited into his home.

Arriving at the church seemed like stepping into a completely different world to me. So you can imagine how thrilled I was when, on one very memorable day, I got invited to join the choir. How incredible was that!? At first I felt so nervous but it didn't take me long to appreciate that I had been given the opportunity to sing my little heart out; which I proudly did. This always made me feel absolutely wonderful, as well as giving me the idea that I was actually involved in doing something which meant a lot to not only me but everyone else around me as well.

I soon found that I could produce my singing from a really special place deep within my soul. This allowed me to express my true feelings for someone who I felt must surely be somewhere close by. At those times when I was in full flow, I just didn't know how there could possibly be a 'God' who would be anything other than kind. Because, to my way of thinking, if anyone like that existed then no one would ever have wanted to make up such wonderful songs and then sing them to Him. This was my reasoning and it felt perfectly right to me to look at it in this way; even though I didn't have the courage to say so to anyone else.

Whenever I sang the words '*Jesus loves me*', it always made me feel so special. Somehow, as they flowed enthusiastically out of me, I knew without doubt that he really did; and still does. Sometimes when I hit a certain note it had the effect of making me tingle all over. This made me even more convinced of being right about what my heart wanted to tell me about God. My singing always enabled me to make a connection with a higher power, but it was also a way for me to get more deeply in touch with a part of myself that I needed to trust in. The words that I sang echoed so much of what I wanted to express while allowing me to connect with my own innate sense of 'rightness'. It wasn't until I got to the part where I had to listen to sermons that my uncertainties began to surface once again. This was where I would find myself being confronted by those who insisted on asserting their unenlightened authority over me.

Unfortunately, on one such occasion, I remember listening intently to a passage being quoted from the Bible which the minister had been delivering with a great deal of passion. His captive audience was, in his view, no doubt in need of a strong dose of unadulterated moralising which he was in the somewhat overzealous process of obliging them with. He threw himself into his 'mission' with a great deal of arrogant gusto and with what seemed to me like a very threatening tone in his voice. No one spoke during the whole of his riveting admonishment from the pulpit where many, like me, were wide-eyed with fear at what was being said. Even now, I have no trouble at all in recalling how really upset I was as a result of his disturbing performance.

I well remember listening transfixed as the fearsome minister painted a quite startling picture in all of our highly captivated minds. He sternly filled every attentive ear with a grim story about some mighty figure ominously descending out of the clouds on a big white horse. His arms flailed the air as he described this heavenly apparition landing in the midst of a great crowd of people; who were no doubt just as terrified as me. As though the drama of the story wasn't enough he thumped his bible for added effect when he got to that part about the horse trampling all the sinners under its mighty hooves. There were a few moments of wordless drama which followed while he allowed the full effect of his 'message' to sink in as everyone contemplated the obvious implications of this part of his sermon. There was not even a murmur from the traumatised audience and no one moved a muscle. No one dared hardly breathe; especially me.

I will never forget the look of pleading anguish on his face when he delivered the fiery passage which told us all of how the 'saved' ones frantically rushed to hang onto the horse's mane and were then mercifully carried off. To where and to what wasn't made clear at the time, although I may have missed that part as a result of my brain being totally frozen up in abject fear. I'm sure that I wasn't the only one not to have taken in much after the stunning climax of his performance which only the most robust of souls could have failed to have been affected by.

He made it all sound so real while impressing on the congregation that it was indeed a truth which would surely come again in one form or another. With the recent traumas and consequences of a world at war still relatively fresh in everyone's memories, he seemed to have no trouble at all in convincing people of this fact. Unfortunately, I was far too young to appreciate just how manipulative and dreadfully deceitful his actions were; but I'm sure that my feelings were echoed by many others. I have no doubt that those in the congregation who were equally as impressionable as me, and who succumbed to the power of his zealous rhetoric, had the same overwhelming reaction.

I can so clearly remember feeling myself trembling at the horror of such a vision but I just couldn't stop thinking about the scene that he had painted so graphically in all of our minds. Whatever I did in my attempts to make it go away then I just couldn't seem to get it out of my head. It was as though his dreadful story kept insisting on confirming what I didn't want to feel, but I seemed powerless to resist it. Sadly for me there were further repercussions which added an extra disturbing dimension to my encounter with this poor misguided man. Ones that had a much deeper impact on me.

In retrospect I can see that his theatrical performance had the effect of making me feel very insecure. This it did while I was keenly aware of being in the sanctuary of an environment which I considered was intended to cheer people up and not scare them half to death. This realisation did nothing to alleviate the battle between my heart and mind which continued unabated as a result. There was a part of me that just couldn't accept that what he had tried so hard to convince me as being the 'truth' of, could actually be so; even though his words had affected me so emotionally. Unfortunately I couldn't stop myself thinking about how I felt or what he had implied in his 'sermon from hell'. He appeared to have pushed open a little wider, the door to a place within myself that I didn't want to look closer into; even though I had to admit that it was there.

As a direct result of my encounter with this man's doom-laden tales of wrath and vengeance, I had the most awful nightmares which often needed my mother's gentle, self assured presence to comfort me. When she found out what had happened, she wasted no time at all in calling the church to tell the, no doubt, 'unmoved' minister that I wouldn't be attending his dubious 'house of God' ever again. I never did, but more importantly it left me feeling that I never wanted to go to church ever again; until, that was, I thankfully met Susie and then her wonderful mother.

She came to my rescue as a result of my entering the highly fertile teen-filled 'ecosphere' of Eastern High and I am so grateful to her and the Divine hand which guided me there. Pennsylvania Avenue in Lansing, Michigan, led me to a gateway of education not all of which could be found between the pages of any text books; however eloquently they may have been crafted. My particular avenue took me to a kind of freedom that, for me, rivalled any which could ever have been formulated on Capitol Hill. Lincoln would have been proud.

Susie was my little angel sent by God to bring me back into the sight of his loving care. Her mother's gentle understanding and kindness helped me find the confidence to not only acknowledge but really trust in my own intuitive feelings as well. Maybe I needed to go through that period of feeling so disconnected from a deeper understanding in order to get back to a place where I would be more firmly anchored to the truth; which I intuitively felt in my heart. Whatever the reason may have been, or the real extent of the lesson that I learned, I was certainly very glad to have stepped out from under the dark dispiriting cloud that this poor deluded man had thrown over me. I can only bring myself to bless him now for the valuable gift which he had actually given me.

The Dawning of Awareness with the Coming of Age

Whenever I look back on how things were for me when I was young then I am able to see little reminders and indications of how I must have had a strong sense of my spiritual nature; even though I wasn't aware of it. Signs and symbols had always been important to me. They were a constant reminder of something close to my heart in those frenetic action-filled days of the rush towards adulthood and self determination. Those often hectic days when there had been so much to take in and so little time in which to do it while endless distractions continually popped out of the woodwork. Aahh, how wonderful it was to grow up, but where on earth did all that time go?

I clearly remember one stage in my life when I longed to have a pretty necklace with a nice shiny cross. Something beautiful to wear but also a precious piece of jewellery which I felt would bring me a kind of reassuring comfort. I had no conscious idea as to why I should have wanted it to do this for me, but a part of me must have been trying to guide my attention to an emotional issue which needed to be resolved. I was too young to appreciate this at the time and only had my emotional compass to steer by. In this particular instance the needle had been pointing towards the image of a jewellery store but the sign on the door said '*closed*'. I clearly recall being very frustrated by this.

The necklace was in itself a relatively simple thing but it did mean a lot to me although I had been under the false impression that you had to be a Catholic to wear one. I thought that I had only ever seen them worn by people who belonged to this religion, so I assumed that no one else had the right to have one. I didn't know what to do to get one or even why it felt so important for me to possess something so apparently unattainable, but I was certainly conscious that I wanted to wear a cross for much more than merely making a fashion statement. It got to the point where I wanted it so badly that I could almost imagine how it would look while I was wearing it. Sometimes, without thinking, I would raise my hand to my neck and just gently pat it while feeling the sense of comfort and reassurance that it would give me. It seemed to bring me closer to something or someone although I had absolutely no idea of what or who it could be at the time.

Before moving to the 'big city', my parents had originally lived in a town nearly ninety miles north of Lansing called Weidman. This meant that I had relations still living there and so I used to go visit them whenever we had family outings. On one particular occasion, the town was hosting something they called Weidman Day where they held what could be described as being a fair; which formed a colourful part of the celebrations. Naturally I went along to join in the fun and while trying my luck at one of the stalls I was amazed and really pleased when I won a prize. To my absolute delight I got a cross which thrilled me beyond measure and meant the whole world to me at the time. I never gave a thought to the fact that I had wanted it so badly and that it had so miraculously come into my life as I was far too busy being excited about finally having something so precious in my possession.

That proved to be a very memorable day for me and one which I keep dear to my heart. The most important thing about it was that I gained an appreciation for the power of intent and what can be created as a result of it. My cross had been a wonderful gift but by coming into my life it showed me what I was capable of if I listened to my intuition while remaining true to myself. Owning my necklace brought up feelings which helped me get more deeply in touch with my true self but it took me some time to appreciate that this aspect of me already existed; while just waiting to be discovered.

It wasn't until much later in life, when I looked back on those formative years, that I realised just how much I must have had an innate understanding of something which I later came to appreciate was my intuitive connection to a higher power. It seems highly significant to me now that I chose to grow up in a time where there existed little or no understanding of God's eternal love. An era of our evolution when people were happy to accept whatever anyone gave them in the way of much needed guidance; especially if they looked to be an authority figure. I feel now that I must have known from very early on what this love truly was and is. However, because I had been so immersed in a society which had little or no true connection to it, then inevitably I was destined to be confused.

Fortunately, within the midst of my uncertainty there was to emerge a great clarity and strength of purpose. This would make itself known to me through the process of my consistently being asked to walk the truth of my heart. The pathway which I followed as a result of this repeated request proved to be one that I have come to acknowledge as being an integral part of the Divine 'plan'. In my opinion, this 'way of the heart' which patiently waits for each of us to inevitably discover its beneficial presence in our lives, is indescribably magnificent in its eternal mystery and infinite wisdom.

When Pandora had let all of the evils and ills out of her box into the world at large, what remained after they had all gone was the beacon-bright light of eternal hope. One of the consequences to the deprivations and sustained discouragement, which a world at war had produced, was that hope had become a much sought after commodity; and in apparently very short supply. People from all walks of life were in great need of seeing and becoming reacquainted with the 'light' in their hearts after struggling so resolutely through the long darkness of human conflict.

Sadly, as I had learned to my cost, some of those sources who people turned to for comfort were quite evidently in great need of illumination themselves. A new era was being born where the foundations of the previous one were no longer sufficient to support our needs or to carry us forward into the new dawn. The teachings of the past seemed outdated and misplaced which left many in the position of having to find their own way while trusting to themselves for guidance and direction. I found myself being one of their number, although I had been much too young to appreciate exactly what was happening to me or taking place all around me in the social environment which comprised my world at that time.

Those were indeed testing times but I seemed to have a sense that hope was never far from anyone's reach while always being ready to come rushing forward whenever it was called upon to do so. My parents were a 'constant' in my life whose supporting presence showed me what love could do to keep the flame of hope alive and burning brightly in the hearts of all who allowed love to guide their footsteps. My family was my rock and my anchor in a life where many around me were temporarily adrift on the turbulent sea of an uncertain destiny after the passing of the storm. It seemed that there were so many things to be contended with in every aspect of life at that time. However, I realise now that this also corresponded with the existence of a whole raft of opportunities. They awaited anyone and everyone who cared to take advantage of them in order to grow and evolve into a more spiritual and aware 'us'.

Those times were like riding the roller-coaster of life while experiencing much of what it had to offer; the highs and the lows in varying proportions. As a result, my experiences were both shocking and uplifting while making equally strong impressions on me. But what I see as important now is how I made my choices to accept one and not the other. By knowing what I didn't want, and wouldn't accept, then I began to find my way towards what I did want and what I would accept. Even in the face of such stern authority figures and being as unsure about certain aspects of my life as I was, it seemed as though I had the ability to draw on something; some force more powerful than little Alice who could already see Wonderland much more clearly than many others.

I knew that life existed to be enjoyed as much as possible and that to do nice things for myself, as well as others, was always what gave me the greatest pleasure. There seemed to be a need in me to heal others through my actions but I had always been aware, to one degree or another, that first of all it was necessary to heal myself. Singing beautiful songs to God, who was forever in my heart and who knew me better that I knew myself, certainly felt like much more fun than listening to some poor lost soul who thought that he would find safety in the neediness of those he sought to instil fear in. How empty a life was that? Certainly not one that I would ever want to lead.

Winning my beautiful little cross made my heart soar as though I had been lifted up into the clouds by a pair of gentle hands while being surrounded by the sensation of an unconditionally sublime love. A quite spectacular love which appeared to be so familiar to me, even though it seemed to have such an exquisite quality to its nature that simply took my breath away. It came rushing irresistibly in from an indefinable place which appeared to be situated far beyond the capabilities of my understanding. I seemed to have no concept of just why this should be or where it had arisen. However, a wise and quietly influential part of me existed which encouraged my letting go of the need to achieve any kind of a 'knowing'. I think that this was my first meaningful encounter with the Divine concept which states that it's okay not to know while simply 'allowing'.

Having my nightmares, after being subjected to that highly memorable sermon at a most impressionable time of my life, actually resulted in something very positive for me. Through experiencing the terror of my imagination running wild, while fuelled by the darkness of my benighted bedroom, I also got to feel the protective power and gentle comforting love of my mother. This helped me to appreciate that love always triumphs over everything, however scary it may appear; although it took me a while to be able to see this for absolute certain.

At those times of being so young and easily influenced, as I struggled to erase the upsetting images and chilling impressions of what had been so graphically described to me, I also found myself wrestling with my inner 'truths'. Even at that tender age I could appreciate that while all this was happening to me then I had also got to encounter and feel first hand the compelling healing power of love. This awareness had struck the most influential chord within me which no doubt underpinned my unconscious choice to reject what a religious authority figure had demanded that I believe. I just knew deep down inside the very heart of who I felt myself to be that his truth wasn't mine, however zealously he had tried to make it so.

I just couldn't accept what he had so vigorously asserted even though the era in which I was growing up had been steeped in the time-honoured tradition of having children believe unquestioningly all they were taught. This needed to be done while simultaneously respecting their elders in the process; especially if they were authority figures who dressed themselves up to look different and set themselves apart from everyone else. Evidently I was not an ordinary young girl and certainly not one who had been prepared to just go along meekly with anything that anyone cared to say to me that is. This strength of character and trust in my innate wisdom proved to be of great service to me in the years to come when even greater challenges were to present themselves to me. I had no idea of this when I was growing up, but I can see now that it turned out to be an important preparation that I had needed in order to find what was already in my heart and waiting for me to discover; once again.

In many other ways I was a child of my times and I enjoyed my innocence while letting it have as much free rein as my parents allowed me to get away with. I did everything I possibly could to express myself and one particularly enjoyable way of doing this came about through my being able to go dancing. My city encouraged both music and dance and so it was, in this most creative of atmospheres, that I let my feelings lift my heart above the limitations of how others wanted me to see the world. Dancing set me free just as much then as it does now. Music speaks to my heart and as it does so then it lifts me up into a place of eternal happiness. I used to feel this each time when I would up-end the clothes hamper, much to the annoyance of my very patient mother, where I tap-danced in the clouds while being caressed by the music of the eternal winds. I was literally in heaven and I felt even closer to God whenever it took me there.

I often asked my father if I could have tap-dancing lessons but he told me that it sounded like a silly idea as I would grow up and then get married so as to raise a family; which meant that the money would have been wasted. Such was the mood and consciousness of the times where women were regarded in society as only ever being suitable for marriage and bearing children. The war had decimated nearly an entire generation of males and so good breeding stocks were considered essential; or so we were encouraged to believe.

Undaunted and undeterred I would go to the roller rink and there I would watch other children having dancing lessons. Then I would secretly practice all the moves and steps that appealed to me. As a result of this, my up-ended clothes hamper performances improved I'm quite sure, but even though my techniques may have changed, that feeling of being in heaven never did. To me it was my platform of self expression which took me to a place where I could be myself while feeling all the joy that wanted to come bursting out of my heart. Whenever I would perform my 'routine' high up in the sky then I could almost see God smiling at me; while I loved Him right back each time He did. Any time I look at a clothes hamper now, I remember those wonderful feelings so well.

Surrounded with the love of my family, being able to dance and sing in the clouds while feeling that magical lightness in my heart, allowed me to keep the harshness of life's trials at bay. All this it did while I searched for that illusive completeness which I so longed for. It was to come, but there were many more experiences that I had to go through before I found it.

In this respect, my childhood and the situation that I grew up in proved to be absolutely invaluable to me in many more ways than I could ever have imagined. Life has been, and is, a never ending source of magic and mystery to me, but it's also something that I have come to appreciate has many more layers to it than just the purely physical; or even the dimensional. It appears that time is no barrier when it comes to the subject of love, but never did I hear anything of this nature mentioned to me by anyone in organised religion when I was young. This I had to find out for myself. It had to be this way otherwise I would never have believed it for sure.

It made me realise that life is very much this way for everyone in that we have a need to experience things before we accept the truth of whatever they may bring to us. This awareness has served to explain much to me about why it is that many of us choose lives with so many challenges when others appear to sail along on calm seas. I often wondered what these people knew that I didn't. However, since travelling the path that I have, it appears to me that the richness of my experience has changed me because of what I have been able to come to a true appreciation of. In a sense, it's made life more understandable to me where I no longer look at the highs and lows as being good or bad, desirable or otherwise.

In coming to this life with my fears, doubts, apprehensions and insecurities then I faced my challenges only to find a deeper and stronger connection to my faith as well as my trust. By facing my shortcomings while seeing what happened when they influenced my choices then I got to appreciate what it was that I really believed in. Through doing so I also found my true self along the way. The whole incredibly complex process of my life has led me to a point of awareness where I can fully appreciate the extent to which I really do value myself. It has also taken me to a place in my heart where I have a wonderful sense of peacefulness which goes way beyond anything that can be achieved through any other process.

I used to see people who had a great deal of money as being without problems, but now I realise that they too have to cope with life's challenges just as I do. They inevitably have problems but theirs are simply different ones, although none the less valid than mine in leading them to a similar position of self awareness and self respect. Their life journeys are planned to reflect those qualities which they come into this incarnation with while giving them the greatest opportunities to achieve exactly what I have; but via a route which best suits their needs.

Through my awareness of this I have come to understand that we each have the same opportunities no matter what our particular circumstances may be. The only difference being that we approach our true selves through charting a course which is determined solely by the choices we make according to the situations that we find ourselves in. We are all very much like ships that are navigating across storm scattered oceans while reaching our home ports via unique routes that will have involved many diverse challenges. Each encounter which brings us ever closer to our objective will be completely relevant to the nature of our journey and what we need to experience on the way.

Our vessels are all afloat on an ocean of human existence where, to reach our destination successfully, we must make our own way wisely while being guided by what we feel most drawn towards. In this respect it is absolutely vital that we search for the right 'star' with which to steer by while making absolutely sure that it's the one that is truly reflected in our heart. Thankfully I have found that particular star within the realms of my personal firmament and so it is my sincere wish that you will find yours too. Maybe you already have. Hopefully, what you will read in the forthcoming chapters will enable you to confirm your feelings on this subject or it may even lead you to a better understanding of your true direction in life. Whatever else, it will provide you with a way to gain a valuable insight into how brightly your own star shines while illuminating what it is that you will discover in the process. Everyone has their own personal star but precious few take the time to look for it while many are not even conscious of its existence. Fortunately for you this awareness has already been awakened and so I trust that by the end of this book you will have been able to see things even more clearly.

- Chapter 3 -

Twin Souls - My Initiation into Awareness

My parents were both born and raised in the small sleepy farm town community of Weidman in Isabella County, Michigan. Weidman is situated in a relatively remote rural location, albeit that it's only just less than ninety miles north of Lansing, where the community of less than a thousand inhabitants is surrounded by lakes, farmland and forests. The town itself is quite close to the Isabella Indian reservation which had been established in 1855. It was through the influence of growing up with many of the Indian children that my father gained a deep understanding of, and close connection to, the timeless mysteries of Nature.

As a result of their encouragement he learned to see the world around him from the perspective of a cultural consciousness which had existed for countless millennia. Being so removed from an evolving society, which had little or no regard for anything that couldn't be profited from, my father had been afforded the opportunity to explore many of the wonderful gifts which our amazing planet bestows so freely on us all. His childhood sensitivity and caring personality flourished in such circumstances where he developed a lifelong respect for not only the world which we inhabit but the ancient wisdom of those who shared their knowledge with him.

I'm sure that this is something which he passed on to me as I love all animals and wildlife as well as the plants, flowers and trees which we share so much of our environment with. Since as far back as I can remember, I have felt a great affection for all the creatures of this beautiful world. Although he didn't really share much with me about his times with the Indian people, until he was in the latter stages of his life, he very often showed me by his example. Being as sensitive as I am then it proved to be inevitable that I would be influenced by his attitudes towards not only Nature but also everyone who he came into contact with.

My father also encouraged the compassionate aspect of my personality by what he would allow me to do when it came to caring for whatever I felt drawn to, as I was growing up. This wonderfully kind-hearted and amazingly patient man indulged so many of my various fads and passions. He let me keep everything from parakeets and tadpoles to turtles, my 'huge' Alaskan husky dog Tootsie and my adorable cat Mitzie; plus all the cats I used to feed on the streets. Both my mother and father were so supportive in this respect and so I am eternally grateful to them for the wonderful introduction they gave me to this life.

Due to his having been raised in an area that had always been surrounded by such a diversity of Nature, and then learning about it via the wisdom of the Indian culture, my father was able to pass on to me a much deeper appreciation of the world; far more than any classroom could ever have given me. With very little in the way of entertainment in the early 1900s, and no access to the big city lights to distract him, he had been free to focus on anything which the land around him had to offer. The Indian children were a great source of information insomuch as they knew the ways and customs of the culture which had taught them how to relate to their surroundings and to respect the earth and what it offered. They showed my father the secrets of the woodlands, how to catch fish, all about the animals and wildlife as well as how to respect the 'spirit' in everything.

Through his initiations into their sacred ways of honouring all life, and the world in which they lived, they also taught him how to converse with the trees. I'm sure that they must have recognised a kindred spirit even though he had come from a different cultural background. As a result, my father was able to 'bridge the divide' and in doing so he gained a very special appreciation of our world while treasuring and respecting very many aspects of it. I have no doubt that this contributed greatly to his being able to express his love in the way that he did and why it became so easy for my mother to feel so close to him from such an early age.

By virtue of his upbringing, my father had been given the opportunity to rise above the limited conditioning of Western boys and men who were, and are, so often encouraged to suppress their sensitive emotions in order to succeed in a competitive world. Being so isolated from the major influences of this kind of society, and being schooled in the ways of understanding the natural rhythms which govern all life, my father erected very few barriers to expressing his love from an early age. No doubt this was what attracted my mother to him in the first place and why they became so attached from early on in their childhood. To have shared so much from the point of being so young no doubt helped them to forge the wonderful bond which would be needed to sustain them through what proved to be the very troubled times to come.

Growing up together must have been wonderful where the carefree life of a child of those times probably seemed next to perfect. However, as they approached adolescence the prospect of starting a family in a very small town like Weidman was not at all appealing. When it came to the subject of how best to provide for their future then obviously there were much higher wages to be earned in the capital city of Lansing. It must have been a difficult decision, as well as quite a scary one, but at the age of seventeen my father decided to leave behind the sleepy environs of Weidman so as to move to the 'big city'. Once there, he would become a part of the ever expanding industrial workforce; albeit that it proved to be an environment which was completely alien to him.

I have no idea how he did it or how he coped with the dramatic change but to me it demonstrated his determination to provide for his future wife and family; even though it meant living in a 'concrete jungle'. From the quiet, unhurried, rural community of a few hundred souls, he gave everything up while plunging into the heart of a huge metropolis while having little or no understanding of what to expect. Fortunately it didn't take him long to find employment with the Motor Wheel Corporation automobile plant where he stayed until he retired after forty six years of service to the company. Going from living in the heart of Nature to spending the whole of his working life in the harshness of a sterile manufacturing environment surely was an absolute labour of love and a priceless gift to our family. I am so grateful to him for all that he did for us.

In the early days of his having moved to the city he would travel back and forth to Weidman every weekend so as to see my mother until she eventually made the move to join him. After they were married she too bravely gave up her relatively insulated existence while having to leave behind her close-knit community of family and friends. I certainly admire her courage and commitment in heading off into a very different world and a highly uncertain future while following her heart along the pathway of true love. Together, with only their love and determination to guide them at first, they made a life for themselves in Lansing. So it came to be that my brother and I were born and raised in the city.

In the latter part of his life, my father would often tell me about the many pressures that he'd experienced through being a 'city dweller'. From how he spoke then I could appreciate that he accepted them as being the inevitable consequences of living in a highly urbanised environment. However, in his telling I also realised that life in Lansing must have been such a contrast to that of living in Weidman. This, no doubt, was why he felt as though he'd lost touch with all that he had been shown and taught about Nature by the Indian children. I can see that it must have been a huge change for him in having to adjust to the relentless demands of city living while working in the challenging and unnatural atmosphere of an automobile manufacturing plant; but, to my way of seeing him now, he really didn't lose anything. He might have thought that the monotony of factory life had caused him to change, as I'm sure that on the surface it must have to a certain degree, but who he knew himself to be in his heart could never have been altered by anything as far as I was concerned.

All of the many influences from what he had been exposed to, and his experiences in those impressionable days of his upbringing, served to firmly mould and shape who he had become. Nothing could ever alter this in any significant way and, although I never knew exactly how he had been in those times, I could easily imagine what he must have been like in his younger days. Even though he had ended up being a 'capital city citizen', those really important formative years were forever within him; so he was still very much a country boy at heart. In truth, he lived up to the old adage that you can take the boy out of the country but you can't take the country out of the boy. I came to realise this for sure when he was nearing the end of his life.

When he could no longer get around very well I used to fetch books on the Indian tribes from the library for him which he would read to satisfy a longing for a life that he missed so very much. He had always been interested in subjects of native cultures, and lost civilisations, as well as very many aspects of spirituality. However, it wasn't until he'd retired that he could spend any time reading up on them. He was very interested in a lot of subjects that people of his day didn't take the time to consider or even want to discuss if they did.

Whenever he would tell me all about what he had found so fascinating then it always gave me such a lot of pleasure in what he shared with me. It also made me feel even closer to him in times when I needed his steadying presence in my life as well. My children were well into their teens in the late 1970s. This was a time in my life when I felt very insecure about many things where the passing of my father was not something that I really felt in any way prepared for. He had been my rock and my inspiration. My essential guide who would steer me steadfastly to that special place wherever I felt it was that I wanted, or needed, to go. It proved to be very difficult to think of his not being with me for very much longer.

Whenever I read to him then I somehow knew that his heart always returned to those carefree times in Weidman where he had felt such an intimate connection to the rhythms of life. I so often had a sense that he was getting ready to go home. In a way I'm sure that his preparation for that eventuality had been greatly helped by allowing himself to renew his close spiritual relationship with Nature. That intimate bond with the mysterious essence of all things which he previously thought had long since been lost to him. Looking back at those days from how I see life now, I am sure that he was aware of a time approaching when he would once more be reunited with my mother.

He often spoke of his deep feelings over her passing as well as how he recalled their being so wonderfully close as they were. Those were such delightfully happy days that it's not hard for me to appreciate the deep sense of loss that he must have felt at their separation. His flame still burned brightly, but it was constantly looking for a way to feel the closeness of its other half until one blessed day in the October of 1978 the angels came to take him home. Once again the two flames could feel their much longed for 'oneness' of an eternal companionship while also sending me their loving energies so as to help me fully recognise my own.

An Emotional Moment of Breathtaking Realisation

To me, in the days when I was growing up, my parents looked as though they had always been together since the beginning of time. I could never for one minute imagine them not being as they were because they seemed to fit together so perfectly; so naturally. Neither could I see them ever being anything other than an inseparable couple who would eventually walk off hand in hand into the sunset of eternally blissful togetherness. For all I knew at that time, they could have actually been born in that state of being a devoted couple. It never entered my mind to think otherwise. However, there would come a time in the not too distant future when I would need to face a challenge which required me to dig deep into my innate faith. It would also serve to remind me of my unresolved sense of aloneness.

Within their loving care, I was raised thinking that all parents were like mine, but from what I saw happening in the families of my neighbourhood and school friends, I learned that this often turned out not be the case. Much later in my life I wondered whether it had been my exposure to the loving togetherness which my parents' demonstrated virtually every day of their lives that gave me the notion that I was incomplete without that 'special' someone in my life. On reflection it appears as though I had actually planned to be with them in order that they would remind me of the fact that there was indeed a 'Mr Right'. That marvellously unique male presence in my life who would prove to be much more than simply an ideal companion and a father to my children; he would be altogether much more than this. My own father had so lovingly presented me with a wonderful example by which I would be able to get much more deeply in touch with a 'sensing' that I had brought with me into this lifetime.

On one occasion, when I was travelling along the highway with my parents and riding in the back seat of our family car, I remember studying my mother and father. I wasn't quite yet ten but my powers of observation were already very keen for my age. I noticed everything, but on this particular day I found myself watching them as they sat in the front seats. They were just being themselves and responding to one another as I'd seen them doing on so many other occasions. This time however, I seemed to be very much more aware of their special 'togetherness' which, for some reason, brought up an emotion in me that I didn't like at all. It proved to be so uncomfortable that I felt as though all I wanted to do was run away and hide; but run away to where and hide from what? I had absolutely no idea as I took in every tiny detail of the two people who loved me most in the whole wide world and who were my devoted protectors.

I just didn't understand why I should be feeling so awful and why I would even contemplate running away from such a loving and caring environment which was so obviously important to my very survival. My mind seemed to be slowly turning to stone as I searched for some kind of explanation to my dilemma, but absolutely nothing came to me. At the very least I was able to appreciate that there had been nothing particularly special about this particular day where my mother and father were just being their usual loving selves. It all seemed so totally unreasonable but for some reason I appeared to be noticing their closeness, their 'togetherness' much more than usual.

I could almost make out the invisible strands of the strong bond which they felt so connected by. It was so strangely magical that it appeared like many precious, sparkling threads woven by some angelic hand which had wanted to ensure that they were never lost to one another. Right at that moment of seeing this I wondered if I would ever be blessed with a similar angel who would come to bind me to my eternal love. To my innocent and inexperienced mind it seemed like an impossibility. This suddenly made me terribly afraid where, even in the presence of such brilliant love, I felt as though I was a captive of some incomprehensible darkness.

The more I looked at my loving parents the more I couldn't imagine them ever being without each other. They seemed to be in such contrast to how I viewed my future existence in having nothing but the companionship of an emptiness that was unconcerned by the yearning of my soul. As my mind reached out to imagine such a prospect I found myself immediately gripped by an overwhelming feeling of my being desperately alone. Not so much lonely but more like being without something so vital that had been lost to me and which felt as if it was in danger of never being found. This sensation proved to be quite overwhelming while pouncing on me right out of the blue.

It made no sense at all for me to feel this way as I was with my parents while being surrounded by their love and protection. Even so, I felt this awful hollow hopelessness in the pit of my stomach which almost made me feel sick. I was terribly confused by the presence of such conflicting emotions which I had no way to understand at that age. I found myself becoming so panic stricken that all I could think of doing was to scream out in the hope that I would suddenly and mercifully wake up from some unbearably suffocating nightmare; but I didn't. My world at that moment seemed to contract into the desperate need for the comfort of a reassuring answer to my dilemma.

Wherever I looked out of the window at all the passing cars then it seemed to me as though there were so many couples of all ages where every woman had her 'man'. Everyone, that was, except me. For some reason I had an overwhelmingly urgent need to know if I would ever find mine. I suddenly wanted someone to tell me if I would ever have one like my mother had and, dare I even contemplate the prospect, would it be possible for me to be happy if I never did. The thought of not finding someone very special to share my life with was almost too much for me to bear. My emotions went into turmoil when I considered even the merest possibility of being alone for the rest of my days. It was so totally devastating to me that it felt as though a heavy weight had suddenly fallen on my body. My mind seemed to freeze as it tried to visualise how any woman could exist without a truly loving husband who would cherish and protect her just like my father did for my mother.

Time suddenly appeared to compress for me where I was clearly able to see myself leaving them so as to start a life outside of my family. I could almost feel the moment when I closed the door of our 'togetherness' firmly shut behind me as I moved across to the cold sidewalk of fearful footsteps and out into the unknown. On to face the uncertain future that time would demand of me. One which I could see no way of enduring without the love and companionship of my man. But where was he and how would I find him? It was all so incredibly scary.

I could see first hand what being in love and sharing yourself with your perfect mate was like and, right at that moment, I wanted that same thing for myself so badly that it seemed as though I couldn't take one more breath. Unless of course, I knew for absolute certain that I would find whoever it was whose presence in my world would make me equally as happy; who would make me feel just as complete, as safe and as loved. As soon as that thought entered my head I looked at my father and wondered if my mother could have ever been happy with anyone else; but then I instantly knew that she would not have been.

I had thoroughly convinced myself that if she had married anyone other than my father then it would never have been the same. They seemed destined to marry and to be happy together while bringing my brother and me into this world. However, in coming to this realisation then it only served to make me panic even more through reanimating my original question. Where was my other half and would I ever be able to find him like my mother had found her cherished other half? Her completeness, her protector and her very best friend in the whole wide world who she happily shared absolutely everything with. What I felt at being able to appreciate this was such a contradiction in the respect of sensing an ultimate happiness as well as the awful panic. This I knew came from the prospect of never finding it for myself. All this seemed to hit me in the very same moment which resulted in my desperately wishing that someone would come to take all the scary feelings away.

Little did I know that my twin soul had actually been making his somewhat faltering way towards me and, in the not too distant future, would be very close by while waiting for us to discover each other. However, looking through the eyes of childhood innocence, and the apprehensions of growing up into an uncertain future, I was simply overwhelmed with fear. Thoughts and feelings raced through me to the degree that I began to become overtaken by a sense of dread which seemed to go way beyond the reality that I existed in. I prayed hard for an answer to my plight as I just couldn't contemplate a life without the man that I knew I wanted to spend the rest of my days on this earth with. I so longed to experience the happiness that my mother and father demonstrated to me each and every day of their togetherness. They were my guiding light towards the promise of a safe harbour which would be filled with the deepest and most abiding love. It was a place that I so desperately needed to reach while feeling cast adrift on an ocean of naive uncertainty and gut wrenching loneliness.

That particular car journey seemed never ending as I wrestled with my deep emotional state. But from how I am able to look at my life now, I can see that it was my awakening into the appreciation of calling my twin soul to me. At that time I could have no clear idea as to how powerful the magnetic influence of the twin soul energies can be in shaping your emotional state and what they encourage you to appreciate. Even though I had been unaware of it within my consciousness, there was actually a part of me which did understand the message and it was speaking to me in a language that definitely did get my attention.

My acute sense of loneliness proved to be my innate sensing of what I was missing, but the strength of the emotion itself resulted from it having been so brightly illuminated by my twin flame energy; although I had no way of knowing this at that time. To me, the whole experience was like waking up in the middle of the night and finding my dearest love not lying beside me in our bed. That awful moment of panic, within the partial state of wakefulness, when a sleep-laden mind tries to figure out what has happened only to conjure up fearful thoughts which then come rushing in to provide some kind of answer.

Those times of panic are the deepest and most disturbing where your emotional defences are at their lowest ebb while your mind offers nothing but anxious confusion. The longing for protection is acute to the degree that escaping back into the shelter of deep sleep is seductive, although not acceptable until there is an awareness of what has happened; and so it was for me. But in the back seat of our family car I had been wide awake and not in any cosy bed.

However, that very same feeling appeared to be present through my 'twin flame' awareness which had alerted me to the fact that someone familiar was missing from my side. This resulted in my desperately wanting to know where he could be found and what had happened to him. My whole being cried out to him but I didn't get any answer; or so I thought. I was to learn that no entreaty to the Divine presence, my guides or my angels ever goes unheard or unanswered. I would come to appreciate that there is always an answer; it's just that the timing of the response where the solution may not come when you expect it to. '*God moves in mysterious ways His wonders to perform*'; never a truer statement had ever been penned. Life is all 'God in Action' where what we perceive as time is simply an illusion.

My illusion at that moment in the car had been one where I was apparently destined to be alone for eternity. However, in truth I was actually awakening to the guidance of my heart through the urgings of my twin flame energy. It had begun the process of leading me to discover a happiness which it knew well from a place that could never be limited by the constraints of time. Had I been able to appreciate it, I was about set out along a pathway of an unprecedented spiritual experience. A quite extraordinary journey that would lead me towards my ultimate fulfilment where the intense sensation of aloneness had been the first indications of a gradually unfolding process.

This thoroughly confusing situation had come about through my having liberated a mysteriously potent energy which I had no understating of. Its only purpose being that of propelling me on that journey so as to ensure that, however many times I lost my footing along the way, I would inevitably reach my intended destination. It would prove to be an amazing adventure and one which I could never have anticipated in my most vivid of dreams. In actuality, my twin soul would shortly be in my life but I had no way of knowing this at that time. He had been making his own remarkable journey towards me and in a few short years would even share the same year of high school while he attended Sexton; which was on the opposite side of the city to mine.

He was getting so tantalisingly close, but in the back seat of our family car in my state of abject aloneness, it felt to me as though he was at the very least on another planet. He seemed so unattainably far away to my overwrought mind but there existed a very wise part of me that knew otherwise. My heart knew where to find him and it wanted me to listen. In time I would do just that but it took a while for me to understand its language. Fortunately for me I had always been keen to learn, so the ever compassionate Divine presence kept gently leading me back to school for more tuition. The lessons, however, would not be listed on my high school curriculum and nor would my grades appear on any kind of report card. God does not judge in any way whatsoever and so we always get an 'A star' no matter what we do.

- Chapter 4 -

Settling for the Fashionable Norm

Bob and I first started dating not long after I had turned 14 and we were both attending the same year at Eastern High School. I was attracted to him partly because he had a similarly confident, self assured manner to that of my elder brother Leonard Dean; who was more than nine years my senior. Having grown up with someone who was keen to sample just about everything that life had to offer in those days, I had already been exposed to the world of adolescent males from an early age. L.D. seemed to have an amazingly large circle of friends, and others who knew him, from all walks of life which often left me wondering how he had managed to meet so many people. It made me curious about how things would be for me when I got older and if my social world would ever be anything like his.

Even though we were typically elder brother and little sister, who would often endear herself to him by doing things like flicking toothpicks into the mouth of his saxophone whenever he was practicing, he was always very protective of me. I realise now that it was just his way of demonstrating his love for me, but at that time I had got into the habit of having it around; so moving 'solo' into the world of seniors proved to be more than a little scary for me.

Starting at Eastern High, while having to wait for my slightly younger best friend Susie to catch up with me, I naturally felt the need for someone else's protection having been so used to that of my brother. High school felt like I was actually stepping into the sacred echoes of his world while walking the hallowed hallways which had once been shaped by his influential presence within them. So, when Bob came along with his air of intriguingly cocky arrogance and he seemed to find me irresistibly attractive into the bargain, I kind of latched onto him quicker than you can say 'freshman'. I must have attached myself to him pretty firmly because, before I knew it, he and I were considered as being an 'item' by almost all of our classmates and budding friends.

Even before I met him I'd had been keen on boys for as long as I can remember; after having been exposed to the often intriguing social language and behaviour of males who were a lot older than me. None of L.D.'s friends really took any notice of me as I was too young to attract them, but I was certainly conscious of their presence in my life while often wondering how things would be when I grew up and started dating. Observing my brother, especially with his girlfriends, was fascinating as it all seemed so different than what I had experienced when studying how my mother and father were with each other. It appeared to be like two different worlds to me. So by the time I met Bob I have to admit to being more than a little curious in wanting to find out for myself.

Fortunately for me L.D. was a popular guy who had been into everything, including playing sax in a band, which meant that he got invited to lots of exciting places. Sometimes I got to go these places with him and he even took me flying while throwing his little plane around the skies, no doubt to impress me and my somewhat ashen-faced best friend Susie. He treated everything as an adventure where he was like a kid who had been given the keys to the candy store. So, by way of his example, I got to see life through the eyes of a 'pioneering' teenager who I looked up to for inspiration and also secretly admired. I have to admit to being very proud of my very own personal 'superman', aka L.D., and I'm happy to report that I still am.

Even though I wasn't old enough to fully appreciate much of what was happening in the world around me at that time of my life, he did open my horizons up in the respect of showing me what was possible. L.D. seemed to always be probing the boundaries of a slowly transforming society and his attitude towards it. In the process of doing this, he gradually uncovered the steps of a pathway which his intuition showed him that he wanted to tread. I didn't realise exactly what he was doing at the time but somehow, somewhere in the alertness of my consciousness, I must have understood what he was trying to achieve. This is something which I am very grateful to him for showing me. As I moved into my teens, it really did help me find my way into exploring many of the often confusing traits and capricious tendencies which kept appearing within my developing personality.

High school turned out to be a wonderful environment for me to delve into the uncharted depths of a quickly emerging 'me' while indulging this dimension of my needs. In this respect I found myself taking advantage of every available opportunity to venture tentatively into the realms of my budding sexuality. The inhibiting uncertainty of my younger days, where I so often felt that I didn't fit in, had gradually given way to a greater confidence in my attractiveness. There was however, always a subtly nagging feeling in the recesses of my consciousness that it hadn't been completely eliminated from my emerging femininity.

Sometimes it would make an unexpected appearance while often getting the better of me where my 'antidote' would be to throw myself into lots of different activities and some pretty intense experiences. During these times of venturing quite far outside of my comfort zone I would actually get to appreciate how I truly felt about myself and my life. Whenever I threw caution to the wind, just like L.D. had shown me was possible, I would revisit and revitalise the feeling which he had so firmly implanted in me. Each time this happened I would once again get to appreciate that life exists to be sampled to the fullest while wishing that nothing would ever get in the way of my doing so.

All throughout those days of youthful exploration, there seemed to be so much that I wanted to know a lot more about. It was obvious to me that I wasn't about to waste any opportunity which presented itself. Whatever happened, I was determined not to allow even the slightest potential for any feelings of insecurity to come creeping back into my consciousness and then undermining me. At that time I had no idea where this level of determination came from, but looking back I certainly am glad that I paid attention to it. I realise now that it was actually an aspect of something, some wise guiding force, which helped me keep moving in a direction that I really needed to have my attention firmly focused on.

The mid 1950s were still overshadowed by the remnants of pre-war oppressive conservatism but my generation was fast growing up into a mood of wanting to usher in a new spirit of freedom. The generation gap was already starting to be quite noticeable, even at my age, where teenagers were creating their own society guidelines which were often a lot more broadminded than many considered acceptable. One particular area of this liberated attitude, which got my attention early on, was in the expression of physical attractiveness and how it affected relationships. I enjoyed this particular facet of my 'world' very much and, in this respect, I often gave thanks for the fact that I had been born female. It felt right to me to be a girl and I was, by that time, comfortable in being who I considered myself to be; even though I didn't always see eye to eye with the society around me.

From what I observed, there appeared to be much more in the way of expectations of how women should behave in all walks of life than there were for men. The rules seemed to be completely different for us girls, which I found perplexing although they could also be quite intriguing, not to mention advantageous at certain times as well. The less attractive aspects of this situation were some noteworthy characteristics of my society which I very much hoped would change; but again, they reminded me of how important it was to have a man in my life. I had no idea what made me notice this so much as, at a conscious level, I simply took it for granted that most every girl felt the same as I did.

There was no way for me to know that what I could feel so acutely was actually the need for just one 'special' man; my Mr absolutely Right. Neither did I understand how I could be so sure that he existed and why I felt the unremitting urge to keep searching for him. In hindsight I can appreciate now that something amazingly powerful was always present which kept reminding me of this particular need, although it's taken me a lifetime to understand the true nature of this mysteriously compelling force. Not simply what it is but precisely how it works in all of us as well.

In those frenetic days of exploring not only the world around me but also trying to find myself as well, I had no appreciation of just how much I needed a 'compass' to steer by. I was completely unaware of the fact that we all come with one 'built-in' and that all we ever need to do is to be constantly watchful for whatever it shows us. In this respect I'm certainly very glad that I did, on certain important occasions, actually take notice of mine as there always seemed to be so much that was vying for my attention; especially when it came to the subject of modern fashions and beauty.

In those days of budding commercialism I found myself being surrounded by all manner of competing messages and images which others wanted me to accept. Sometimes it seemed as though the preacher of my past had found a new vocation after having moved into a different area of sales! I have to admit that there were quite a few of his new 'sales pitches' which I found more than a little seductive, but there were also many aspects of his emerging 'idealised' world that I really didn't like too much at all. Somehow there seemed to be a sizeable element of dishonest manipulation to it all, in almost the same way as that which I had encountered while listening to the sermon from hell. None of which did anything to inspire me. Back then, the fiery rhetoric had been delivered to a totally rapt congregation of highly impressionable listeners, myself included, but now the 'con' was much more subtle and carefully tempered while reaching a vastly wider audience.

In the first instance the preacher had been pretty obvious to spot through the sheer forthrightness of his personality and the theatrics which accompanied his messages. Not so easy to discriminate were the subtle messages of advertising as well as the accompanying commonly held social opinions of those who could influence me; along with many others like me. Mostly I tried to ignore the obvious negative aspects of whatever I deemed myself to be in disagreement with but it wasn't at all easy given the constant bombardment which I found myself faced with day after day.

I am so thankful now for whatever guided me to create those precious interludes in my everyday life. Those brief pauses where I could enjoy a quiet time and then journey within so that I could stay in touch with my true self as much as possible. I have no idea how my life would have turned out if I hadn't done this. I can see now that there was already an awareness and sensitivity within me which must have been the catalyst for so much of what I did as well as the choices I made. It may explain why I had such a strong sense of association with L.D.'s principle of whatever we do in life then it ought to be fun. This was his 'teen-wise' opinion and I wholeheartedly agreed with it.

One thing I used to do, which certainly fell into that category, was to go to see school football games. I loved doing this and hardly ever missed a match between the Eastern High School team and their rivals from Sexton High. The whole spectacle was always so stimulating and thrilling where it gave me a sense of being surrounded by an atmosphere which felt as though I belonged within it. For me, the spirit of the whole occasion seemed to embody just about everything that my generation was growing up with; not to mention the fact that it gave me an ideal opportunity to check out all the latest female fashions as well.

I was thoroughly fascinated by the amazing bright colours, all the animated enthusiasm from the spectators and the players along with everyone who dressed in a way which made such a strong social statement of our times. Every aspect of what I loved to immerse myself in seemed to form an essential part of some sort of cultural commentary on how quickly our world was changing. Everything seemed to be so full of youthful potential while creating a living representation of our place in society as individuals and as high school students. Imaginatively motivated teenagers who aspired to a much brighter future. It really was a lot of fun to be a part of as well as being very freeing to be this way.

I remember getting so totally caught up in all the action on the field that sometimes I could almost forget that the rest of the world existed. Something inexplicably fascinating so often drew me completely into the spirit of the contest while I found myself surrounded by so many different people of my own age who were enjoying the games just as much as I was. The frequent high energy struggles between the opposing teams really used to capture my imagination. Not to mention the fact that they caused frequent stratospheric peaks in my adrenaline flow while I did all that I could to encourage my side to win. Wanting them to triumph over the other army of 'warriors' seemed like the most natural thing for me to want to do, but for some strange reason it also felt as though I'd done it before.

I somehow had a sense that not only had I experienced these same feelings at some other time but I could also appreciate that I had expressed them equally as passionately in a completely different setting altogether. Whenever I caught a glimpse of this emotional parallel, I would get a kind of momentary feeling like déjà vu. However, at that time I had no idea why I should feel this quite stirring sense of familiarity with what I often found myself getting so involved in. It wasn't until very many years later did I get to understand what significance two sides battling it out in pursuit of victory actually had for me. This would come as something of a stunning revelation when I was told the reason behind this quite evocative emotion.

Aside from the actual matches themselves, I especially loved to watch the Sexton marching band parading up and down the field while their music lifted my spirits in anticipation of what I knew would come next. I always thought that it was the music which had attracted me so much but this turned out not to be the case. Little did I suspect that in the midst of the musicians there was someone who kept calling to me in his unique and compelling way while my heart responded; even though my head had absolutely no idea what was going on.

How different things would have been for me if I had realised that my twin soul was so close by while sending out his messages in the hope that I would recognise them. I surely did hear his messages at one level but sadly there was far too much else going on around me at another level for my consciousness to make any sense of what they were telling me. My mind had only been aware of what I was seeing and hearing in my immediate world, but thankfully another part of me altogether turned out to have been listening quite intently. This wonderfully innate aspect of our humanity is present in all of us but, like so many others in a similar situation, I had not understood the language of its communications or even what 'frequency' to tune-in to.

There was no doubting that my ever-vigilant antennas were highly sensitive while being attuned to any incoming transmissions. Sadly for me the receiver was situated in an area of my intuition which I hardly ever visited. I didn't even know it existed at that time so I really had no clear way of knowing what was being said to me. Fortunately these messages never get ignored in any of us while something quite magical, a powerful unidentifiable aspect within each of us, carefully and lovingly stores away all of this information. In doing so it patiently waits for any suitable opportunity, however small, to bring to our attention whatever it is that we need to be aware of at that point on our journey. On those times of listening to the heart-spun communications of my twin soul, which came drifting lightly into the core of my yearning twin flame self, I could hear the calling of the ages. In so doing I became aware of a very special part of me which resonated with more than just a sympathetic musical harmony.

This in turn enabled me to discern a highly intelligent and eternally powerful energy which had threaded its way through limitless dimensions of time and was now only a short distance away from me. My true love, my knight in uniform who played such wonderful music which spoke directly to my heart, was so tantalisingly close; unfortunately he would not come close enough for me to fully recognise him until some point later in my life. Long after that blessed time did eventually arrive I would get to appreciate just how irrepressible this unerring energy had been while ceaselessly searching for its beloved 'split apart'. Only then would I be able to marvel at the true magic of how I had been presented with an attraction which I simply couldn't ignore. There was no way that it was ever going to let me and I am so incredibly grateful to it for being that way; although it did take me quite some time before the incredibly magical revelation of its message finally got through to me.

As it was, I made my way through the highly distracting maze of teenage life while largely basing many of my conscious choices on the influential opinions, images and expectations which surrounded me. Bob seemed like a really nice guy and we got on well together while sharing a lot of common interests which gave me an even greater insight into the still confusing world of men. In my opinion he was good looking and respectably ambitious so he made me feel as though he measured up to the image of what was considered to be a 'good catch'. This worked in well with what I had been taught was the way that a girl should be in the 'modern' society of those times.

I could confidently hold my head up when I dated him while feeling that we were a 'couple' who could hang out with other couples where we all played 'house' in preparation for things to come. Marriage was not far off on the horizon of a mid teen's mind where our society seemed to demand that you make a match early in your life. This, apparently, was so that you could begin building your nest while hoping to start a family of your own as the nation needed to replenish its prime 'breeding stocks' after the ravages of war. My country needed me; or so I was led to believe.

This proved to be yet another 'social' pressure on all the teenage girls of my time and was a message that came loaded with expectations which left little room for liberal choices or thinking. We were constantly told in no uncertain terms that those awful years of conflict had taken far too many of our men and boys. It was said that an entire male generation had been severely depleted which left us females in no doubt that we would have to compete to find a good one. The not-so-subtle message to us all was that we should grab a prize early on and then hang on to him for dear life. Inevitably this resulted in a great deal of status being gained from 'getting your man' and then doing your bit to raise a family; while he went out to work so as to provide the necessary support of course.

I had been a willing contributor to this particular notion of the great American dream because I knew no different; or, at least, that's the impression I created for the sake of all those around me. At that time it suited me to play along as I felt confident that there was a purpose for me even though my heart appeared to be somewhat reticent about the subject as I recall. In this period of my life, when my twin soul messages were piling up on the desk in the backroom of my intuition, I made a detour; albeit one which contributed a very important stage to my journey while bringing something very precious into my life.

Serendipity is a Mind-Made Myth

Through the hormone rush of my later teens, Bob and I had walked the unsteady path towards the altar where I was eventually married at the tender age, as it seems to me now when I look back, of eighteen. I had chosen to do what had been expected of me; even though I wasn't exactly certain of how love was playing its role in my opting for a destiny which meant leaving my single 'free-spirited' life behind. I told myself, in my moments of doubt, that I had just been successful in my quest to become a 'woman of my age' while I looked forward to being accepted into the adult world of married couples. Again I was to realise later on, that the ever-present need for me to find the completeness which I lacked had also played its part in the influencing of my choices.

It certainly had been a strongly motivating factor when it came to the subject of my getting married. However, my problem was that there were too many messages coming at me for there to be any sort of clear understanding or sureness of purpose in my footsteps. At that time I was functioning on a level which made me susceptible to a variety of socially conditioning influences. Many of these were quite convincing to the degree that it often felt as though this idealised marriage would be the perfect solution. It wasn't, but thankfully there most certainly was a Divine purpose to it. This proved to be yet another hidden aspect of my journey that I would come to fully appreciate later in my life.

So I made the trip down the aisle and into a different existence which I hoped with every fibre of my being would herald the start of a brand new chapter in my life. This I did while praying with all my heart that it would be a happy one. Even so, my footsteps were a little hesitant almost as though they knew that I was not yet treading the path of my heart's true intent. Patience and trust were needed in equal measure. My guardian angel watched over me, as ever, but I had been far too caught up in the confusing emotions of the occasion to appreciate what was actually happening; or why. However, I must have been aware at some level that there had to be a good reason why I had chosen to do whatever I had set myself up to experience. Somehow I must have known that the outcome of my decision would eventually lead to the production of three absolutely wonderful children.

Three beautiful souls who would come to grace my journey through motherhood by agreeing to bless my married life with the gift of their unique presences. My first two were boys, Elde (pronounced L.D. after my bother) and Dale Dutter, who were shortly followed by my beautiful daughter Robin in 1964. Even though it may appear very much as if my first experience in being a wife was something of a detour, it certainly turned out to be one that I was very happy to have made; if only to have created my three precious children. Married at eighteen and my first child shortly before my nineteenth birthday. What a 'rush' in every sense of the word! But this had been just as it was expected to be. It was the norm for that era. Nothing would be viewed as being out of the ordinary where I was simply another wife and mother of the times who would be seen to be doing her bit so as to live out the 'dream'.

But it turned out to be someone else's dream and one which I would need to change in order to be completely true to myself. It took a lot of drama and inner searching to do this but what my choices eventually led me to, happily turned out to be the peacefulness of a fulfilment which defies description. All throughout the time of my marriage, and while I was growing up, there had been an ever present 'pull' within me which kept wishing to guide my footsteps. I had no conscious appreciation of this as it so often proved to be very subtle, but its constancy kept bringing things into my awareness so as to get my attention; whenever I was willing to take notice. Fortunately for me I did, whenever it really mattered, and so it was to be that I eventually followed my heart; despite what my head would very often insist that I consider as being the 'right' thing to do.

Thank God for the brightly burning wisdom of my twin flame spirit and also for its wonderfully illuminating and enduring presence in my life. Thank God for football matches where they had a band that played music which carried messages that I so much need to hear. Thank God for my infinitely patient guardian angel who kept giving me little clues so that I would eventually spot the next breadcrumb on the trail towards a happiness which exceeded any of my most fervent expectations. Thank God for Ron's guardian angel who did the same for him as he made his convoluted way towards me; while battling through the often darkly wooded areas that lay strewn across his pathway.

How incredibly complex is this life that we lead but what truly remarkable and mysterious intelligences there are at work which play such a vital role in all of our journeys. Where would any of us be without the guidance of a benevolent wisdom which tirelessly keeps us heading towards our ultimate happiness? No one who has truly experienced 'life' in the fullness of its expression can honestly say that they don't believe such a thing exists. If it didn't then how on earth would any of us navigate the myriad pitfalls that await us along every step of our journey, rich and poor alike? In comparison to the truly awe-inspiring wonder of the universe, we are but children playing in the kindergarten playground who desperately need the supervision of enlightened guidance and compassionate understanding. I find it inconceivable that anyone could possibly believe that we get through this life without any help from supportive sources which we have no comprehension of.

Whenever I reflect on my own journey, and all that I chose to do, then I constantly marvel at how things turned out for me. But when I consider how it was possible for me to eventually meet up with my twin soul, after appreciating what had happened to him as well, then it just addles my mind in trying to figure it all out; so I don't bother. Ron's eventful journey had brought him across from the other side of the border in Canada and through state after state until his final move from Illinois. He left Peoria to come to Lansing and got himself a place playing in the high school band which I watched at every football game. It just amazes me every time I think about his journey in that, just one different choice by his parents would have meant that I may possibly have missed him in this lifetime.

Could this all have been put down to mere coincidence, purely happenstance? Out of all of the places on this planet he simply happened to end up living just a short distance away from me and then playing in a band which marched right in front of me. Some people simply call it good fortune or a product of fate or even that it was a random event which could be explained away by the law of averages; or whatever. Let me assure you that anything which is said in this manner is the result of a feverish mind which desperately wants to rationalise something in terms which will make it feel safe. My journey and Ron's served to teach us both that to evolve in this life then we have to move beyond the confines of our limited thinking. If you doubt this assertion then take a good look around you for tangible evidence of what 'mind' has created.

Becoming a mother so young in my life opened my eyes to a new way of looking at a great many things that had once influenced me so strongly. After all the uncertainties which the world around me had created, I suddenly had no doubts at all about the preciousness of our existence when I held my first child in my arms. From that moment on, the focus of my world was directed towards someone who depended on me every minute of the day. He was suddenly my reason-to-be and, within the atmosphere of our wonderfully intimate bond, I got to find out more about not only myself but also the magic of creation; with all its unfathomable mysteries and unanswerable questions in the process.

In my arms I held an incredibly beautiful creation which I could never get over the fact of being blessed with. This little bundle of joy had come into my life while trusting me to look after and protect him come what may. A little life who knew instinctively that I would love and care for him without his being able to communicate with me in any way which society consciously recognises. Every mother understands this, while 'science' has absolutely no comprehension of what constitutes this quite remarkable interchange of awareness. It must be evident from this state of affairs that there are forces at work which are way beyond our abilities to understand. Similarly within the nature of our Universe, so it is with the way in which our soul energies communicate with their twin. There truly is much more to life than what we observe simply happening around us. Our blinkered society insists that '*Seeing Is Believing*' but we really have to move far beyond the limitations of this unhelpfully naïve assertion if we are to make any kind of meaningful progress in our evolution as a supposedly intelligent species.

I firmly believe that no matter what may have happened to Ron and I on our journeys, through whatever different choices may have been made along the way, then somehow we would still have found each other. I just know it to be true. I can't explain it and I don't want to because any explanation would simply be misleading, in that our language is just not adequate enough to convey what's needed. There's also another reason.

In the process of constructing any rationale, I would be appealing to your mind and what I'm asking you to do in this book is to move beyond this state of limiting your awareness. I know you can do it because I have, and we are the same. We may appear to be different but in essence we all come from the one source; no matter what anyone else chooses to call it.

The Wise Guide that Dwells Within

When I allow myself to think about all that I eventually came to learn of what happened within the incomprehensible process of Ron finding me, I very often imagine myself acting as his true North. Through doing this I am able to appreciate how I played just as big a part in attracting him to me as he did in stimulating the longing in me to find him. In the same way that he was sending me his messages, I had been transmitting my own magnetic appeal to him which served to constantly influence his 'compass' needle. I realise that these are only metaphors for something which we cannot at present understand, but it's the closest that I can come to describing to you how the process works; and what happens between all twin souls wherever they may be.

Whenever I recall the longing which was in my heart from so early in my life, I can see now how this powerful force further served to light his way forward in those uncertain and needy times of his journey. He, like me, had no conscious knowledge of his deep-seated impulse to search for that certain very special someone, his completing other half. But he had always been aware that something felt as though it was missing from his life. I can see now how this common yearning in each of us was symptomatic of our exuberant twin soul energy which helped keep us motivated towards making those 'course-correcting' choices that would bring our paths ever closer together.

Throughout our teens and beyond, both Ron and I had to wrestle with all manner of different situations which necessitated our making important decisions. Some of them resulted in us moving a little farther away from our intended pathway, but we always ended up doing something that would get ourselves back on track once again: even though we weren't consciously aware of doing it at the time. However, it's apparent to me now that at one important level we were thankfully able to ignore a world which constantly tried to tell us what we ought to accept. A society which demanded that we comply with the norm, the status quo. This it did while insisting that it knew best when it came to the subjects of 'desirability', 'sufficiency', 'fulfilment' or even 'contentment'. Fortunately we were able to rise above these controlling influences through acting on impulses which, at the time, often made no sense to us; or others around us at all.

This sacred level is where our twin soul inspiration comes from and, thank God, it's impervious to any influences which come endlessly flooding in to our consciousness. If you take a moment to think about it logically then it must make sense to appreciate that there has to be an unassailable place within each of us where we can get to pull up the 'drawbridge' so as to resist the onslaught. This world in which we live relentlessly bombards us with all manner of concepts and beliefs which people foist upon us as being their truths or 'ideals' for the formulation of a society in which they can feel safe and accepted. It's important to very many of those people that they are seen as being 'right'. While achieving this they naturally make others wrong. In so doing they create a much needed sense of security for themselves, not to mention creating a sense of superior identity which fits in to their program of survival.

So many people want us to accept at face value every single thing they tell us as being their 'truth' while insisting that it's universally trustworthy. They do this without any appreciation for its suitability or correctness of individual purpose. If we were to simply take on board and act upon absolutely everything which came at us, we'd go nuts in a very short space of time as our lives spin inexorably out of control. So where do we go for guidance if not to the heart of our true self where an answer or a solution, however nonsensical it may appear at the time, is always waiting to be found.

Even though Ron and I were both very grateful for what we had before we met, especially in respect of our children, each of us instinctively knew that there was more to life than what we had experienced up to that point on our individual journeys. Something kept us both searching for that Utopian extra dimension. That magical place in our hearts where a certain peace and joy can be found which only comes when you connect so powerfully with your other half. Our problem had been that neither of us understood why we should feel that way or what this 'more' actually was that we so earnestly wanted. Thankfully what we did do, however, was to trust ourselves to act on our intuitive feelings and to follow where they encouraged us to go at those crucial times when we really need to listen to our inner guidance.

This is not to say that we simply indulged ourselves in catering to the demands of our ego by becoming eminently self-centred, as this is not the way either of us are. I certainly have a strong will, just as does Ron, but many of our decisions which led us to find each other were very often made for genuinely selfless reasons. On numerous occasions this actually resulted in a temporary increase in the level of hardship and unhappiness that we had to endure, but this too is all part of how twin soul forces work in our lives. It's ultimately all for our benefit but it's just that we so often choose not to see it that way.

I'm sure you can appreciate that this is why life doesn't come complete with a handbook included where you can simply refer to any kind of index or oracle when faced with a problem which is in need of a solution or an answer. Our quest to find what we need presents us with the opportunity to learn and evolve while making choices which always bring their inevitable consequences. How we choose to label the results of our actions is up to us while using terms such as 'good' or 'bad' is unhelpful to say the least. The perfect solution to anything which perplexes, confuses, perturbs or even frustrates you must always come from within; and that's why it's important to trust whatever you hear when posing any question. Carefully listening for the quiet voice which comes to give you this answer is the key; but it takes practice! I promise that I will give you some very important and helpful pointers on how to go about doing this later on in this book.

In Retrospect Wisdom Reveals Itself

Whenever I look back to whatever my feelings may have been on the subject of my being somewhat 'socialised' into doing what was expected of me, I am now able to see things as they really were. On the one hand I can be that anxious, fresh-faced 18 year old who had to contend with the prospect of becoming a new mother and wife while not knowing what the future held for me. But, on the other hand I can be the patiently wise grandmother who is able to calmly look down on the 'illuminated' pathway through the maze while knowing that everything always works out for the best if we only ever follow the directions which come from within.

If I'd chosen to take notice, I would have seen the signs early on that my marriage to Bob wasn't ever going to be one that was made in heaven. I had latched on to him in the early days of high school as there was no one else to help me navigate the confusing environment which I found myself in; as Susie wasn't yet on the scene. In keeping with the old 'modified' adage that 'familiarity breeds consent', I chose to spend a lot of time with him while putting inconsiderate behaviours down to the immature growing pangs of an adolescent male. He took me to the football games and dancing where we quickly grew to be a couple who seemed set to make a life for ourselves through getting married and raising a family. I have no regrets at all about any of this as Bob gave me three wonderful children and I am grateful for all that we shared together on the briefly converging paths of our separate journeys.

Things look quite different to me now than they did back when I often had difficulty imagining what was going to happen the very next day, leave alone what may possibly happen in another part of my life. I had heard it said on many occasions that wisdom comes with age but it really is no use telling a pregnant 18 year-old this when a new soul is shortly to arrive and there is no helpdesk number which comes with it either. Life is very much a process of 'learning-on-the-job' but where is the teacher when you are most in need of instruction? In those situations, waiting to get older is not an option so I give thanks to my guardian angel or whatever it was that inspired me to listen as well as I did. I don't even want to contemplate how my life would have turned out if I hadn't been encouraged to pay attention to what I felt were the right choices for me to make when it really mattered. God bless my twin flame wisdom for its amazing presence in my life as well as its infinite patience while it kept on presenting me with whatever I needed to be aware of. I'm so glad for all those occasions when I chose to listen to whatever it was telling me. How well do you listen to yours?

It's quite obvious to me now that I was being guided along my pathway from very early on in my life so that, at one point, I would meet Ron. Then I would know that I was done with my searching. It's also amazing to think that even during those years when we were both in our first marriages we actually lived only just a few short blocks away from each other. This must have meant that our paths crossed or came very close to crossing many more times than we will ever know. Sometimes I imagine that we could have been walking around in the same store or the mall while each of us was just out of sight of the other. Maybe we even just missed bumping into one another in the same doctor's waiting room, or anywhere similar in the area where we lived. I still can't believe how close he was to me for all of that time until we finally met and 'recognised' one another.

His journey had been very different from mine but it really does show me so clearly how he is my other half in the respect of what he chose to experience on his way towards me. Whenever I visualise him wrestling with all of his trials then I see myself with much greater clarity because he is the mirror of my spirit as well as the brilliant light that reflects the power and quality of my own. He truly is my twin soul, my eternal twin flame. Through my appreciation of this I came to understand that our twin soul shows us, in a truly unique way, a characteristic quality of our personality which has no language to describe it. Whatever else you take from this book, I sincerely hope that you will consider listening for your twin soul while trusting to your inner guidance to take you where you most sincerely need to go. In doing so you will come to appreciate a great deal more about yourself than you ever thought possible.

To give you a better feel for much of what I have said about Ron, I would like to give you a more complete insight into his life which will hopefully bring you a greater depth of understanding for what I have made you aware of up to this point in time. His story is really fascinating for more than just the reason of knowing about someone else's journey, as there is more than one dimension to what he has experienced. This you will come to understand later on as it will lead you into a quite challenging perspective of our humanity which may well surprise you in its content and implications. It will also very probably expand your personal horizons when you come to consider and reflect on the path of your own journey in this incarnation.

Trust me, there is far more to it than you ever imagined.

- Chapter 5 -

My Twin Soul's Journey

Ron was born in the early part of September 1940 just a couple of months before me and was the only child of Stanley and Marie Darling. At that time his Canadian parents were living in Kitchener Ontario but early in his childhood, when he had just turned eight, they decided to cross the border into America so as to seek a better life for themselves. This was the start of the pattern for the forthcoming years as his ambitious father chased after more remunerative positions in his line of work. In those uncertain times, just after the end of the Second World War, Ron's father did his best to improve the prospects for himself and his family even if it often meant relocating to wherever it was that presented the best opportunities.

America was in the process of rebuilding and rediscovering itself after the long years of struggle with its military efforts in Europe and the Far East. This meant that skilled people were in demand as all areas of industry and commerce looked forward to the rewards of peacetime; as well as the uninterrupted period of economic growth that was to follow. News had always been big business as it served the needs of those who wished to be kept up to date on whatever was happening in both the local and national worlds. This inevitably meant that newspapers needed staff and supplies. Ron's father had always been astute when it came to recognising the prospects which were frequently springing up all around him and so he made sure that he took advantage of everything which came his way. Constant relocation became a way of life which he considered necessary to achieve this.

The Darling family actually moved a total of seventeen times while crossing from state to state before they ended up in Peoria Illinois when Ron had reached the tender age of thirteen. The outcome of all this, for Ron and his somewhat overanxious mother, was that they experienced nearly six hectic years of disrupted home life while never having the chance to settle for very long in any one particular place. After having to cope with the stressful uncertainties of a world at war, his mother then had to struggle with even more disruption to her life through never being allowed to create the stable loving home environment that she so longed for.

This all took its toll where her fears and anxieties led to her being overprotective of Ron to the point where she developed a dread of even the slightest disease or illness which might affect him. He was however, never in any doubt as to how much she loved him, although her way of expressing it often caused him to withdraw very much into himself. The consequence of this, in combination with his having to relocate so much, was that he didn't enjoy the kind of socialising childhood that others of his generation experienced. As a result, Ron became studious and hard working so that he could easily adapt or be readily accepted into whatever environment he found himself having to survive in.

This self taught ability was to serve him well in his adult years but his perceived lack of a normal home life proved to be a big challenge when it came to making the difficult choices that he would have to face during the latter part of his first marriage. The constant upheavals that he had to endure, combined with the nervousness expressed by his mother, caused Ron to feel that the world which he inhabited appeared to be anything but a safe place to live in. It also gave him the impression that it was quite a lonely existence. This feeling no doubt resulted from his lack of developing the social skills that would have naturally evolved from his having enjoyed a stable and settled childhood. Inevitably this all took its toll on his emerging personality but nothing ever touched the wonderfully sensitive and caring soul that was his true self.

It was from Peoria in the state of Illinois that the Darling family embarked upon the final leg of their long journey to my home city of Lansing; after what must have seemed like a never ending trek through one temporary home to another. I can only imagine what his school life must have been like in having to adjust to so many new environments time after time while never being anywhere long enough to make friends or to forge meaningful relationships. One of Ron's challenges was that he had to constantly adjust to being the 'newcomer' in grade school while setting himself even farther apart through his having a different accent. This did nothing to encourage any kind of outgoing nature in him or to inspire a positive degree of self-assurance in how he related to his social situation and people in general.

In those formative years of his life it was so important for him to have the experience of interacting with other children of his age over a long period of time; but this was not to be. So, instead of making his way confidently in the world of his peers, Ron withdrew into the solitude of his own company where music and reading became the mainstays of his young life. This left him in the unenviable position of having to grow up while dealing as best he could with his own emotional issues; which must have been a real challenge for such a sensitive soul.

There was also another disadvantage to travelling so much in that it meant leaving behind his ties with friends and relatives in his home town of Kitchener. As a result, he didn't even have the constant influence of an extended family in the form of cousins or aunts and uncles. This must have made him feel ever more dependent on his mother and father for support. All of this certainly did have an impact on the aspect of shaping his personality but Ron was a resourceful soul who had come to this life with a certain indomitable strength of character, although it wasn't until much later that I discovered why this was. His challenging start in life had actually been that way for a purpose and one which he would learn a great deal from while his twin flame energy guided his footsteps through many difficult trials and soul-searching tribulations.

Everything that he experienced throughout those impressionable days of his youth proved to have a lasting impact on him. This was something which later served to form his strong desires in wanting to create a stable home life for his own family. It was however, also a contributory factor in causing him substantial problems in his married life when it came to making decisions about disrupting the stability of his own children's wellbeing. Ron's early experiences naturally made him very sensitive to the needs of a child. After going through all that he had encountered while growing up, he was especially protective when it came to the subject of breaking up the home that he had created for his family.

This degree of his sensitivity would also present him with yet more challenges when it came to choosing between his own needs, while listening to the influential energies of his inner guidance, or holding on to all that his experientially conditioned mind kept telling him that he had worked so hard to create. Ron was never one to shrink from any challenge, however daunting a prospect it may have appeared, but there were some that I would have preferred him not to have faced in how I saw that it affected him. I found his sensitivity to be one of the very many qualities which attracted me to him but it certainly did present him with a lot of high mountains to climb while on his pathway towards the fulfilment of his life's spiritual quest. Fortunately there was always the guiding light of his twin flame that kept his path illuminated however deeply he wandered into the various detours of the darkest woods.

It seems remarkable to me now, when I consider all that he went through in moving from place to place, that he actually managed to get here to Lansing at all. So many unpredictable circumstances which spanned the thousands of miles they must have travelled while his father chased down the ultimate prize or opportunity. Along that precarious route it would only have taken just one different choice to have produced the unthinkable; me never having found my twin soul in this lifetime. I shudder to think of it even now as I have no concept at all as to what my life would have been like without my beloved Ron; my most precious, eternal other half.

As so much of life has taught me, in how I have seen things pan out in such amazing ways, quite evidently there was a Divine hand at work which unerringly guided our paths toward the same destination. The truly mysterious nature of that Divinity would take me a long time to even begin to comprehend but the journey towards it would be more spectacular than any physical one that I could ever make.

Whenever I would listen to Ron tell me about all the different places that he lived then I could only marvel at what incredible intelligence and wisdom had been at work behind the scenes. Whatever it was, it somehow got him from Ontario through seemingly endless moves until he was only just a few short miles away from me in my home city. How could I not believe in the sublime nature of a compellingly Divine power through appreciating what had happened to bring us together? Putting aside all else that has happened to me in my life, this alone would have been enough to convince me.

Differing Lives - The Contrast of Twins

Ron's life had been very much different from mine in that he grew up in a family of three where his father was often absent from his upbringing. It wasn't so much the absence of his physical presence, because of his work commitments, as that of his inability to express his emotions to him. Ron's father was an intellectual who encouraged his son to an academic way of life while teaching him that achievement and material rewards were all that really mattered in life. Consequently, Ron didn't get to experience the 'togetherness' of a truly loving family such as I did, where both parents are able to express and demonstrate by their example what unconditional love actually achieves. His mother did treasure him greatly but she couldn't compensate for the lack of his father's loving input in his upbringing.

I feel sure that if his parents had been aware of just how lonely Ron felt his life to have been, in having to amuse himself for long periods, then things would have been different. Love had certainly always been present in his family; albeit that it was expressed in ways which he found difficult to appreciate in how he saw things through young eyes. In having to move so often then it proved very difficult for him to make any close friends which meant that he didn't even have the comfort and companionship of someone his own age to confide in. How he managed to cope with his schooling I can only guess at but, despite all the disruption and uncertainties in his life, Ron actually did achieve a lot; not only in his education but also in the world of music as well. From very early on he learned to turn his disadvantages into his strengths, which also fired his determination to excel at whatever he did. Ron was intelligent, just like his father, and so he developed this aspect of himself to compensate for the absence of love that he perceived was missing from his life.

As a consequence of this he escaped into the written word where he read everything from newspapers to comics and encyclopaedias so as to satisfy his insatiable quest for information and knowledge. His reading also enabled him to expand his vocabulary above and beyond his years, but unfortunately it came at a price. The result of this was that it ended up further removing him from the world of potential friends his age because they found it difficult to communicate on his level. Typically, Ron adapted and so he developed a preference for the company of older boys or adults who he could talk to in the way that he wished to; while also getting to know more about a world which increasingly fascinated him.

This meant that he constantly needed to dig deep into his own resources so as to find the confidence which he considered necessary in order to be accepted into society. His way of compensating for this was to become good at whatever he did to the degree that he sought perfectionism while putting his great resources of enthusiasm and effort into anything he'd made up his mind to do. Music became very important to him, either listening to it or making it and so, early on, he began to learn to play instruments one of which was the marimba; it's like a xylophone but has a broader and deeper tonal range. He discovered that he actually had a talent for it and so got very good to the point where, while living in Peoria and playing in a band which he really loved, he had thought about whether or not he would like to take up music as a profession. His father, ever the opportunist, briefly considered being his agent so as to promote his son's talent in a world of endeavour which seemed as though it might be profitable.

His mother tried her best to compensate for the relative lack of a nurturing role model in their family life but this really only served to further isolate Ron from the loving male influence that he needed. His sensitive artistic nature would have benefited greatly from the gentle guiding hand of encouragement, but it was not to be something that he would experience from his father. So, Ron grew up missing something in the same way that I did where he longed for the companionship of another loving soul who he could relate to at the depths to which he felt the need.

His mother had certainly always been very openly loving, in contrast to her husband's intellectual way of expressing himself to his son. Sadly, as a result, it turned out to be a very frustrating childhood and early adolescence for Ron where hard work became the anaesthetic that dulled the pain of unfulfilled love. Although he didn't appreciate it at the time, Ron also had a hole at the centre of his being and was looking for a way to fill it while not understanding how to go about it. He had already started searching for his twin flame, but like me, he had no idea that this was the case while learning to listen to the one thing that would unerringly guide him towards what he so desperately wanted. The quiet but powerful urgings of his heart were already being heard by him. It was a lesson that we both had to learn where the road to true understanding would prove to be a long and bumpy one; albeit that the arrival was certainly well worth the trip.

Much time would pass before Ron got to appreciate just exactly what it was that he wanted, although he told me once that he did have an idea that something had always been waiting for him to find it; even though he didn't have a clue as to what it could be. So he distracted himself by working hard at everything where even at the age of fifteen he joined his father in a venture to provide services to the printing industry; and so they formed the company of Stamp-Rite. This would set him firmly on the path of his business career after abandoning his ambition to become a professional musician. This came about shortly after he began to appreciate how difficult it may have been to make money in the entertainment industry. It must have been very difficult for him to come to this decision in understanding that his talent was never going to be appreciated in the way that he would have hoped. By that time in his early teens he had become so accomplished at playing the marimba that his father actually did go looking for a professional agent who would promote his son into the music business.

Ron's father had obviously been keen to encourage his only son to emulate his ambitiousness while achieving as much, or even more, than he had. This, no doubt was his way of demonstrating the love for him that he couldn't otherwise express in the manner which he may have wanted to. As a result, Ron certainly did inherit his father's drive but it was only harnessed in the direction of making money and being successful in the material world. This, however, was not what would sustain Ron's underlying need to express and receive the love which he so earnestly longed for. The world of business ambition proved to be superficial to Ron but he was never one to do anything half-heartedly and so he applied himself in the only way he knew how.

The one period in his life which had offered him any stability in contributing to his development as a young adult was the time he spent at Sexton High School where he graduated in the class of 58. Fortunately for me he got to join the marching band as a result of his talents where he played the baritone horn. This as what called out so powerfully to me every time I heard him playing at the football matches, albeit that I wasn't consciously aware of it at the time. Ron's ability as a musician and a performer thankfully made him a lot of friends at this school, but having little experience to base friendships on, he was not aware until later life just what a significant effect his presence had made on them. Many would recall a really nice guy who played great music and who gave them all a lot of pleasure at dances, concerts and all sorts of public appearances.

He was greatly admired for his talent at playing the marimba and the organ by very many who had the pleasure of listening or dancing to his music. Even after all that he had been through, in moving from place to place and feeling so insecure as a result of it, Ron proved to be such a bright light in the lives of others who he had once felt so alienated from. In just over three short years while attending Sexton he managed to make a lasting impact on very many people who, at the time, he considered took little or no notice of him. Such was the lack of confidence that he'd developed over the years of his growing up but his ability to excel proved to be his compensation which covered what he truly felt.

This was who he had become and how he continued to be in the way that he lived his life. No matter what the circumstances, Ron would always rise to the challenge while presenting a steadfast example of determination and compassionate expression to the world around him. Nothing would get him down, not even his inhibitions or the insecurities of his youth which he'd coped with for such a long time and even taken on into adulthood. He would always work to find a way of turning disadvantage into advantage and in so doing he would uplift not only himself but very many others whose lives he touched in the process.

Ron actually loved people and only ever wanted to make them happy. This no doubt came about through keenly appreciating his own lack of happiness at being alone so much when he was growing up. His sensing of being without me, even though he didn't understand it at the time, must have contributed to his yearning to search for the love which he knew instinctively that he needed and wanted. Much of his life, like mine, was tied up with experiencing love's desired presence or expression to one degree or another. As a consequence he had developed a keen sense of knowing when it was needed to be given, but he also constantly looked for it in his relationships. This could be with his friends, within his romances or eventually with his children until he finally found me. I was his homecoming to the love which he had been seeking for most of his life. However, in the same way as me, he hadn't realised it until we were finally together.

Ron's unique journey had conditioned him, through his experiences and his family environment, to make choices from the perspective of his need to survive and flourish in a world of competitive males. Through walking this pathway, he got to discover many important things about himself in the process while also developing a determination that would sustain him through what proved to be his ultimate test. We both shared the experience of a family life where each of our situations presented us with what we needed in order to appreciate that there was something missing. Even though it may have appeared to be different for Ron, it actually came down to the same thing for both of us; although we had no true understanding of this at the time.

This common factor led us both to search for whatever it was that we considered necessary to bring about the completeness which we sensed as being absent before eventually finding each other. In those pre 'us' times, neither Ron or I had any idea what it was that motivated our desires to find this vital 'something' which very often didn't make any logical sense. It seems that neither of us ever questioned our urges or sought to get a better understanding of it. This was because we had precious little in the way of wise counsel to draw on within the bounds of our social environments. Obviously this did nothing to alleviate our individual sense of aloneness, but it certainly was an important factor in keeping us in touch with that truly magical force which had always been there to guide us.

That mysteriously magnetic attraction which constantly worked to draw us together. In so doing it inevitably influenced our choices whenever we took the time to listen to what was being said. Ron's parents graciously gave him the opportunity to experience loneliness while being deprived of the love which he felt in need of. Whereas my parents showed me through their example what I felt to be missing from my life, albeit they did it in a very different way. To me, the whole incredible process of our lives is one huge mystery in appreciating how things happen; but the most mysterious of all is the question of 'why' they should happen in the first place. By this I mean, where is the unimaginable intelligence which is behind what we experience?

It's just so much greater than our limited human minds can even begin to comprehend. Ron and I eventually found our ultimate happiness but along the way we had some truly amazing experiences, not the least of which was the gift of bringing six wonderful souls into this world. How could all of this have been made possible for us and what is it which makes life so rich in its diversity of 'adventures' for each and every one of us to experience? Whoever, or whatever, it is that creates this awesome roller-coaster ride of a journey which we call life, it surely goes way beyond whatever I have considered my understanding of a supreme Divine being to be. In my heart I know the answer because I can touch the flame of an eternal consciousness which encompasses the truth of all things, but it's something that I can never put into words. This same truth exists in the heart of every living soul.

- Chapter 6 -

Ron's Passionate Determination and his Trials

Joining with his father in forming what he considered to be the new family business was something that Ron hoped would bring a deepening closeness in his relationship with him. Being only fifteen he really had no idea what to expect but was glad of the opportunity to participate in an adventure which he felt would earn him not only the respect of his father but also that of others who were beginning to form a stable part of his much needed social world. Ron considered that starting Stamp-Rite, as it was called, represented not only the beginning of new possibilities but it would also mark the point at which the family's constant upheaval would end.

To him it was like a big sign that they were putting down roots at long last and that their lives would change from that point on. This time the change would be for the better. Change would mean no more changing places but, instead, changing from insecurity to certainty; choosing to make a stand with confidence while finally giving up the almost itinerant family lifestyle which they had known for so long. Change would hopefully bring love to a place of fertile pastures where it could grow and flourish while being tended to in the peacefulness of its undisturbed surroundings; such was his eternal optimism. To Ron it represented an irrefutably positive omen which convinced him that the long and arduous trek across the desert of seemingly endless loneliness was over at last.

Finally and most thankfully they had reached the oasis of peace and plenty where their new life could prosper undisturbed. For Ron it felt as if his life was really beginning in earnest after having been put on hold for so much of his youth. It came as such a relief to be making a home even if the creating of it felt as though it meant putting yet more effort into something completely new. Although it appeared to be a 'something' that he hadn't exactly dreamed of, to him it represented a start. A wonderful new beginning which promised to be another step, albeit a welcomed step this time, towards wherever his heart wished to lead him; and so he was happy to follow.

Even though he wasn't able to visualise the future in any clearly defined way, it gave him hope through feeling that his freedom was at last more than just a tantalising phantom of his unfulfilled desires. Now it seemed more like an actual possibility. To Ron it offered a new reality but more than that it was something which he felt that he could influence by his own efforts. This fired his aspirations to a level which he'd never experienced before where the undaunted flame of his heartfelt dreams grew brighter inside him at this realisation. The freedom that he so longed for which would allow him to live the life he so desperately craved where the unseen hand, that had controlled so much of his youth, would once and for all be banished to the desert which he'd so recently escaped from. Now he could resist the forces which had so influenced his life up to that point in time, and having appreciated that he was no longer powerless to affect his future, Ron had never been one to shrink from grasping his opportunity to fight for what he wanted.

It didn't matter to him that he knew nothing at all about business because, whatever else, he respected and trusted his father's ability to understand the complex world of finance and commerce. Stanley was Ron's 'commanding officer' in the battle for the Darling family freedom and so it was to be that they took to the campaign table so as to plan for the encounters ahead. Ron was happy to start out as a 'private' in the ranks while he learned the art of business operations and 'tactics'. His father proved to be a good teacher and strategist who soon had their business flourishing while gaining a reputation for the quality of their work and products. Ron was in his element where everything that he'd gone through in the past had almost seemed worth it to have got him to that point. All his reading and fascination with learning about the world around him seemed to be paying off as the business grew while his life at high school also turned out to be just what he'd always wanted.

Wherever he'd been placed at schools in the past then there had never been any problem with how he was received by his teachers. Ron always impressed them as being a model student who appeared to be quiet and attentive in class and who regularly achieved good grades. It was obvious to most everyone that he had a bright mind, but this didn't always sit well with his classmates who felt challenged by an example which they sensed the need to live up to or compete with. Ron only knew how to be himself and had no particular desire to compete, but whatever he did and wherever he went then he was seen as representing a standard which others could aspire to if they chose to do so. Many children, especially in those days, didn't react well to a newcomer who upset their status quo while making waves on their pond although there were always those who admired him and would sometimes even ask for his advice. Ron came across to many as being a kind of talented 'geek' who put more value on studying and playing his instruments than fooling around in class or playing games after school.

His attitudes of perfectionism and diligence were just his way of expressing himself as a result of what he observed his father doing while being his role model; but his classmates had no way of knowing this. From those times of feeling at odds with his generation, Ron now found himself in a position to take advantage of all that he had 'trained' for; which must have seemed as though his destiny had come rushing in to greet him. Without hesitation he threw himself into helping make his father's new enterprise as much of a success as he possibly could. He regarded this opportunity as being one where he was determined to make all of his hard work pay off. In so doing Ron had begun setting out on the path to become a successful businessman while his father paved the way for him by providing the guidance that had been so lacking in the years leading up to that point. Finally, father and son were united but not in a way that either of them could have ever envisaged before that time.

Taking Charge of the Journey

Being in business with his father gave Ron the opening to explore the possibilities of his true potential. In working his way through his graduation as well as being able to make music such as he loved to do, then this combination of circumstances helped him overcome so much of what had been detrimental to him in the past. As the business developed and Ron became more involved then he was exposed to not only understanding how to make money but also how to manage men and machinery as well. He suddenly found himself in a period of his life where everything seemed to be working well for him and for once the chips seemed to be falling completely in his favour.

Everything that he wanted in the way of feeling valued had suddenly become available to him. This in turn provided the platform on which he was able to climb out of the pit of self doubt that had haunted him for so much of his youth. In those latter years of his teens Ron allowed himself to actually appreciate that, finally, he really did belong somewhere and that Lansing Michigan was where he would make his stand while claiming the right to command his own destiny. Ron, while working with his father, had found the courage to reach out for self determination and in so doing he left behind the dark times of uncertainty and loneliness of his past. All of his hard work had paid off in that his knowledge and talents provided him with a foundation which, when laid in a place where he felt safe, would be the basis for building the life that he wanted.

Stamp-Rite was to be the beginning of a new chapter in his life and Lansing proved to the blank pages of the book which he wished to write it on. The capital city held much promise and opportunity with its thriving manufacturing base but it also held the qualities which most supported Ron in his quest to find himself. Had it not been for its nurturing diversity of art and music then Ron's story, and mine, may have been very different but Lansing was filled with the vibrant and stimulating nutrition that his soul had been deprived of for so long. It hungered for so many things which the environment he found himself in supplied in abundance but the one commodity that was still so important to him remained as elusive as it had ever been.

No matter, Ron's optimism was the brightest of beacons which could never have been extinguished however often the dark, stormy night of a difficult past came back to haunt him. It had always been an irrepressible light which had guided him purposefully on towards a secretly dreamed of destination; one which he treasured above all else. This time however, he found himself at the helm and so it was to be his choices that would determine which course his life would take on the pathway to the fulfilling of his desires. His new 'home' had given him the opportunity to finally listen to the quiet voice within but it had always been one that actually called to him from a dimension that he was completely unaware of.

Ron's Poem to Me

- To My Wife -

A few short years ago, a gift of love came to the earth

An infant whose future was an expression of beauty unfolding

Who could know what a priceless treasure had been given that day

To the fortunate people to touch her way?

And the privilege was given to some

To watch something special become

And the child grew and bloomed, like a beautiful flower

Maturing, blossoming, her bubbly fragrance spreading

Touching all in her path with her lightness and love

Now a special lady is here, lighting the world as an angel would

With brightness, femininity, as only she could

She is loyalty, and strength

She is beauty, and charm

She is caring, and delicate

She is Janet

And now the world is warmer, and it smiles

Do you see her? I do

I love you Honey

Ron

- Chapter 7 -

The Gifts and Challenges of a Twin Flame Journey

Although Ron and I had no conscious idea as to the nature of our very special connection before we met, we had both chosen our life pathways to provide us with a deeper insight into love's mysterious magnetism. Ron's childhood experiences allowed him to see love expressed in ways which he considered to be unfulfilling, while I witnessed a display of loving togetherness that I desperately wanted for myself. As a result, our individual journeys proved to be the catalysts which inspired our search to attain that missing essential 'completeness' which we felt eluded us. In our 'aloneness' we each sensed an attraction towards something so real that it almost appeared as if we could touch it. Neither of us had any kind of awareness as to what it was that seemed to call so insistently to us and which kept on motivating us to find it; even though in doing so then what we eventually found was each other.

Ours turned out to be a kind of happy ending story because we never stopped following the breadcrumb trail through the maze, even though much of the time neither of us had any idea that we were doing it. Each of us made important choices for reasons that we didn't fully understand until one day we eventually arrived at a strangely familiar place where our 'prize' was revealed in all its glory. For both of us it had been a completely unexpected discovery which came bursting into view when we had least expected it to. In so doing it took us quite a while to recognise just exactly what it was that we had been led to an awareness of and just how incredibly precious it actually was to us. I don't think that either Ron or I could believe that we had really found what we had been searching for or, more precisely, that either of us even appreciated that we had been searching at all until that moment.

Such had been the disorientating nature of our journeys, with all the twists and turns that they had taken along the way, where our minds had got so caught up in a variety of distractions and diversions that they had somehow almost 'lost the plot'. Our hearts, of course, were well aware of just exactly where we should be heading, but as is the constant dilemma of human existence, we so often didn't take the time to listen as carefully as we should have. Little did we appreciate, however, the amazing persistence and compelling power of a flame which only ever wishes to illuminate our true course through even the most deceptively testing parts of the labyrinth which life presents us with.

Mine was a relatively straightforward route in comparison to Ron's, but it certainly did have its own fair share of un-signposted crossroads and dispiriting dead-ends. Whichever way we chose to view the journeys which we made towards our 'completeness' then they unquestionably were eventfully challenging ones. In the course of their unfolding we definitely got the opportunity to take in a lot of very interesting, and sometimes dramatic, scenery along the way until we finally realised our destination. Nevertheless we did arrive, albeit a little careworn and frayed around the edges but certainly a lot wiser for the trip.

Orientation to our new situation proved to be another challenge, but one which we were happy to take on board while trying to appreciate where we actually were without having a clue as to how we had got there. As a result of this, we both spent quite some time cautiously unwrapping our gift just to make sure that it was real; which of course it was. Neither of us could quite take it all in at first. This was because it felt almost like hearing our lottery numbers being called out on the TV while sitting in a dream-like state and waiting for someone to tell us that it was true. Initially there were fleeting moments of tension where I could imagine holding a priceless gem in my hand while wondering if the jewellery sales assistant would suddenly ask to put it back in the display case.

The only thing that I can compare the experience with is that feeling which comes at the moment when you first hold your new born child. Those precious few seconds where your mind just can't seem to take in the indescribable magic of creation; while trying to understand that you have been a major part of the process. Then, to suddenly realise that an amazing soul has chosen to come into this world while honouring you with its presence, this gift is completely beyond words; but it's a similar depth of feeling that I have for Ron. At times like these you get to appreciate that language has severe limitations when it comes to conveying the true impact which love can bring to your emotional state of being.

So much of the time prior to our finding each other was taken up in the pursuit of exploring our various levels of happiness, which we felt had already been achieved, that we had been quite unprepared to look any further. At that point on our journey it seemed as though our respective lives were very much settled in that we both had our family ties and commitments. In consequence of this we had naturally assumed that these responsibilities would very likely keep us chugging along that same predictable track well into the future. Little did we expect things to change so abruptly.

Apart from the immediate physical attraction that my beloved and I felt for each other, there were signs that started popping up early on in our courtship which let us know that what we had found was something, and someone, quite extraordinary. Ron couldn't seem to get over the fact that I always appeared to be genuinely interested in all that he had to say, just as I was flattered by his attentive manner while I told him all about my life and myself. As a result we shared a great deal with each other, during our wonderfully cosy times at the restaurant and anywhere else we could find to meet, which I have no doubt provided both of us with some very much needed healing.

I could tell that Ron was really pleased to finally have someone who he could confide in and who would listen to the tales of his childhood while being genuinely interested in what he had gone through. I would like to think that my compassionate support helped him come to terms with so much of what he had experienced while having the benefit of my concerned and sympathetic input; which, I'm very happy to say, he respected. Talking brought us ever closer together while feeling that it was the most natural thing in the world for us to do. Sometimes, in the very early stages of our getting to know each other, I used to get the strangest feeling as we were talking that we had done something similar on very many previous occasions. It wasn't until much later that I got to appreciate just why I felt this way as well as what it implied when I happened to meet up with a very gifted psychic while I was in Florida.

In this way of our being together, I got to the opportunity to share my life and my 'troubles' with him as well. I just found it so easy to talk to him. In what seemed like no time at all, I realised that I was telling him things that I hadn't shared with anyone for a long time; certainly not a man. Of course, he would often give me his take on my dramas which inevitably gave me a lot to think about in those early days. Being that we were both parents and having the same number of children, albeit mine were a few years older, we found even more common ground when it came to the subject of parenting.

So we talked and talked as often as we could while simply enjoying the thoroughly disarming familiarity and fascination of each other's company; which tore down so many barriers in an incredibly short space of time. Things just seemed to flow between us where, as I look back now, it feels as though we were playing catch-up. I imagined us as being two very best friends who were so keen to tell each other absolutely everything that had happened to them since they were last together. There was a kind of instant rapport between us which quickly broke through so many years of our social conditioning. So much so that it was easy to imagine us as having been that way forever.

I clearly recall that on many occasions it appeared as though several lifetimes had passed us by where the hours seemed to have disappeared in a haze of blissfully rapt togetherness; which felt so completely familiar to both of us. Those really treasured times were so important to us through their providing a kind of emotional oasis which we were so much in need of at that stage of our journey. To me it gives a lot of credence to the spiritual wisdom which states that there are no such things as coincidences. I have learned that life is anything but haphazard where everything that happens to us and around us is present in our lives for a very good reason.

The down side of all that arose out of my finding Ron was that it threw quite a few of the remaining aspects of our lives into comparatively lacklustre perspective; where it became increasingly difficult to sustain the 'unacceptable'. The lives which, up to that point, we had considered as being what we had strived so hard to achieve suddenly appeared as though they hadn't lived up to our heartfelt expectations. This certainly did cause us problems and a lot of soul searching, especially on Ron's part in that he had no thoughts of ever breaking up his marriage before he met me. I, on the other hand, was already somewhat disenchanted with my marital situation but, even so, we both had to consider the well being of our children in whatever we decided to do in the future. As a result, it certainly turned out to be one spectacularly memorable rollercoaster ride.

Misperceptions about Utopia

You may be surprised to learn that twin souls often don't experience the enduring Mills and Boon type of romantic earthly encounter which many people, especially women, fantasise about. They may choose to experience a different kind of relationship. This however is also an important and valuable aspect of their journey. No matter what, the spiritual 'magic' is always present in whatever situations arise, despite what the external circumstances may persuade the observer to believe otherwise. Indeed, the breathtaking beauty of what evolves from the potential of this truly heavenly 'togetherness' is often difficult to comprehend from an earthly perspective.

My own journey with Ron was to teach me the depth of awareness which is to be gained from walking through this adventure we call life with your twin soul. There is something completely indescribable about sharing this physical existence with your eternal other half while being able to explore aspects of your individuality which would otherwise go unnoticed. This divine flame, which burns brightly in each and every one of us, reaches a spectacular new intensity when in close proximity to its immortal counterpart. When this happens then the light produced by the boundless energy of transcendent love will penetrate into even the darkest recesses of your true self. Oftentimes it takes great courage to look at what is revealed on these occasions as absolutely nothing is hidden from view.

The precious closeness that I was able to share in this lifetime with my beloved twin flame allowed me to explore so many things about myself where his gift to me remains just as powerful now as when he was here on this earth plane. Through his presence in my current life I have been able to experience not only the truly magical energies of a deep and abiding love, but also the challenges which arise as a consequence of our mortality. Life, I came to appreciate, has a multitude of facets each of which reflects an aspect of our 'self' that, at one point or another, we must acknowledge and address in order to evolve. Ron taught me that even suffering and death, when regarded from a higher perspective, are actually opportunities to grow and learn from; in the respect of what is presented to each soul at the time.

From what I have been able to understand then I can appreciate that the degree of challenge encountered on a twin soul's journey is quite specific to whatever is essential to be learned. It also depends on the level to which the individual is capable of progressing along his or her spiritual path. Take comfort from the fact that there is never any situation or circumstance which arises in anyone's life that is beyond the limits of the individual's ability to successfully deal with; this is also true for every other journey we make as well. Each and every opportunity which is offered during our time of incarnation only ever arises for the benefit of moving our consciousness even closer towards a deeper and more meaningful understanding; while existing solely for the highest good of the soul.

Twin flames are gifted with the ability, while being incarnated together, to gain a level of awareness which would otherwise have required countless lifetimes to arrive at. They provide each other with the opportunity to achieve, in one or two lifetimes, what it would be very difficult to learn from any other situation or through being with anyone else however spiritually gifted or enlightened they may be. Inevitably it is always possible to gain certain valuable insights, as is the case with any earthly experience, but corresponding twin flame energies on an earth-bound path bring with them an extra dimension of possibilities. A potential that when it occurs, allows us to touch another dimension of ourselves. This in turn accelerates our spiritual progress while bringing with it an ever deepening sense of fulfilment and inner happiness.

I had often read that the occasions of twin souls actually incarnating together were once considered to be quite rare; but now, fortunately, this is no longer the case. Apparently, the rapid evolution of humankind's spiritual awareness over the past few decades has made it possible for many more souls to benefit from meeting up with their other half. It is however, still far from a common occurrence so imagine my surprise when I discovered that Ron and I had got to share not only this lifetime together but at least one other incarnation that we are aware of. The one before this present lifetime you will read much more about in the following chapters, as well as Ron's amazing story from a different dimension which is his gift to you. His amazing insights which come from a truly fascinating journey will guide you towards an appreciation for many things that will hopefully bring a greater depth of understanding and happiness to your life. Along with this you may well experience a more peaceful sense of contentment to how you view your present situation, as well as how you deal with your future challenges. I sincerely hope that this is the case.

Whatever the circumstances of our lives may be, the lesson is always the same. Love is encouraged to be the sustaining force which brings about the healing and happiness which will result in the raising of our individual vibrations. Along the pathway of a shared physical relationship, not only do the twin flames themselves experience the benefits but so do those who are in close proximity to their powerful energies. Twin souls are like blazing beacons who do much more than just bring healing and evolvement to themselves. They are instrumental in moving others farther along their journey and towards an understanding that would have been considerably more difficult to achieve without their illuminating presence. The combining of their bright flames makes the overall light more intense and so all who come into its sphere of influence are able to benefit; whether they are aware of it or not.

The manifest energy of twin souls however, can oftentimes create varying degrees of discord between them which runs contrary to the popular notion of blissfully never-ending physical attraction; where each walks around on cloud nine all day. Twin souls, you may be interested to know, can actually be brother and sister or mother and son or any other combination as well as two apparent strangers who meet across the illusion of distance. It's also quite possible for them to dislike each other intensely which may result in bitter arguments and feuds, but within every circumstance which presents itself in the physical dimension there is only ever one creative force at work. This is the sublime energy of love.

Love is everywhere you look and is behind every circumstance that you encounter. This may come as something of a revelation to you as well as being somewhat difficult to comprehend at first, but as you will come to appreciate later in what you read here, it really is a fundamental truth.

The Questions I Had to Ask Myself

From the moment I met Ron then it was obvious to me that he was very different from anyone that I had ever come across before that time in my life. In those days, when things weren't working out with my marriage in the way that I had hoped they would, then I needed to be cautious. Or so I thought. I could feel that it would be all too easy just to throw myself into a relationship so as to escape what my married life had turned out to be. So I had to ask myself, in my quiet times, just exactly what it was that I had let myself in for as well as why I felt as I did.

My head was often in a spin where little or nothing made sense as I tried to figure out what had happened as well as how it would affect my future. At that point in my life I had nothing else to go on except what I had heard that every woman goes through when faced with the potential of entering into an all consuming affair. Is this real and what are my true feelings about the situation? This is promptly followed by the big question ... What will come of it and will I get hurt?

From all that I understood the world to have taught me during my many years as a wife and mother then I was probably indulging myself in some sort of infatuation which allowed me to escape into my fantasies. As a result, my head kept coming up with all manner of excuses 'why not' but my heart constantly leapt forward so as to cause me to feel otherwise. It was such a difficult time emotionally in that I had a strong sense that what I felt for Ron went way beyond anything that I had ever experienced before. But how to stop my mind labelling it as simply pandering to my vanity, while satisfying my unrequited passionate nature, was another matter altogether.

Something deep within my very being kept telling me to ignore my conscience while allowing myself to abandon any and all reservations as I let Ron see the person I truly knew myself to be. Somehow I knew it was right to let my barriers down while allowing matters to take their natural course and then seeing what came as a result. It helped me to do this by how I felt Ron responding through his openness and sincerity towards me. Never once did I detect any hidden agenda where I felt that he was trying to take advantage of me by manipulating the situation. He just wasn't that sort of man and somehow I knew this to be true.

We seemed to be just as I remembered my parents being when they were expressing their togetherness. Something which I had so often watched while longing for what they had. Suddenly, miraculously out of the blue, I seemed to have found it, but there was no point in hoping that my mind could rationalise it because that wasn't ever going to happen. I didn't appreciate it at the time but I had really been functioning on purely intuition although I had a strong sense that it was absolutely the right thing to do. I also had no idea about how strong and motivating the energy of twin flames really are. Oh how easy life would be with the benefit of 20/20 hindsight.

From what Ron shared with me then I'm sure that he experienced a similar battle with his conscience while also following the dictates of his heart. If we both had known then what we later came to appreciate about twin souls, and our reason for incarnating together, things would undoubtedly have been much more straightforward; but then, if they had been, what would we have learned? This is the somewhat frustrating paradox of life itself in how it's necessary for us to grow through experiencing the consequences of our choices. We are each born with free will and so we can choose as we wish, but life teaches us to make those choices wisely.

To be forearmed with reasons, outcomes and a general 'map of the future' is to fast-forward to the destination where there is nothing to be gained at all in having skipped over the pathway of uncharted possibilities. Many say that the convenience of modern day travel has ruined the charm of distance and I tend to agree. There is something especially inspiring about any journey that offers the opportunity for adventure and unpredictability which makes the arrival all the more meaningful when you eventually get there; and so it is with life.

It didn't take me long to appreciate that my getting together with Ron was for much more of an important purpose than merely satisfying my long held desire to find my Mr Right; my fulfilment of womanhood and my statement to the world that I was loved. Our deep need to be reunited, however it had expressed itself along our journeys, caused us to have to deal with lots of different issues that were necessary for us to learn and grow from. Similarly, with our becoming ever closer. We both needed to explore parts of our true selves so as to understand more fully just exactly who we were in how we perceived ourselves to be. In order to have a life together then both of us had to work through issues which were quite difficult and which sometimes even challenged our faith in not only ourselves but many other aspects of our beliefs as well.

From the point in time that Ron and I found each other to the time that we successfully sorted out our lives in order to allow us to marry, it took a total of nine years. During that period we found it necessary to lean on our 'other half' quite a few times in order to get through what we did, but there was never any doubt as to how we felt about one another or what we really wanted. We did, however, get to appreciate that life has a way of throwing curved balls at you when you least expect them, and in this respect there were plenty of trials which tested our ability to stand firmly within the courage of our convictions and our love. Listening to our hearts at those times was absolutely essential but it really is amazing how the mind comes rushing forward to insist that it knows best. The wise and enlightened spiritual traveller is not at all impressed by its insistence and has learned how to tame it; or even ignore it. For us mere mortals it's not so easy.

After more than fourteen years of marriage and raising three wonderful children, I found that facing my ideal future required me to question very many things which had become the norm for that era of the early 70s. First there was the issue of standing before a minister while promising in front of a congregation of witnesses that I would love, honour and obey etc until death us do part. I had never been one to make promises lightly and neither was I in a mind to have God on my case for having decided to opt out of my commitments; despite the fact that the other party had abandoned his a long time ago.

In that period of humanity's gradual evolution towards greater awareness we were only just coming out of the era when people would stay married for the sake of the children and where divorce was often frowned upon. Somehow, to me, it always seemed as though ending a marriage reflect badly on the woman in that she was frequently judged as having failed in her duties as a supportive and successful wife. Those times, and the lamentably puritan attitudes which prevailed, were very much different from how they are now. In the space of just a handful of decades we have come to regard things so much more liberally and with a greater degree of tolerance, but I'm not convinced that the benefits entirely outweigh the disadvantages. It seems that in the process we may have lost something of our sense of responsibility to not only others, and the world in which we live, but to ourselves as well.

Secondly there was the issue of having matured while leaving behind my childhood notions but then suddenly being reunited with them and having to almost reconcile the two very different eras of my life. My time as a wife and mother had made me more pragmatic in order to deal with the demands of everyday life, but Ron's appearance propelled me back into the heart of that little girl who envied her mother's closeness to her father. My mind had asserted its need to be listened to but there I was doing a one hundred and eighty degree turn on the fast-track to middle age while feeling that my life had started over again. It was all very seductive and had come at a stage on my journey where I felt myself to be more than a little susceptible.

The universe had appeared to put the ultimate temptation firmly in my way where all the ingredients were presented in such a manner as to ensure my unconditional surrender to it. Or at least this is what my mind wished me to believe as I allowed myself to be guided by a totally different part of me which didn't have any intention of debating the subject at all. It almost seemed as though I had gone through all that I had, and got to the point of being caught up so much in my mind, when I was suddenly faced with the greatest challenge of needing to listen solely to my heart. It would have been so easy not to, but something about Ron's presence kept pulling me forward in a way which gave me the confidence to rise above my doubts.

My adult conscience wanted to know just how much I had been allowing some childhood yearning to influence my judgement and whether I was being wholly irrational in continuing to see this man. It insisted on knowing whether I had considered the consequences of what the future may hold but when Ron and I were together then I just knew in my heart that everything would be alright. With him in my life I was certain that whatever may come in the future, or even the next moment, we would be able to deal with it together.

Come what may, something assured me from a place which resonated deeply within me that he and I would rise above any challenge. It told me that we would prevail over whatever circumstance, however difficult it may be, if we were together. Such was my confidence in him. But more than that, there existed a kind of knowing in me about the scope and power of our capabilities; almost like we had been through some very difficult times together before. It wasn't until much later that I was to find out just exactly what we had been through and how our trials, especially Ron's, had actually played a significant part in our country's history. That really turned out to be a huge and fascinating revelation.

For the time being I had little to go on but my strong sense of faith in my feminine intuition as well as my overwhelming feelings of rightness. Whatever my mind wished to question and undermine, it could never get past the sentinel of 'sureness' which emanated from a place within me which had always been unassailable. My resolve was absolute, although I readily admit that there were occasions where my nerve certainly benefited from the reassurance of our physical closeness. It most definitely was a highly memorable and eventful trip.

Being Brave through Difficult Times

Our journey to the altar was also a somewhat faltering one in the respect that our pathways to the church were anything but direct. Ron had a lot more to deal with than I did, but being conscientious souls we very often put the needs of others, who we loved and cared for, in front of what either of us wanted; however important it may have appeared to us at the time. It just wasn't our way to be completely self-centred and so there needed to be periods in both our lives, prior to us being able to marry, where adjustments had to be made; so as to give support and consideration wherever we felt it was necessary.

There were, I'm pleased to say, many very happy times that duly compensated us for the frustrations which we felt along the way. Finding ourselves as a family of eight, on those occasions where we brought our children together with us, proved to be an absolute delight which gave all of us some wonderful memories. Sharing our children seemed just as though it was a natural extension of sharing ourselves, but there also appeared to be something which felt very familiar about being part of a large family. We both fell into the roll of parenting a 'team' of children like it was a perfect way for us to be. When we were all together then there seemed to be a strong sense of 'rightness' about this way of being, as well as a kind of wonderfully comforting familiarity.

I don't think that either of us consciously gave it any specific attention at the time but it certainly was a factor in allowing us to feel our togetherness much more keenly. The fact that Ron's children readily accepted me, while mine got along well with him, made things a whole lot easier for us; especially as we were both so keen to protect their emotional well being. After everything that Ron had been through in his childhood then he was very tuned in to the needs of his own children who he wanted only the very best for in the way of their upbringing. This was one of his many qualities which reminded me so much of my father's wonderful sensitivity.

There were also very many little things that happened which, when viewed individually didn't seem to amount to much in comparison to some of the hurdles that we had to overcome. But whenever I look back at so much of how things were in those times then I can see how important these little 'starry signposts' really were. Those little sparks of brightness on even the gloomiest of days were actually a real blessing in how they kept encouraging us both to make those all important choices. The ones which moved us ever closer to a state of happiness which we both longed for. If either Ron or I had looked up then we would have seen the canopy of stars above us as they twinkled away while watching over us and smiling at everything we did out of a purely loving motivation. Such was their gift to us.

Finally we did make it to the church and, while stood in front of the most beautiful stained glass window with the light pouring through it, we made the sincerest of vows to each other. I remember the portrait of the figure in the big circular window so well as he knelt in a humble pose of gratitude while expressing just exactly what was in my heart that I wanted to say. His sentiment said more than I could ever express as that little anxious girl in the back seat of her parents' car finally found her completeness. Her prayer had been answered and no matter what life would hold from that moment on, she knew that it could never be as scary as being without her twin soul. She had found her home at last.

Even while being caught up as much as I was in the ceremony, when I was so immersed in the captivating atmosphere of the beautiful little church, there were precious moments where I had the distinct feeling of déjà vu. For an instant, when it first happened, I considered it as being a reminder of my marriage back when I had only just turned eighteen. The next time it hit me however, I was able to appreciate that the feelings of familiarity were coming from something quite different as though they weren't a part of my present lifetime. With all that I needed to concentrate on, I didn't have time to ponder whatever I had sensed so strongly. As the ceremony progressed then Ron and I standing together in front of the altar in a lovely church began to feel more and more like a replay of another almost identical occasion. I would clearly remember these feelings later on in our journey at the point when we were told about our time together as Nathanael and Kitty. When we did learn about it then I had no doubts whatsoever about the truth of what we were told.

The ceremony and the atmosphere which surrounded me were all that I could have ever hoped for where, whatever doubts and misgivings my mind may have wished to present me with before that moment then they were banished forever. At the instant I stepped through the doorway of the church, I absolutely knew that I was doing the right thing. More than that, it was something which I realised had actually been waiting for me to do it; that certainly felt very special indeed. Ron was there, our children and friends were there, what more could I have wanted than for them all to create a truly magical moment in my life; the memory of which I will treasure for all time. I am so grateful to have been granted the opportunity to have experienced such intense love in a wonderful situation and then to have enjoyed that same love throughout each and every day which followed.

And so it was that we entered married togetherness after what had seemed like an epic journey over some fairly demanding terrain. The destination had certainly been worth it while the lessons along the way often came from some quite unexpected directions. But there was always the presence of our twin flame which kept us focused on what our hearts' most sincerely wanted, even when things got pretty confusing. Everything which we had encountered along our pathway towards that time proved to be invaluable in what it was necessary for us to face in the years to come. Neither of us had any idea of how much more of a journey we would need to make, in that we would eventually view it as being a very challenging one which waited to bring us experiences that we had no way of anticipating. As it turned out, the pathway which we shared would be a long and eventually mountainous one where our twin flames certainly were needed to burn their brightest. This powerful light would blaze the way forward through all of the forthcoming dark areas that we were to face in the dense forests.

Only just three short years into our marriage, Ron was diagnosed with M.S. In the years that followed this completely unexpected news we needed to face very many tough hurdles in our search for a possible cure as his condition progressively worsened. I'm sure that my twin flame presence in his life provided him with an extra dimension of fortitude which sustained him in the most trying of his times; when he needed every ounce of strength to stay positive and determined. It certainly wasn't what I had envisaged as being the outcome of our finally getting together but he was my man and whatever came to pass then we would face it together.

His protracted battle with the many debilitating and often demeaning phases of a terminal illness, along with his eventual passing, was a huge challenge for both of us. It took great courage on both our parts to do what we did as there were very many aspects of both the physical and emotional trauma which we had to come to terms with. Being so incredibly close as we were, Ron and I shared everything at a level of intimacy which goes way beyond the intellectual or emotional. I really can't begin to describe just exactly how strong this sensation is, but I can assure you that once you experience this same feeling then you will know it instantly. It will be as though you have forgotten something quite precious that has just been remembered, but more importantly you will immediately know it to be a truth which is beyond question. You won't know why you are so sure, or even be able to explain it to others, but there will be a part of you that has total confidence in your conviction about the depth of your belief.

Given this insight into the realm of powerful emotions then I'm sure you are able to appreciate how Ron's parting was the ultimate test for me, even after twenty eight years of our being together as man and wife. Nevertheless, it had been something which he helped prepare me for through teaching me how to look at it from a higher perspective. It was an act of absolute love through which he gave me the opportunity to expand my awareness while enabling me to grow as an evolving soul. He had been and always will be my soul 'companion in love' as well as my twin flame; although the two energies are almost indistinguishable in their alignment.

Ron took me with him on his journey through romance and physical attraction to the dizzying heights of enduring passion and ultimate fulfilment. On many occasions I found it difficult to know where he actually ended and I began as we appeared to be 'one' in all but our physical forms. He was, and forever is, my most adored other half but I had to learn to let him go so that I could gain an understanding of love's enduring dynamic in this third dimensional reality.

This would not have been possible for me to do in any other way unless I had lived through many more incarnations to achieve it little by little. Ron taught me to do it in one giant step. It hurt like hell at the time but his resolute love, which constantly surrounds me, has enabled me to heal and to move on in the way that I needed to. It has been a truly remarkable process and one which I sincerely hope that you encounter; albeit in a way which benefits you through providing whatever you most earnestly need to propel your footsteps further along the pathway of your ultimate spiritual happiness.

Twin souls bring each other an intensity of 'being' which allows them to make great leaps in their progress back to the source. It's where we are all headed and where we all want to go, but to get there then we have to remember who we are and what the purpose of our existence is. Ron showed me this. Our purpose is to be the love that we are and to anchor that love on this planet. We are beings of light where withholding this aspect of ourselves only results in discord and disease (dis-ease). When we all step into our Divinity then all the ills of the world will vanish and there will be no more need for Pandora to keep hope locked up in her box so as to counter all that she let loose in the first place.

Discordant twin souls who fight and argue are allowing themselves the opportunity to appreciate that all the negative qualities expressed by humanity are simply calls for love to be given in response. Those who cry out are in actuality offering the opportunity for others to give; and in so doing love is recognised at every instance. To not appreciate this is to walk blindly through an experience which offers us the greatest potential for learning than any other place in the universe. Here, in this physical dimension, we can see love in action at its most polarised which makes it visible to even the newest awakened perceptions of spiritual 'eyes'.

Twin souls blaze their uplifting light not only to all those around them but also into the collective consciousness of humanity as well. This precious gift enables many others to become aware that the opportunity exists to learn valuable spiritual lessons while working with twin flame energies. This expanded understanding may then result in their choosing to incarnate another time where a twin flame encounter of their own will be experienced. From this will come ever greater illumination which then brings with it more awareness whereupon other similar opportunities will be created; and so the process expands exponentially.

If you imagine twin flames dotted all over the surface of the earth and then each instance of them shooting out brilliant white sparks then it's easy to see the outcome. Sparks ignite to become other flames which in turn create sparks of their own and before long you have a light spreading all over which holds out a challenge to the sun in its brightness. Twin flames serve to illuminate as does each and every soul on earth, to one degree or another. Some burn so dimly that they appear to have almost no light at all but there is never any instance where the Divine spark of a soul is completely extinguished. Even the tinniest of embers can be fanned back into a flame of the most compelling intensity within the blink of an eye. Twin flames are the light of the world and can set the universe ablaze. This is exactly what they will do.

A Time of Previous Togetherness

From all that we learned along the way, it appears as though Ron and I were blessed with at least one other opportunity to offer our combined light to this world. During our quest for a cure to his physical dilemma we came across a very gifted psychic in Florida (now living in Asheville N.C.) called Mary Pompeo. She was able to tell us that we had been together over two hundred years previously where our lives had been well documented and could be researched.

We did just that and found a great deal to interest us and much which seemed to explain what we had experienced in this current lifetime. It turns out that Ron had chosen two quite testing journeys, although his previous one was a challenge of a much different nature. In those times we were known as Nathanael and Kitty. Our story is absolutely fascinating and one which I would very much like to share with you now.

- Chapter 8 -

War - The Unlikely Link across Time

In order to more fully understand the true nature of our enduring twin soul love, and that of love in general, I would like to take you quite far back to a time which was very much different from the one that we know at present. This particular era had been a period in my country's history when there was much unrest and where feelings of love appeared to be in lamentably short supply. These were the days of the 1760s when the aspirations of our citizens were so harshly limited by what many regarded as being an occupying force from another land. Dark clouds were slowly gathering on the political horizon as people began objecting to increasingly unfair laws which were passed by a remotely situated government. One that had no apparent interest in the welfare of its 'colonists' or even had any representation from them.

The final straw came for many with the passing of the Stamp Act of 1765 which enraged the British American colonists. This resulted in protesters increasingly taking to the streets from places as far apart as New England to Georgia, some thousand miles to the South. This unjust tax was imposed by a heavily indebted British government in order to help pay for the highly expensive seven year war which had been waged against the French and the Indians. The British felt justified in making demands that the colonists contribute towards what they saw as being a gainful enterprise; which had been undertaken for their ultimate benefit. Unfortunately it was an ill conceived attitude and onerous tax which created a financial imposition that many increasingly felt to be unreasonably penalising and intolerable.

The upshot of all this was a sharp rise in the level of discontent to the point where action gradually began to replace heated words of collective dissent and anger. Out of this transition towards active rebellion was born a movement which called themselves The Sons of Liberty. From within this somewhat secretive organisation there emerged ever more violent and destructive demonstrations which inevitably paved the blood-thirsting road towards armed conflict and outright war. The most memorable of these pre-war violent outbursts was the much reported Boston Tea Party. This rebellious outrage proved to be the tipping point which garnered popular colonial opinion firmly against the rule of British forces and government.

Over the period of a few short years, the American colonists saw fit to respond to what they saw as grossly unfair and unjust British rule by establishing their own governmental institutions in each of the thirteen major colonies. The forming of the Continental Congress in 1774 was the prelude to the American people making a momentous stand against what they considered to be a flagrant violation of their birthright. In the full knowledge that they were almost certain to engage in a war which threatened to tear their country apart, brave men and women elected to stand against intolerable subjugation; as they saw it. Sedition became the byword of the times where huge numbers would be called upon to follow their passions in pursuit of justice and the right to self governance.

In the process of striving to achieve this end, people of all ages, especially our young men, were encouraged to set themselves against an unwanted oppressor or even, God help us, one another. Men and women from all walks of life would soon find themselves needing to be called on to act upon the convictions of their beliefs. In many cases they would discover levels of courage, perseverance and resourcefulness which they had never expected to find hidden away within them. The newly emerging American political and cultural society would need many such brave men and women to champion their cause while untold numbers would forfeit their lives in the bitter and protracted struggle.

In spite of those terribly gloomy times, there were still opportunities for love to flourish. It did so among many who would not allow the fullness of their true feelings to be subjugated to the darkness of an approaching era that was destined never to be forgotten. This whole traumatic period served to highlight many whose names would eventually be deemed noteworthy while their unique contributions and inspired actions found their way into the history books for all to read. The most memorable of these would be men and women who had clearly demonstrated the many enduring and beneficial aspects of human nature which have enabled and engendered mankind to evolve and prosper over the centuries.

One such person was born into a society that had little or no time for any thoughts or aspirations in the direction of political empire building or promoting civil uprisings; especially if they would ultimately lead to armed aggression. His would be a name to remember by those who were to draw a great deal of inspiration from his example.

Born in 1742, Nathanael Greene was the son of a Quaker farmer and smith whose religious sect did very little to encourage the modern education of its children. Nathanael, being naturally bright and astute, grew up being inquisitive while soon finding the narrowness of his upbringing much too inadequate for his needs. Determined to rise above the academically lowly and restricted status which he felt himself to be bound by, Nathanael soon took matters into his own hands. He decided that there would be a need for him to expand his education far beyond what his immediate society offered him and so he schooled himself in the subjects of his 'time'; mathematics and law. Even at an early age he sought a certain freedom from the restrictions of a way of life that appeared to be, in certain respects, unreasonable and irrational to him.

His 'weapon' of that era in his life was education and this he used as a means to escape an existence of limited potential through having no other options than to work in his father's various enterprises. Nathanael had a great interest in books which is where he gained the majority of his worldly knowledge, but there was one particular book which he drew on for his inspiration and much of his spiritual support. His love of reading the Bible was to be his mainstay in the years to come where living and quoting its fundamental principles would endear him to a great many in positions of community influence and power.

His upbringing in the Spartan and somewhat restrictive world of the Quakers, and his wish to rise above its limitations, was to set the scene for much of how his adult life unfolded; given the quite momentous events that were to come. Nathanael was a man of his time in that he had a vision of a more independent way of living where people were free to express themselves without having others impose their will on them. His strong sense of self-determination very much reflected the growing spirit of his era while representing an 'ideal' that he, and very many others like him, would feel the need to fight for in either word or deed.

And so, inevitably, there was to be an intense period of great upheaval the like and scope of which had never been seen or even envisaged by a fledgling country that desperately sought to discover its own identity. It would be a birthing cycle which inescapably entailed an often perilous as well as tempestuous emergence into a notional maturity which involved the vigorous flexing of its wings. The outcome of these seismically historical events would be the recording of a dramatic reshaping which affected more than just political boundaries. The evolutionary 'growing pains' of a united sense of sovereign purpose was to change not only Nathanael's own life, but also that of the national consciousness as well. This new ethos, this consensus of patriotic spirit and mind, would have a substantial impact on the very nature of the world in which he lived, where nothing would ever be the same again.

At that point in his young life he was completely unaware of the active and decisive role that he would play on the stage of provincial as well as national politics; and how history would judge him as a result. Those studious times alone in his bedroom, while immersed in his books on military heroes and religion, were born out of a fascination for many things which would later prove essential to his survival and that of his family. Little did he appreciate that so much of what influenced and inspired him at that time would also have a profound impact on many others who would come to depend on him for his astute guidance, his wise counsel and compassionate support; such was to be his contribution to society.

The Greene family were among the earliest settlers in Rhode Island and were instrumental in helping to establish the colony in that relatively small state on the North East coast of America. In 1770 Nathanael moved the relatively short distance from Warwick to nearby Coventry in order to take over the running of his father's foundry. There, he was the first to urge the establishment of a public school and, in that same year, he was chosen as a member of the Rhode Island General Assembly; to which he was re-elected in 1771, 72 and again in 75. He sympathised strongly with the 'Whig', or Patriot, element among the colonists which led to his helping organise a local militia in 74; in anticipation of the inevitable war that was to come.

At this time he began to acquire many expensive volumes on military tactics while setting about teaching himself the art of war, even though he had absolutely no idea of the physical and mental horrors involved. It would not be long until he found out first hand. Coincident with this he was also serving as a member of a committee which had been appointed by the Assembly to revise the militia laws. This drew him ever deeper into the preparatory stages of conflict, but his chosen path of following the road to war went very much against the societal principles of his upbringing and his roots. It is thought that his passion for attending to his ever increasing military duties led to his expulsion from the Quakers in 1773.

It was just a year after this happened, while still in Coventry, that he married the daughter of a long term family acquaintance although she was nearly twelve years his junior. Catherine Littlefield Greene, as she became known, didn't catch her future husband's admiring eye until she began to blossom attractively in her late teens. At the same time that he began turning his attention to her then she found herself being drawn to his mature masculinity and wisdom; a mutual attraction which culminated in their marriage. Their first meaningful romantic encounter took place at a dance where Nathanael experienced another type of passion that was to sustain him for the remainder of his life. Catharine appeared to be everything he could ever have wished for in a woman while she in turn viewed him as her perfect 'knight in shining armour'.

Nathanael's tall and strong male appearance noticeably contrasted her relatively small and somewhat delicate feminine form, although she was blessed with a quite disarmingly enthusiastic nature as well as an engagingly flirtatious aspect to her character. The combination of her striking personality, her soft complexion and alluring figure made her irresistible to Nathanael who very quickly fell deeply in love with her just as she did with him. Even the quite frightening spectre of a looming war was not a powerful enough deterrent to make any impact on their dreams of happiness together as they embarked on their journey as man and wife. Little did they know that the depths of their love would be tested by what the historians would come to record as a momentous episode along the evolutionary path of an emerging nation.

Not only were children to be born to Nathanael and 'Kitty', as he affectionately called her, but a struggling new world would also be gripped in the throes of similar labour pains at the very same time. In the meantime, they both took advantage of every opportunity to enjoy their social activities within their extensive circle of many influential friends and acquaintances. This also was to prove invaluable to them in the years to come when relationships and special bonds of affection, along with mutual understanding would be called upon to bring a healing to a damaged society that was in great need of support and guidance. Even though men of great influence held ultimate sway in a world which did not encourage or invite the opinions of women, the quiet female voice of support behind each of them would be invaluable in shaping the social fabric of their emergent world. Kitty was certainly one to willingly and enthusiastically play her part this respect.

In the very same year as Nathanael and Kitty were married, the landmark meeting of the First Continental Congress also took place. It was an occasion of great significance which would later be regarded and noted by historians as representing the deep desire for independence which pervaded the atmosphere of the land. The joining of two people in a spirit of mutual love and affection corresponded to that of the joining of minds which, even though contemplating the unthinkable, were intent on acting out of a mutual love for their country. The national mood of the moment was surely one of great love which could be seen in retrospect as having appeared in its many obvious forms as well as its various often misinterpreted guises.

Nathanael was certainly a passionate man who made no secret of his love for his new wife, as well as that of his dream for a bright and happy future which he held very dear to his heart. He was typical of very many of his countrymen who also felt the urge to express their independence of not only thought but their heartfelt wish to self governance as well as self determination. He epitomised the spirit of his time while recognising in his wife those very special qualities which so aptly complimented his own. His was a valiant dream in which they would raise their children in a land filled with opportunity. A place where freedom of expression and the right to live in harmony would be the guiding force to a better way of life. A greatly liberated way of living which would allow them, and every other like-minded countryman, to achieve their ultimate happiness within the expression of a deep and abiding love for one another. Time would provide the irrefutable evidence that he was not dreaming alone.

Kitty proved to be his enduring inspiration with her vivaciousness and enthusiasm for life where, between them, it appeared as though no battle could ever be too great for their powerful love to overcome. She was his twin flame who had come to be re-united with her counterpart while being unaware that the ultimate test of their infectiously magnetic attraction was soon to appear. Precious little time would be afforded them in which to enjoy the undisturbed bliss of their married life while the momentum of an impending storm carried the dark battle-crested waves of disruption swiftly towards them. It would be a long and oppressive storm where the bright lights of incandescent twin flames were very much needed to burn unfalteringly intensely in the face of such desperate times.

Love Prevails over Conflict

Shortly after a year into their marriage, the Revolutionary War of Independence broke out as the escalating skirmishes of various militia groups turned sharply in the direction of organised battle. On May 8, 1775, Nathanael was promoted from that of a lowly private in the militia to the exalted rank of Brigadier General in the Rhode Island Army of Observation which had been formed in response to the siege of Boston. He was appointed a Brigadier of the Continental Army by the Continental Congress in June of 1775. George Washington, on recognising his skills and leadership abilities, assigned him the command of the city of Boston after it was evacuated in March of the following year. All that Nathanael had planned for in preparing himself for battle, even from a time when he could have absolutely no idea of what the future held for him, had come to fruition. His years of studying the tactics of war meant that he was now a vital link in the chain of command which would inevitably bind him to the campaign trail while being parted from his young wife.

It surely is impossible to imagine how he must have felt in following a cause which so deeply inspired his patriotic heart while having to leave behind his dearest love and eternally treasured other half. His only consolation could be drawn from the belief that he was fighting for a better future for them both where, hopefully if they were to be blessed in such a way, their children would grow up never knowing the oppression which he had experienced. Such were the aspirations of his heartfelt dream, but he could have had no way of anticipating what measure of sacrifice he would be asked to make in order to achieve it.

As the historians would record, Nathanael would often be absent from his home for long periods of time while he moved ever farther down through the north eastern states with each successive battle. There was very little time to return to his native Rhode Island state and house in Coventry while the fortunes of war constantly shifted; as did the political situation at the seat of government where his presence was often requested. This same pattern persisted for nearly eight exhaustingly long and bloody years while one campaign after another proved to be just one small, but very costly step towards ultimate victory. At each pivotal point along the way his contribution was essential where not only his military skills were required by his troops but his inspirational presence as well.

Married life, in the traditional sense, was virtually non-existent as he travelled great distances across the Eastern states from Rhode Island to South Carolina while fighting the British forces. Kitty suffered greatly as a result of his absence and would often make arduous journeys through the most dangerous of situations just to get to visit him at his camp; wherever it was located. Her wonderfully determined spirit had always been identical to his own, in that her flame burned just as brightly and equally as passionately in her need to support him. In consequence of this she would not let her ambitions or her love be thwarted by any force which offered any opposition however perilous it might have appeared.

Circumstances were no obstacle to her desire to be with her beloved husband where her legendary courage and determination undoubtedly proved inspirational to very many who were in great need of holding fast to their own. Against seemingly impossible odds, she had seven pregnancies which resulted in the birth of six children; only five of which survived past infancy. One pregnancy was a miscarriage and one child died as an infant. In those days of limited medical knowledge, and the arduous conditions which she had no other choice but to endure, it was unquestionably no small miracle that any of them were able to enter this life in the first place. After their children were born, and they were all able to travel with her, Kitty would often take them on her trips to visit Nathanael. This was very often his only opportunity to see his children growing up and to create an atmosphere of family togetherness as much as it was humanly possible under the prevailing conditions.

Raising children in the midst of an army encampment on the edge of a battlefront had surely not been factored into his dream, but no matter what the circumstances both Nathanael and Kitty were determined to do the best for their loved ones. Whenever it was considered too hazardous or too arduous a journey to take the children with her, Kitty would reluctantly leave them with family or friends. She would very often go to the ends of the earth in order to be with her precious husband where no battlefield was too daunting a prospect for her to be so close to. Bearing in mind the rudimentary transport and the nature of what was then huge expanses of wilderness and undeveloped land, journeys of a few hundred miles could often take several gruelling days in very basic horse-drawn transport.

No foe, of whatever nature or however powerful, could ever be any kind of match for the strength of love which they shared as their twin flames lit up everything around them. Nathanael longed for her visits while spending many lonely nights in the makeshift camps at the edge of the 'firing line' or when his army had laid siege to a fortified town. Even so, he would never be one to dwell on the impositions of his office and the traumas of war. Not only to bolster his own spirits but to ensure that he kept up the morale of his men, there was very often some form of entertainment to be enjoyed even if it was only listening to the tales of a skilled raconteur or a fiddle playing a simple melody.

Quite often, whenever the opportunity presented itself, there was fun and dancing to be found at the camps and never better an occasion arose than when Kitty came to be with Nathanael for a while. This always proved to be most enjoyable as it allowed her to be near her beloved husband in a way that reminded them both of how they were together in the time of peace. Nathanael's style of command was not one of being a remote and dispassionate authoritarian but someone who would lead by example and that included dancing with his wife in the midst of a large and happy gathering of his men. As a result, their public displays of 'togetherness' soon earned them the affectionate title of the 'bride and groom' where the lasting allure of their love was obvious to all who witnessed their example.

In the latter stages of the war, when circumstances became treacherous or too dangerous for visits, they endured their enforced separation in the hope that there would soon be an end to the hostilities. The resulting pressures were hard on both of them as Nathanael struggled with the remaining crucial battles; as Kitty did likewise with her domestic duties while raising their five children. Letters were their only salvation in the way of being able to communicate with each other, but nothing could undermine the depth of love which they had for their beloved other half. It was a truly testing time for each of them in their own ways where being apart felt so unnatural and unwanted, although neither of them ever had a moment's doubt as to how they felt towards one another.

The Detrimental Legacy of War

When the dark days of conflict did finally come to an end, Nathanael was able to be reunited with his family where he immediately set about creating the togetherness that he had always hoped for. Kitty was so pleased to finally have her husband home safe from the rigors of the long war but she was also concerned by all that he had so obviously endured in his effort to prevail over the opposing forces. The effect which many years of bitter struggle had levied on him seemed to have taken such an ageing toll on the comparatively young and vigorous man who she had married just a short time before the onset. It must have saddened her greatly to have appreciated that so much had been taken from them where her husband had aged far greater than his years in the process.

Those long years of conflict had oftentimes seemed interminable especially towards the end where, at certain seemingly intractable stages, it looked as though victory was anything but assured. However, Kitty never gave up hope of having Nathanael back while not once allowing herself to believe that she may lose him permanently to the war effort. His return was a blessed relief in so many ways, not the least of which was the security which she felt in having his confident male presence so permanently close after the dragging years of his absence. She was also very thankful for his much needed help while sharing the responsibilities of bringing up their fast growing family; the task that she had faced alone for so long. At times it seemed as though they had both been doing the same thing, whereas Nathanael had now swapped a large army of fighting men for a small army of often rebellious offspring. In this respect she was also glad to have a much needed fatherly influence for their dearly loved children.

At last it seemed as though they could put all the years of conflict and personal deprivation behind them while the biggest challenge in front of them was the adjustment to a new world of uncertainty. Gone were the dark clouds from the horizon but the smoke from the fires of intense confrontation were still rising to cast many shadows across the land. Those fires would burn for many a long year as the after-effects of large scale armed conflict stayed etched on the memories of all those concerned. The repercussions of those decisive battles and times of ultimate struggle in his country's formative history would ripple on for a very long time into the future. Unfortunately, Nathanael was to feel the debilitating effects of this quite substantially as well as that of his unceasing efforts to bring about victory.

Although he had no further obligations to his country in any military sense, he did have a personal liability which he felt duty-bound to honour. In the lead up to the battle of Valley Forge, he had taken on the responsibility of a substantial financial commitment to feed and clothe his men in the absence of any support from a dithering Congress administration. It was during the long encampment in the valley, at which time he was made Quartermaster General by George Washington, that he encountered severe supply problems with respect to basic essentials for his men who faced long exposure to winter conditions while being totally unprepared for them. The army he commanded was continually plagued with shortages of food, clothing and equipment while his soldiers were forced to rely on both their home states and on the totally inept Continental Congress for these basic necessities. Unfortunately, poor organisation and obstructions caused by Congress, a shortage of wagoners, lack of forage for the horses, the devaluation of the Continental currency, spoilage, and captured supplies by the British all contributed to prevent critical provisions and materials from arriving at camp.

Nathanael's naturally inspirational nature, coupled with that of his innate compassion, kept him constantly motivated to ensure that the morale of his men was always kept at its highest level possible. Even in the face of the most appalling conditions and severe deprivation he worked tirelessly to petition on behalf of his troops. In one memorable letter to George Washington he wrote of their predicament *'God grant we may never be brought to such a wretched condition again.'* Had it not been for Nathanael's timely personal intervention in providing a solution to their dire situation then the course of the war may well have been very much different. In order to secure suitable winter clothing and food for his men, Nathanael agreed to personally guarantee many thousands of dollars to Charleston merchants in order to support and equip his soldiers during the unusually harsh winter of 77 to 78.

Unfortunately for him he had chosen to conduct his business dealings through an unscrupulous agent who systematically defrauded the chosen suppliers which meant that, after the war had ended, Nathanael was held personally responsible for all the debts. Due to his protracted absence from his businesses, and the difficulties faced by so many during the harsh conditions and privations of war, he found himself without sufficient funds to meet the increasing demands of the merchants. His appeals and petitions to Congress for financial compensation fell on intractably deaf ears in those turbulent political times which immediately followed the cessation of hostilities and the establishment of a precarious peacetime.

The result of this was that his and Kitty's dream of a happy life filled with family togetherness, and leisurely times spent in a home which they loved, seemed to be in grave danger of collapsing. Only one option remained open to them and that was to sell everything they had while relocating to Savannah where they would attempt to build a new life for themselves. There the family would take up residence on a property that had been gifted to Nathanael by the Georgia legislature in gratitude for his services during the war. Mulberry Grove is situated close to the Savannah River and had been previously owned by a wealthy merchant, John Graham, who had chosen to abandon the property at the outset of the war after crossing swords with members of the Sons of Liberty. During his period of occupation, however, Graham had shrewdly developed it into a large plantation which included not only, what Nathanael termed, a magnificent house along with a coach house and stables but many hundreds of acres to grow crops as well.

Two hundred and fifty of these acres were tidal which the entrepreneurial Mr Graham had turned to his advantage in successfully growing rice crops. Along with rice production, the Mulberry Grove estate yielded many other saleable commodities such as timber and various kinds of fruits. All this came as a welcome surprise to Nathanael and Kitty but it also meant that the land would have to be worked in order to provide them with the income they needed. This could only be achieved by the raising of another type of 'army' in order to provide the necessary labour for working the fields, the orchards and the forests.

Nathanael's plan was to pay off his debts by cultivating the rice and other cash crops while selling their Rhode Island properties when the markets appeared favourable. His strategy proved to be a much more difficult and daunting prospect than he had anticipated and one which would challenge his already weakened resolve, given all that the war effort had taken out of him. Added to this he had to cope with the fact that his beloved wife would undoubtedly be required to pitch in and help as well. This was something he had not wished for but he needed all of his family to work together as a team if there was ever to be any likely hope of securing a successful future family home in those lean years of post-war peacetime. This move certainly took its toll on Kitty in that it not only required her to work on the plantation but also meant that she had to leave behind their many friends and allies in the North.

Along with the loss of her social life, she also had to contend with being deprived of the very supportive connection which she had enjoyed with her family. They still lived in the small close-knit community of Block Island which is situated just a few miles off the south coast of Rhode Island and where she was born. Now she found herself hundreds of miles away while being relatively isolated in a state so far removed from what she had been used to. Added to this she had to somehow cope with raising her family while caring for her hard working husband and then learning all that she could about farming; while also helping him in the fields. It surely was a very challenging uphill struggle which must have seemed completely overwhelming to her at the beginning through having had so much to get used to. Only a strong-spirited woman of pioneering stock could have handled such an apparently insurmountable prospect without crumbling under the sheer weight of her impending responsibilities and the consequences of not succeeding.

To add yet more stress to this already formidable burden she could also see how the struggles of the long war, and the enormous personal debt which had been incurred as a result of it, had taken so much out of her beloved husband. He was certainly not the same man of vigour and vitality who had marched up so confidently to join the Continental militia while feeling that he could overcome any adversary with ease. Kitty could see that a different kind of campaign awaited him at Mulberry Grove where she was resolved to do everything in her power to help him make their life together a success. More than anything she wanted to experience the loving togetherness of family life which they had both dreamed of; but her aspirations were to be short lived.

Life on the plantation was lonely and intense at first where so many things necessitated the whole family adjusting quickly to them while the process of creating a new home for themselves got rapidly underway. After all the long years of arduous conflict it was rest that Nathanael really needed but crops wouldn't wait to be planted or harvested while the seasons made their inexorable march across each page of the calendar. From the very first day of their arrival at Mulberry Grove, the byword at the start of every morning became 'toil'.

As though their already unenviable burden wasn't enough, there was the constant battle with Nathanael's creditors to cope with as well. Despite his best efforts they became increasingly impatient where, eventually, one by one they started taking him to court. Every merchant wanted payment in respect of the food, clothing and materials supplied for the campaign at Valley Forge which his duplicitous agent, for reasons best known to himself, had seen fit not to pay. Repeated entreaties, both personal and by representation to the newly formed Congress, fell on continually deaf and stubbornly dismissive ears. No sense of relief seemed to be forthcoming in the shape of any compensation which Nathanael considered he was rightly owed. The family struggled on while not knowing whether any kind of secure future awaited them which must have been an impossibly heavy strain on his already depleted emotional state of health.

Having fought nearly eight long years to be free of an unwanted and unacceptable subjugation, it must have appeared to him as though he had only achieved exchanging one kind of yoke for another. All that he had ever wanted was the right to live in the secure knowledge of a freedom that would allow a man and his family to prosper while not fearing the tyranny of another. Slowly he was beginning to appreciate that oppression can come in many forms, as well as misleading guises, where the 'enemy' often turns out to be one who had once been seen as a supportive friend and ally.

In those early days on the plantation it must have seemed to him that his life and beliefs were to be held in question as his Congressional overlords continued to bicker and argue while casually dismissing his financial problems. Having won the battle for the survival of his newly democratised country he was immediately faced with yet another battle of a different kind where this particular one would determine the very survival of his family. This time the enemy turned out to be impending poverty but it was one which fought a guerrilla campaign from the shadows; from there it exploited every weakness imaginable. It was a formidable opponent and one which took its toll on an already very weary Nathanael Greene.

Despite all that stood in their way, the Greene family did indeed adjust to life in the labour-intensive crucible of the Georgia wetlands. No task seemed to be too daunting as the months and years rolled by while the crops were sold and the family fortunes steadily re-established. Their hard work paid off but, just four short years into their time at Savannah, tragedy struck. It came most unexpectedly after Nathanael had spent quite some time on his plantation one day while looking over a rice paddy in the intense heat of the afternoon. Through not taking adequate precautions against the incessant pounding from the noonday sun he quickly succumbed to the effects of his exposure and died suddenly of sunstroke on June 19, 1786. He was just forty four years old. It was a devastating blow which seemed so unfair after his having come through eight long years of armed conflict relatively unharmed.

Once again Kitty suddenly found herself being both mother and father to her children, but this time she also had the added responsibility of taking on the management of the plantation finances and welfare. This presented her with an immense challenge while at the same time she was deeply gripped in the process of grieving the loss of her beloved husband. It must have seemed like an absolutely impossible task to her at that period in her life where any other less able woman would have surely perished under the sheer weight of her huge burden. Nevertheless, her twin flame spirit was undiminished even though Nathanael had made his untimely transition to the other side.

With this aspect still burning brightly within her saddened heart, she bravely faced all that she had to cope with while managing to run the plantation with a surprisingly good degree of success. Not only did she do this but Kitty also attended to the upbringing of her children as well as continuing her husband's assault on Congress. She was not without influence and called upon her many friends who helped her personally present a petition to Congress to recover Nathanael's debt. Eventually her efforts proved successful, and on April 27, 1792 President George Washington signed an act which indemnified the Greene Estate against all claims from those who had supplied food and materials to the war effort at Quartermaster Brigadier Greene's request.

At last she had achieved the justice which she had fought so exhaustingly hard to attain, but this freedom from Nathanael's final burden proved to be something of a hollow victory. The rewards of his and Kitty's long fight were to be savoured only by his grieving widow who would willingly have given the earth just to have had her beloved husband with her so as to see out their remaining years together. Even so, she was obviously very much relieved when this long awaited decision and act was agreed to and then endorsed by the President, as her letter to a close friend Nat Pendleton clearly shows. In it she says :

> *'I can tell you my dear friend that I am in good health and spirits and feel as saucy as you please not only because I am independent, but because I have gained a complete triumph over some of my friends who did not wish me success and others who doubted my judgement in managing the business and constantly tormented me to death to give up my obstinacy, as it was called; they are now mute as mice. Not a word they dare utter. Oh how sweet is revenge'*

Her remaining years without her beloved husband were filled with attending to the business of running the plantation while being as much of a mother to her children as she possibly could be. In fourteen short years of married life, almost eight of them had been filled with the struggle and deprivations of the war effort. During that time her beloved twin flame had helped form what eventually came to be known as the United States of America. History would note his contribution as being second in command to the man who later became the country's first president, George Washington.

An Unexpected Ending Creates a
Path to Re-Uniting

Nathanael's sudden and unexpected passing came as no less a shock to Kitty as it did to the people who he had so valiantly fought for. The measure of his impact on their new found society was such that all business was suspended for a short while as the nation mourned his untimely loss. Such was the lasting impression that he'd had on very many people while having the reputation of being a loyal and trustworthy man who would always stand firm in the convictions of his heart. This he would do while selflessly defending the cause of equal rights for all free men and women who only ever wished to pursue a fulfilling and enjoyable life. His true and enduring legacy was one which not so much exemplified the struggle that every conscientious man and woman aspires to, but the love which he demonstrated for his dream of the right to live in a liberated world.

No one would truly know what the pursuit of this dream had really cost him and what it would lead him towards in a way that much of humanity can only speculate on. Nathanael was a brave and committed soldier, but he was also still that sensitive young Quaker boy inside; the one who had spent much of his sheltered youth discovering the world through reading his precious books in the safety of his bedroom. Nothing, however graphically portrayed, could have prepared him for the indescribable horrors of war which brought about untold anguish as he watched many close friends, and those who he sought to protect, forfeit their lives.

This certainly must have caused him, in his times of quiet contemplation, to search within for answers to the age-old questions which very many still ask to this day. No doubt his Bible studies were a great comfort to him, but having faced in eight long years more than most souls face in many different lifetimes, he experienced much emotional and spiritual distress. As a result, Nathanael acquired scars which were not evident to the naked eye and neither would many of them heal on this side of the veil. It would take something very special to happen for him in order that he could overcome many things which his consciousness could not reconcile in his time as Nathanael. It would require another lifetime while assuming a different identity and embarking on a quite remarkable journey so as to do what was needed.

Undoubtedly the time which he was able to spend with Kitty and his children, after the cessation of hostilities, did a lot to restore some of his emotional balance. The handful of years he spent at Mulberry Grove, where everyone worked so closely as a team, must have been very healing for him as he strove to carve their future out of the land. It may have been a short-lived togetherness but it surely was one which gave him the opportunity to sample many important steps towards the fulfilment of his dreams. Kitty and

Nathanael had been parted for so long in a war that had not been of their choosing when suddenly she lost him when she least expected to. It seemed so unfair after all that they had been through.

Their love however, was as enduring as the words which were penned by many a scribe who would commit the acts of a brave and conscientious man to the annals of a great country's birthing. Nathanael and Kitty were a light so bright that the illusory shroud of death could neither separate them nor keep their presence from influencing others. They were, and still are, twin souls who came together in the same lifetime to experience challenging circumstances on a journey through an era which would help them both with their spiritual evolvement and progress. Their twin flame energies were an inspiration to them both as they encountered many of the extremes which this life can offer.

Nathanael lived an intense existence after having experienced the sheltered and often introvert world of the Quakers of his childhood days to then encountering the frantic insanity of brutal human conflict in his adult life. In the midst of all this he was supported by the love of his life who gave him six adorable children, one of whom was only with them for a very brief time. His was a journey of extremes in every sense of the word and one which would have been almost impossible to survive, while keeping body and soul together, without the close presence and support of his twin soul.

Even with the supporting love of his other half, Nathanael suffered greatly in not being able to come to terms with what he had been exposed to during his times as commanding officer. Many issues which appeared to conflict greatly with his religious beliefs posed profound questions that went unanswered while matters of his family survival needed to be attended to. On top of his spiritual and emotional dilemmas, Nathanael must have been further demoralised through witnessing an apparent abandonment by those who he had assumed would support him in his time of need; after he had willingly come rushing to theirs. Being as sensitive as he was, Nathanael took all this as a reflection of his character insomuch as the failures and consequences he presumed were his, in the light of no clearer or meaningful understanding being available to him.

As bright as Kitty's twin flame love was, and still is for him, it proved to be incapable of penetrating the dark areas of doubt, self-recrimination and guilt which had accumulated in Nathanael's conscience. These had all come about as a result of those traumatic times where he considered that he had either caused his men to endure suffering or he had ordered them, especially close friends and boys, to their death. This was a challenge too far for him but there are forces which exist beyond our comprehension which are constantly watching over each one of us where Nathanael's plight was well understood. In this respect, another opportunity was created and devised so as to allow him to experience circumstances which would help a greater understanding of all that still troubled him after his transition. Before he could take advantage of this gift however, it was necessary for him to seek the counsel of wise beings who would offer their guidance in a manner which he could best understand.

What you will read next is his story of how the whole extraordinary process unfolded and what truly amazing things he experienced before returning to this life as my beloved Ron, my eternal twin flame. Kitty and Nathanael were to be re-united so that many things, which they had needed to sacrifice for the good of a common cause, could once more be experienced in a more beneficial and meaningful way. Their love would once again transcend time while giving them the opportunity to discover not only each other but a great deal more about themselves as well. In doing so they would come to appreciate at a much greater depth the unfathomable mysteries which lie behind this most astonishing journey we call life.

- Chapter 9 -

Returning Home - Looking Forward to the Past

I found myself standing in an uncharacteristically thoughtful way amid the bright sunlit land of my Savannah plantation while trying to absorb all that I was seeing. It appeared as though I was looking at something which I had taken for granted over a long period of time, but suddenly I was viewing it in a completely new light. Somehow, in a way that I found difficult to comprehend, the environment all around me appeared to be strangely different. Not in any kind of displeasing way that I could perceive but it just didn't seem to be as I remembered it being when ... well, right at that moment I wasn't even sure of exactly 'when' might be as time also seemed equally unfamiliar.

The more I began to focus on everything then not only did it appear to be comfortingly familiar, but as odd as it may sound, it also looked to be so remarkably fresh as well. In fact, it would be more accurate to say that it was almost bursting with life in a way that I'd never imagined possible. I felt compelled to examine things closer and so I began to wander around while peering into the canopies of trees which I somehow sensed were actually happy to see me.

Wherever I went then it felt like there was an air of excitement emanating from whatever I looked at as well as the very ground that I found myself standing on. It was the most amazing experience but one which impressed upon me a kind of communication with whatever happened to be the focus of my attention. While allowing myself to be swept along with the allure of this sensation, I got the impression that I was being invited to share in its new found delight at simply existing.

Each time this occurred there were a few seconds where I felt myself becoming overwhelmed by the sheer depth and scale of beauty which formed what I can only describe as a three dimensional living canvas. It was the most remarkable spectacle which presented itself to me as though it had very recently been created by the highly talented hand of some Divine artist. Even characterising it in this manner didn't really do it justice, but however my mind attempted to analyse it, I couldn't seem to stop staring at one fascinating aspect of it after another. Somewhere in the furthermost recesses of my thoroughly captivated mind I heard a small voice telling me that I may be in imminent danger of never wanting to leave this place; I agreed with it.

Wherever I looked then not one single structure or piece of equipment appeared to have been affected, even in the slightest way, by the ravages of the seasons. There were absolutely no indications of any ageing where even time itself appeared not to be resting its insistent hand so heavily on my shoulder. That ever present, inflexible grip which, as I recall, always seemed to want to usher me on towards a future which it insisted awaited my arrival. Fortunately for me I was never a willing subject of time's perpetual deception as I thought it to be nothing more than an insubstantial phantom of its own making. If I remember, it perpetually wanted to convince me of its essential part in supporting the foundation of a notional eternity which offered nothing other than oblivion; I wasn't in the least bit convinced by its empty illusion. I had often heard it said that time and tide waits for no man but always recall feeling, in response to that particular sentiment, that I would be very happy for either commodity to pass me by unaffected.

Even as these thoughts flowed into and through my awareness, I began to get a sense of whatever it was that I felt the need to better understand while looking around me. Then it dawned on me. Suddenly I realised that there appeared to be nothing in the way of anything which gave me any impression of time at all. Everything appeared to be somehow in a perpetual state of youthful poise where the prime of life was the preferred state of all that existed. Quite unexpectedly I started to appreciate that I actually didn't have any clear idea of what 'time' was supposed to be; even though I felt sure that I could recall a state of awareness in which I considered that I did. It was a most odd sensation like trying to remember the details of some complex dream that went on for many lifetimes but which also felt as if it had lasted no more than even the briefest of heartbeats.

I found myself suddenly struggling to find my feet, in a manner of speaking, and so I looked once more at the land around me while searching for something that would give me a sense of reality; some kind of grounding that I could relate to. Nothing really helped in coming immediately to my rescue which resulted in my consciousness performing summersaults while attempting to stay in tact. It was then that I started to experience fear and apprehension creep vine-like around my body, but I had no intention whatsoever of giving into this feeling. Besides, I was far too busy immersing myself in a thoroughly captivating experience to allow any kind of distraction to dilute my enjoyment.

I had faced fear many times on the battlefield and had invariably been successful in rising above it, so I was determined that nothing would alter that aspect of my nature. Nathanael Greene had never been known to shrink from adversity. On this occasion however, there appeared to be no identifiable enemy or any kind of threat that I could perceive; so why was fear even present in my awareness? This emotion seemed so out of place in a setting of such apparent serenity where only the expression of unfettered joy should be allowed to exist. Even so, I did feel very much the need for some kind of reassurance although I had no idea as to how it would come to me or even from whom. My resolve began to waver momentarily as my heart picked up speed a little at the prospect of my dilemma.

I stood motionless as I watched a flock of Savannah sparrows swoop low overhead while the cloudless sky swept them gently up into its nurturing arms. It was such a graceful display of loving protection that, for an instant, I felt a little tinge of envy at their good fortune. As though in anticipation of my unspoken neediness I experienced the sensation of a huge wave of the most profound joy come rushing in to enfold me. It swept through my entire being like the tide of some unseen ocean whose powerful currents cascaded into my emotional rift while reinvigorating my spirit. Immediately there was a wonderfully uplifting lightness which I felt in the very depths of my heart.

It was the kind of feeling which left no room for even a hint of any dark emotions where all anxieties, doubts or fears were instantly banished. The irresistible energy of a child-like joy served to fortify my sense of 'self' while reminding me of my true nature which, for the brief measure of a lifetime, I had almost forgotten. As a consequence I found myself feeling quite overwhelmed by this experience but while in its delightful grip I sensed a powerful reconnection with the child I had once been. It was such a precious gift to be revealed to myself once more and whilst immersed in this remembering I got the idea that I was actually glowing with sheer delight. My heartbeat soon settled into a soothingly comfortable rhythm in response to the encouragement of this wonderful emotion.

Once again I looked around me but this time I began to appreciate that everything, wherever I looked, was radiating a similar serene state of delight; which almost reached out to encourage me to join in. I considered it to be a thoroughly welcoming experience which needed no words, however eloquent, to convey its joyful message. I took great pleasure in being the happy recipient of such a sincere overture which had come to envelop me while being carried so lightly on the wind. Through attuning myself to the sweet melody of what was being expressed then I felt an irresistible urge to become a part of whatever I had been invited to join in with. I needed no more encouragement other than to immerse myself in this most heavenly of sensations while I happily went with the flow. The river of life felt to me as if it was in full flood which made me want to stay playing in its delightful currents forever. I was overcome by a sudden sense of being reborn, rejuvenated, rediscovered to myself which felt **so** incredibly good!

While being thoroughly immersed in this amazing sensation, I gradually became aware that the glare from the sun didn't seem to be anywhere near as bright as it had been. But, what surprised me even more was the fact that I didn't get any impression of heat coming from it at all; even though I felt as if there ought to be some kind of sensation at the very least. This confused me for a moment as I searched within myself for a greater depth of connection to my physical senses. As soon as I did then I was pleasantly surprised to realise that my body wasn't so terribly exhausted or painful any more. In fact, it felt just as it did when I was in my early twenties; full of youthful vigour and overflowing with vitality as well as an enthusiasm for life which was an almost forgotten concept to me.

Not only that but my head didn't feel as though it was throbbing and about to explode as I remembered it doing before ... well, at that moment I couldn't recall when exactly 'before' was. It even felt strangely odd to think of this particular word as its exact meaning didn't appear to be present anywhere within my awareness. Even so, I wasn't inclined to dwell on its apparent elusive absence as it just didn't seem to be important to me any longer. Just how incredibly freeing this realisation was to me, I couldn't possibly begin to describe.

I turned to look directly up at the blazing afternoon sun but in doing so I was not immediately conscious of the fact that there appeared to be no need for me to shield my eyes. I stared in fascination at such a familiar object which had never before given me a moment's pause for thought until that precise point on my journey. It was then that I truly appreciated for the very first time that I had been looking directly into the unfathomable heart of the magic which is the source of our very existence on this planet. What I observed in the process was the breathtaking beauty of this unconditionally nurturing star in our little heaven without whose tender ministrations, and eternal gift, then nothing would ever grow or flourish. I couldn't seem to tear my wonder-filled gaze away from it, but then I began to find my behaviour a little confusing.

Somewhere in the back of my slowly awakening mind I had a sense that I really ought to be reacting to the powerful light from such a bright star, but for some incomprehensible reason, I wasn't. It made me happy to stare at it and, what's more, I could almost feel that it was the most natural thing in the world for me to want to do. In fact, when I came to think of it, being exactly where I found myself to be at that moment seemed as though it was just where I would have wished to be. I also seemed to be doing what I wanted to do and could have been happy for a very long time doing nothing else. It was while in the process of contemplating this possibility that I suddenly became aware of just what happiness actually meant to me. I immediately thought of Kitty and I smiled as the unique essence of her femininity seemed to step lightly up so as to enfold me.

This somewhat captivating moment of realisation also corresponded with my sensing the presence of someone standing very close by. I was torn between continuing to feast my eyes upon the beautiful golden orb in the sky, while thinking about my beloved wife, or paying attention to my previously unnoticed companion. For some peculiar reason I had a sense that whoever it was who had come to join me in my little piece of paradise then he, or she, seemed very familiar. Curiosity slowly got the better of me and so I turned to look at who it could be. In doing so I began to look away from the sun and once again I caught sight of the landscape around me.

This time, to my delight, it appeared to be substantially more appealing than it had ever been before; if that was at all possible. To describe just exactly what I saw all around me needed careful consideration but in certain respects I would have to say that everything looked so much more vibrant; simply brimming over with life. Then it suddenly occurred to me that I felt exactly the same. Within this appreciation I was able to see that there existed a certain harmony to everything and I had become, for want of a better expression, an integral part of it; like a kind of One-ness, a belonging. However I phrased it then it did seem to express exactly how I felt, but to say that I experienced a sense of contentment unlike anything that I had ever encountered before would be to get pretty close. It seemed as though I had achieved a sublime connection to everything and it was absolutely **the** most wonderful feeling imaginable.

Even the old buildings that were used for storing equipment and food stocks appeared as though they had been built just a few days ago. All their sad weather-beaten exteriors were gone where every stone, slate and plank had taken on a new lease of life to the degree that they seemed to be a totally natural part of the surroundings. If it were at all possible for buildings to express an emotion then I would have to say that they looked positively cheerful. It seemed an odd way to think about the 'form' of a building but that surely was the impression which they left on me as I tried to take in the entirety of the landscape all around me.

While doing this I realised that wherever I looked then this wonderful quality was being reflected back to me from every dimension and corner of the world which I once thought I knew. A world in which I vaguely remembered observing so much confusion, strife, deceit and despondency. These being the underpinning emotional and mental constituents of a society that was so obstinately blinkered to its innate potential. But here, all around me now, right in front of me in all its glorious splendour, I could see every grain of that wonderful potential expressed so freely and so vividly. So positively and so unencumbered where all I wanted to do was to look at every aspect of it while feeling myself to be as much a part of it as I possibly could be.

I eagerly drank in the entire panorama while satisfying a strong need within me to fill myself up with its magic when suddenly I felt my heart respond as though a huge weight had been lifted from it. The sensation was quite overwhelming as the lightness which I experienced at that moment convinced me that I could take to the wing and fly without any conscious thought as to how I would ever do such a thing. All of a sudden it seemed to be the most natural thing for me to want to do. I just wanted to play in the clouds while enjoying my freedom from the constraints of a burden which I felt no longer able to tolerate in its incessant desire to keep me pinned to the ground. I prepared to flex my 'wings' but there was a movement to the side of me which I caught sight of from the corner of my eye and so instinctively I turned to get a better look at what, or who, it was.

Immediately I realised that I had momentarily forgotten about my unidentified companion. To my surprise I was greeted by the most beautiful smiling face which expressed a level of patience that would have surely challenged the degree which had been attributed to the legendary Job. I smiled back while feeling as though I knew what my companion's demeanour was actually 'saying' to me. At precisely the same instant I also had the sense of being a small child whose parent had indulged it while watching it play endless fantasy games in the park. Now the time had come to go home, although at that moment I just couldn't remember where 'home' actually was. It didn't matter though because I confidently expected that he knew where to go and so I would just follow him to wherever it was that we lived.

I looked directly into his incredibly expressive eyes whereupon a feeling within me instantly rose up which seemed intent on bursting forth with an energy akin to that of childish excitement. I felt the overwhelming desire to share with him just what I had become aware of and what I was feeling about this wonderful world all around me. It seemed as though I had discovered something completely new where my degree of elation was just too much to bear. If I wasn't able to share it with someone very special right at that precise moment then I imagined that I would quite literally explode.

To my heartfelt relief, my radiant companion appeared as though he knew exactly what it was that I wanted to express where no words needed to be exchanged. At the instant I became aware of this then I noticed a beautiful glow coming from all around him which seemed to be in near perfect harmony with the landscape. I found it to be a most peculiar sensation but one which, for some reason that I didn't understand, appeared as a quite natural response to the intensity of my feelings. I smiled at this realisation while becoming conscious of a similar glow surrounding myself at the same time. It was all just the most magical experience that I could ever remember being so intimately connected to, but also one that I certainly didn't want to give up.

Without a single word being spoken, I knew that he completely understood but I was also able to appreciate that he had been waiting for me to accompany him on towards our destination. I was torn, although in my heart I knew that it had become necessary for me to leave this beautiful place while accepting that we must begin setting out on the pathway to wherever it was that we were going. I made him aware of my readiness to go with him but I had no idea of exactly how I did it; I just seemed to think it and he knew right away. In response he turned to walk off along the pathway out of the paddy field and then on towards the big wooden gates in the high stone wall.

I thought for a moment that he would encounter some problems in opening these broken down old sentinels which had so steadfastly protected this part of the estate since before I was even a twinkle in my father's eye. To my surprise, however, they were already slightly open while looking as though they had been installed just a few minutes ago. They appeared to be so new that I felt an urge to look for the carpenters and stonemasons who surely must have been working on them right up to the moment of our arrival. They were nowhere to be seen which puzzled me somewhat; more than a little actually.

The gates opened effortlessly to reveal the most beautiful tree-lined pathway which seemed to go on forever. I didn't understand how I could have forgotten something so picturesque which had always been situated just on the other side of what I once considered to be a broken down old wood and stone portal. It was a structure which had never attracted my attention until that moment, but now it seemed as though, if I had been an artist, I would be happy to sit and capture the entire view on canvas. As much as this was appealing I could sense my friend slowly walking towards the gates while waiting for me to catch up. I felt sure that my reluctance to leave must have been obvious to him but his gentle encouragement persuaded me that he must have a good reason for wanting to set off on our journey.

Even before my mind was able to register any kind of objection, my feet were already starting to tread the course which led in his direction. Something inside me seemed to know instinctively that the moment had come for me to journey to another place, even though it was unknown to me. Just as I neared the gateway I felt the urge to turn so as to look back one more time just to make sure that the vision of such wonderful surroundings, which had become so dear to my heart, would be captured forever in my memory. It was while doing this that I noticed, for the first time, a group of workers gathered around someone who seemed to be in distress. I could see a man lying prone on the bare earth and looking very poorly while his weary, older-than-its-years looking body, remained inert and motionless.

It did not look to be a happy scene at all which made me want to return to see what was happening, but I could sense that my companion was encouraging me to leave so as to follow him on to our destination. Reluctantly I acceded to his request albeit that I seemed to recognise the man lying on the ground. His appearance was quite familiar even down to the look of profound sadness which almost covered him like a thick shroud. I sensed a strong need in me to help him but there appeared to be many other very capable looking people who were offering their kindness and compassion.

As I watched for a moment longer I saw them pick the man up and then start to carry him off in the direction of the large plantation house. My reaction to this was that I seemed to experience a very confusing sensation in that I sensed a certain need to accompany the fallen man; but I had no idea as to why this should be. Obviously there was nothing I could do for him but somehow it didn't seem right for me not to be with him.

My urge felt so strong but just at the precise moment I was about to act on my feelings I sensed a firm hand holding me by the arm. It let me know that I should leave things as they were while heading off with my companion; so I turned back to investigate the long pathway that I had observed leading away from the other side of the entranceway.

To my surprise the pathway was no longer there and neither were the gates. Instead I seemed to be walking alongside my companion as we headed into something which appeared to be, as best as I can describe it, a very bright mist. It was nothing like I had ever seen before but I felt not one iota of fear as I stepped confidently on my way while being enveloped within its fascinating presence. For some reason it just felt right. I had no thought whatsoever as to why this should be although there seemed to be a familiarity which arose from a kind of inner 'knowing'. This sensation appeared to impart a certain freshness in my awareness, just like the one which I remembered wrapping me up in the same way as I had felt back in the fields of the plantation.

That was it! Suddenly it dawned on me that I was walking in the same wonderful feeling that the landscape had surrounded me with while encouraging me to be a part of it. Being in the bright mist had simply been a continuation of that joyous state which I had experienced, but then I became conscious of something else; another dimension that I hadn't been aware of outside of the mist. I could hear some kind of sound. It appeared to be almost inaudible at first but it was surely there, all around me, although it wasn't anything like I had ever heard up to that point. Or was it? Did I remember it or didn't I and what could it be if I did remember it? I listened more intently only to appreciate that what I had assumed to be a sound, actually appeared to be more like a song. Even on recognising this I could appreciate that it was one which came from a choir the like of which went completely beyond the limits of my comprehension. Its sheer beauty seemed to speak to me in a language that only my soul was able to interpret.

No sooner had my attention become focused entirely on the irresistible enchantment of the song than I found myself stepping through a pair of tall, beautifully carved entrance gates and into the wide expanse of a peaceful meadow. As I did so then the sparkling mist simply evaporated to reveal a beautiful summer's day where the high wispy clouds and the light blue sky could have been taken straight from the painting of some master artist. The whole landscape surrounding the meadow was absolutely breathtaking with its rolling hills and tree-lined valleys stretching out as far as I could see.

Everything had such a 'friendly' feel to it where even the delicate scents that were carried on the lightest of breezes seemed to evoke feelings of a deep contentment in me. Within the allure of this salving emotion I was able to appreciate a wonderfully warm sense of the most sincere greeting. As a consequence I felt so 'wanted' in a way which I could not recall feeling before that moment.

It was all so perfect in its appeal to me, but oddly enough I found myself having to just stand still for a moment or two so as to adjust to all that I was feeling while keeping my emotional balance. It seemed illogical that I should want to get used to a sensation which came rushing at me with such unconditional love and acceptance; but my feelings didn't know anything about logic. I was unaware at that point on my journey of just how much I had forgotten about being cherished in such a way. Fortunately I was keen to be reminded while suddenly wishing to know much more about this wonderful location which I found myself in.

Whatever else, I seemed to have the urgent need to share my heartfelt joy with someone in that it felt almost too much to keep to myself. I was just brimming over with unreserved happiness, so much so that even the gentle birdsongs coming from the distant valleys appeared to be speaking to me in a similar way. This I found incredibly exciting which almost made me feel as though I wanted to answer them. The whole captivating experience was so uplifting while seeming to wrap me up in some sort of protective covering which had a wonderful kind of maternal quality to it. As I let myself fall deeper into its comforting attraction then it became very tempting to just rest in its tender embrace while giving up to a nice long restorative sleep. I could almost feel my eyelids getting heavier when I noticed something which got my attention.

Just a little way off I saw a small lake where the surface of the water looked like glass; there wasn't a ripple to be seen on it. For a moment I just let my gaze rest on its tranquil beauty which almost felt as if it was calling to me in some way. I was briefly captivated by the allure of such serenity while something deep within me seemed to urge my feet to carry me closer so that I could set myself down by the side of it. Having done so, then I somehow knew that I would be able to feel its compelling promise of an eternal peacefulness which awaited me. The lake seemed to want to welcome me into the cradle of its compassionate presence and, as it did, a long forgotten memory would stir in the very depths of my being.

I knew this place and it spoke to me in recognition of my remembering. It was the sweetest pastoral scene which my heart held most dear but one that had been kept shielded from my awareness until now. It felt so good to be back although I was tempted to consider the prospect that I had never actually left. The welcoming familiarity which reached out so encouragingly to embrace my entire being made me think about never abandoning its magical beauty ever again. I looked once more upon the brushstrokes of some divine hand that had so lovingly created this perfection on a huge canvas of the most spectacular living colour.

In doing so my attention was drawn to a group of people who were sat in what looked to me to be a charming garden which had been lovingly created just a little way from the lake. Some of them looked familiar, but before I had time to think about where I might have met them before, my companion stepped past me while appearing to head in their direction. As it meant my being closer to the lake if I followed him then I gladly set off towards the gathering in the hope of discovering more about what was happening. Drawing nearer to the garden area I noticed some tents set against the trees where there was what appeared to be a large semi-circular bench in front of them. A few of the men were sitting on it while deep in conversation but they stopped as my companion and I began to approach them.

It was at this point that I noticed a large and quite strikingly beautiful symbol which had been set into an area of the ground which seemed to be at the focal point of the curved wooden seat. One of the men stood up to greet my companion and then, one by one, the others joined in. Very shortly, more people came to take part in what appeared to be turning into a small celebration. As I watched then I couldn't help but be affected by the unreserved happiness which everyone so eagerly expressed. Before I could fully take in everything that was going on then all of them started coming towards me which I found momentarily alarming. That was, until I recognised one of the men and immediately my heart literally overflowed with loving gratitude. I had never expected to see his weather-beaten impish face ever again.

Yet here he was standing in front of me while looking as young as the day I'd dragged him out of the river after he had taken on a man nearly twice his size; and then I had offered him a place in my regiment. What a sight for sore eyes he was indeed. His enthusiastic greeting nearly knocked me off my feet and so I held onto him as we embraced in a manner of the most joy filled friendship. My unreserved happiness must have been obvious to everyone who surrounded me in what I can only describe as an experience of the utmost love and affection that I could ever remember. It was the most incredible feeling and so absolutely addictive that I never wanted it to stop.

Eventually he reluctantly released me from his heartfelt embrace while turning to his companions who were then treated to a long discourse of our time together as well as all the adventures that we'd had. As he was talking then he proceeded to lead us all towards the seating area where I found myself invited to sit on the strange symbol while everyone else sat on the large arc of the bench seat. There were many introductions to people who I seemed to remember to one degree or another but what overwhelmed me the most was the feeling of unconditional love which completely surrounded me.

Everyone expressed their emotions so freely where no one seemed to judge anything or anyone where all were accepted for being just who they were; especially me. It felt so wonderful to be this way but what proved to be more remarkable was that I began to sense the fact that it actually appeared quite natural to respond to each other in such and openly accepting manner.

Suddenly, people began to talk about me and, to my surprise, they seemed to know quite a bit more about me than I did. I listened in rapt attention as I heard story after story told about my past where no small detail was left out. What I found to be the most startling aspect of the entire experience was that I heard what I considered to be not only flattering and complimentary accounts of my life but also many not so pleasing, or even distressing, stories as well. Episodes from my journey that I had totally forgotten about, or at least not wanted to recall in such graphic detail, but in not one of these recountings was there ever a hint of any judgement whatsoever. I seemed to be the only one who felt that my deeds be considered either good or bad. It was highly puzzling to feel myself being somehow unable or unwilling to view my life without judging it in some way or another.

After some of the people had told their stories they left the group and returned to the side of the lake where, eventually, they wandered off into other parts of the meadow or just sat by the water while watching the swans. I realised that, including my companion, there were now only six people seated on the circular bench where all of them were looking at me as though they were waiting for me to say something. I had no idea what they were expecting, but nothing at all came to my mind about what I could possibly want to say as I was far too busy going over all that had been described of my life. There was much for me to think about, especially after having heard it spoken of when seen through the eyes of others. I had been reminded of many instances which had stirred up quite powerful feelings in me, some of which sent uncomfortable ripples across my emotional 'pond'.

I looked across to the quiet lake where many people were sitting close by the still waters while enjoying the tranquillity of their surroundings and immediately my state of disharmony began to subside. No sooner had this happened than a flap on one of the tents swung open whereupon I saw the figure of a tall man step through the opening. The first thing I noticed about him was his quite recognisable walk but his whole demeanour seemed very familiar to me; although it wasn't until I could see his face clearly did I appreciate who it actually was. My feelings were somewhat mixed as I wasn't prepared to see him again, especially after hearing so many stories that surrounded our most desperate times together while gripped in the harshest of battles.

At first I felt a shiver run through me as vivid memories of those times appeared to course through my consciousness where I could almost feel how it was to be back in that era of my life. In one respect it all seemed so real and yet, in contrast to the beautiful surroundings which I was present in, it didn't appear possible for anything of such an appalling nature to have ever happened at all. The contrast of my vivid memories compared to the sheer peaceful harmony of my surroundings made me feel as though my experiences had been nothing more than some horrible nightmare; which I had since woken up from. The idea of this possibility left me feeling more than a little confused.

As the man approached our little group I recognised a characteristic aspect to his smile. It put me in mind of how he would always appear this way whenever he'd figured out a solution to some seemingly intractable dilemma. I remembered his wonderful resourcefulness as well as his ability to lift the spirits of just about anyone who came under the influence of his infectious personality. On this occasion however, he appeared to have the most wonderful extra 'dimension' to his smile which gave me the impression that he had found the answers to just about every question that anyone could ever think of asking. Not only this but he was beaming this wonderful smile in my direction which made me feel that he knew all the answers to my problems as well; whatever they may be.

This pleased me greatly to see his uniquely familiar greeting as it always had the same effect of lifting my spirits no matter what was going on around me at the time. So, here he was again, only on this occasion he appeared to be exuding a certain self-assured radiance which made his presence seem even more compellingly inspiring. Gone were the facial lines that had characterised his often animated appearance as we wrestled with the inevitable consequences of conflict. He had always looked younger than his age but constantly living on the edge of such turbulent and perilous situations had inevitably taken its toll on both of us.

It made me very happy indeed to appreciate that all those times were forever behind us and was heartily gladdened to see him looking so well. I had often wondered about his fate after the war had ended and our struggle began in earnest to create the world of our dreams. Those were times of great confusion where an uncertain future awaited so many and where good fortune would favour those who could adapt and contribute whatever skills they may posses. To my mind there appeared to be little in the way of any encouraging prospects for a musician and poet but quite evidently life had been kind to him in the peacetime that followed. I found myself being anxious to know what had become of him, but thankfully I would not have to wait long to find out.

My companion got up to greet this quite extraordinary man, the 'Battlefield Bard' as we used to call him, and then quickly offered him a seat. He graciously accepted it with a certain humility that was so typical of him while extending his unique greeting to all others present. There were now seven people facing me from the semi-circular seat which suddenly gave me a strong sense of having been in this exact same position before.

"Many times." one of them said which made my mind race a little in being able to appreciate that he knew what I was thinking. While struggling a little to regain my composure, I got the distinct impression that this meeting was

going to turn out to be much more 'interesting' and definitely more enlightening than I could ever have imagined. It wasn't long before I was to be proved right in this assumption.

- Chapter 10 -

The Journey into a New Adventure

For a minute or two I sat looking around me while trying to take in all that was happening in the hope that I could get a better insight into not only where I was, but also why all these people were here with me as well. The group who were all seated on the curved wooden bench seemed to be momentarily engaged in a communal conversation about something which they obviously found very interesting. I, on the other hand, was far too busy to take notice of what they were saying as I let my emotions settle while attempting to adjust to my new surroundings; but this I found to be the confusing part. In one respect it did all seem comparatively new but in another way I was quite sure that I'd been here before. Not just once, either, but very many times although I had no idea whatsoever of how I came to know this to be so.

My mind couldn't seem to make any sense of this 'knowing' at all, which I assumed was more than likely the cause of my stirring sense of unease. In an attempt to gain a more helpful understanding I began examining the nearby landscape of my new 'world' while almost feeling as though I needed to get better acquainted with it. This I hoped would make things come clearer as it uprooted one or two important memories in the process. At first I was drawn to study the lake but quickly I moved on to take in just about everything including the beautiful garden where it appeared as though summer was in full bloom. It seemed to be quite evident from my observations that absolutely everything around me did nothing other than radiate the most profound degree of unreserved joy while apparently existing within the ultimate state of peaceful harmony.

Through my increasing appreciation of this, I also began to sense that the atmosphere which had been created by such a wonderful synergy was actually trying to tell me something. When I 'listened' then it felt as if it was encouraging me to become completely immersed in its universal magic and that somehow my presence had been anticipated. For some reason I didn't stop to question this as it gave me such a nice feeling which served to ease my apprehensiveness. It also helped me to appreciate that the only thing which appeared to be required of me was to simply enjoy the beauty of my surroundings while getting lost in the timelessness of its appeal.

This request was one which made me very happy to accommodate it as I took a few moments to become absorbed in the enchantment of the quite spectacular scenery in and around the meadow. Wherever I looked then people, animals, birds and even the plants, shrubs and trees seemed to be expressing a serene quality which I found to be completely irresistible. It was impossible not to be affected by such a wonderfully natural harmony which unconditionally extended its infectious attraction in such a way that I felt compelled to join in with it. However, this willingness to do so caused another sensation to arise in me. It was one which brought with it even more uncomfortable stirrings of unease. In all honesty I would have to say that it was quite a bit more noticeable than merely a state of mild agitation. What I actually felt could be more accurately described as bordering on the decidedly uncomfortable; which seemed most out of place in the current climate. Through feeling a strong desire to surrender myself to the atmospheric mood of my surroundings, I began to appreciate something else. It appeared to be an equally strong need to first of all lay down a very heavy burden which, up to that moment, I hadn't been aware of.

Somehow the ambience of the meadow had provided me with a kind of backdrop against which I was able to get much closer in touch with myself while also allowing me to see many things more clearly. It was as if I'd been given a personal 'harmony level' indicator. This helped me to get a much better idea of how my own emotional state of balance faired in comparison to the peaceful contentment of all that I found myself influenced by. The results were not looking good. It seemed to be telling me that I should put aside something that I no longer needed to haul around with me, but for some reason that I was completely unable to fathom, I didn't seem able to lay down whatever weighed so heavily on me.

My mind darted around aimlessly like a hapless paper bag caught in a windstorm while having not the slightest clue as to what it was looking for. There had been no indication before that moment of any excess baggage that I had brought with me on the journey so how could I dispose of what I didn't even appreciate was being unwittingly dragged along with me. There could be no doubt that something needed getting rid of as I could feel that until it had been dealt with then I wasn't free to truly enjoy my surroundings. This thought saddened me more than a little but this was yet another emotion that I didn't welcome as my harmony-level indicator edged ever nearer to the 'depleted' mark.

For what seemed like quite some time I sat processing my thoughts and feelings while struggling to regain my balance. This wasn't helped by the fact that I was beginning to have doubts about just what that state of being actually meant to me. It felt so odd in the respect that, on the one hand I did appear to be keenly aware of my surroundings and the peacefulness which they were encouraging me to share in. But, on the other hand, the more conscious of this attractive quality I became then the greater was my awareness of an inability to respond to it as I wanted to. It seemed to be such a subtle process but one which I could appreciate the very powerful nature of in how it was affecting me.

In consequence I began thinking about just what could have caused me to become more conscious of my state of balance when I realised something important. Suddenly I began to appreciate that the atmosphere of serenity itself seemed to be presenting me with a kind of tangible reference to a state of carefree innocence. In doing so then it perceptively held out an emotional template for me so that I would have something to compare myself against. The closer that I allowed myself to move toward it then the more I was able to see just how much out of alignment my state of balance had become. In so doing I also gained an awareness of how 'normal' it had become to walk around in this state without having the benefit of something else to bring it to my attention. It seemed comparable to having a headache for so long that eventually it wasn't noticed any more. This was not by any means a comforting thought as it seemed like a completely unnatural way to be. However, I had to admit that it was more than likely to have been my normal state of being right up to this point on my journey. I shivered a little at this realisation.

Seeking solace in the comfort of my surroundings seemed like a good idea right at that moment, so once more I turned my attention to the beauty of the garden. It was then that I began to notice the colours of the various flowers and in particular how exotic some of them appeared to be as well as how wonderful their somewhat intoxicating fragrances were. Many of them looked to be quite delicate in their nature where it seemed as though even the lightest of winds would be enough to carry them off to the horizon and beyond. Such beauty and poise combined with a delightful delicacy but there was no hint of any kind of reservation whatsoever among them that I could detect. They obviously had no fear for their survival while only ever wishing to share their individual gifts with anyone who cared to be graced by them.

I suddenly became a little envious of their freedom to express themselves in such a naturally unencumbered way. It seemed strange to even consider this, but I could almost feel what it was like to be exactly how they were in not giving any thought to whatever else was going on around them. I had a kind of remembering within me of being this same way once a very long time ago, even though I had never actually consciously considered it to be possible before that moment. Unfortunately, the more I gave my attention to it then the greater was my awareness of the burden that I had been carrying. As a result I found myself momentarily existing in a kind of dualistic state where I could appreciate two quite different ways of being.

The longer that I absorbed the irresistibly disarming charm of my surroundings then the more I appeared to be aware of how weighed down I was with whatever had decided to become a stowaway in my subconscious. I became determined not to give it one further instant's consideration as there were much better things to occupy my mind with; such as continuing to relish my wonderful environment. This was the moment when frustration came to sit beside me while tugging irritatingly at my sleeve in order to get my attention. I had no idea whatsoever why it had come to harass me in the midst of such an idyllic setting and wished very much that it would just go away so that I could be left in peace.

Evidently it wasn't about to humour me by agreeing to my request so I chose to rummage around in the gloomier recesses of my mind to see if I could find a heavy weight that would fit right over it. No sooner had I decided to tackle this unwelcomed spectre, whose shadow had sought to obscure the light of my desired tranquillity, than someone on the semi-circular seat began speaking. This certainly had the effect of interrupting my train of thought. Immediately I looked up to see who was talking and for the first time I began to earnestly study the faces of the people in front of me. My mood changed at the same instant, although I still couldn't seem to shake off the awful oppressive feeling which hung over me.

I realised that someone had asked me a question to which I nodded a kind of agreement even though I hadn't fully registered what had been said. It seemed as though I was still very much caught up in the dilemma of my emotional balance which my mind had been struggling to process while searching for some kind of resolution. Alas, there didn't seem to be any kind of imminent reprieve from my situation which made me feel more than a little dejected. So I decided to simply stare blankly at the assembled group of people and their surroundings in the forlorn hope that it might help. I had no idea what else to do, although it seemed appropriate at that moment to offer a little prayer just in case anyone was listening. Someone always is of course, but I wasn't in the least bit prepared for the answer or for what would happen as a result; even if I could have anticipated it.

To my absolute surprise, the view in front of me slowly began shimmering which made me rub my eyes in response. At first I thought that my vision had somehow been affected by something but it quickly became apparent that this wasn't the case at all. As I tried to adjust to the fact that what I had once considered to be reassuringly solid forms were now appearing to become quite fluid, then things continued to change in the most fascinating way imaginable. I rubbed my eyes again, but this time it was because I wanted to make sure that I didn't miss anything. Suddenly I found myself completely caught up in whatever mysterious process had begun to unfold without realising that my emotional dilemma had been momentarily put on hold. I watched in silent fascination as my immediate surroundings took on a kind of flowing appearance, almost as though I was looking at them through the softly rippling surface of the lake.

Very gently the ripples became less pronounced only to be replaced by some kind of superimposed misty blur. As I tried to make out what it could be, it slowly began to reveal lots of moving patterns; or that's what they looked like at that point. But then I could make out recognisable shapes as well as certain things which started to look familiar. Where there had once been simply earth, grass and plants I looked on in amazement as a new dimension suddenly began appearing in front of me. Within it there were remarkably clear images beginning to form but what was actually more startling to me was the fact that these were images which I had no problems at all in recognising right away.

I stared wordlessly spellbound while trying to make out what on earth was going on as I gradually allowed myself to be drawn more completely into the memories which these images evoked in me. One recognisable situation of my life after another came and went as they seemed to melt into each other before I really had time to focus on anything in particular. There was so much to look at that I could happily have sat quietly watching forever while sincerely wishing, during certain poignant glimpses, that time would stand still. Within this state of sheer fascination then absolutely everything was forgotten, even the tranquillity of my surroundings, while I studied the sheer magic of the spectacle which had so magically formed before my very eyes.

Then, as though from a different world, I heard another person speak but I paid little or no attention to their words as the 'so lifelike' image that I was studying continued to play out in full. Unexpectedly it grew larger to show me a scene from my youth where I could see myself sitting alone in my bedroom while studying a much treasured book. I recognised it right away. It was an historical account of Alexander the Great that I had been given and it was this book which had been responsible for introducing me to battlefield strategies. It also taught me how a great leader of his time had inspired so many men to travel huge distances while successfully overcoming many opposing forces in the process.

To be so realistically re-united with this stage of my youth once again, while recalling so vividly how I felt at reading something so completely fascinating and absorbing, was an experience which brought back a great deal to me. For one thing, I could really feel the pulsating excitement of leading a large body of men into a truly historical campaign as I soaked up every single detail of the description. Surprisingly, coincident with my reading I was also aware of sensing a certain amount of guilt. I'd quite forgotten about that aspect of my warfare studies, but now that I could feel it again then I also remembered why. It came from knowing what it would mean if anyone were to catch me reading about something which my family, especially my father, would not have approved of at all. No matter, I just couldn't put it down while the pictures in my head were so real that I could easily have been a part of the whole amazing adventure.

Such was the level of my fascination with the subject. As I avidly immersed myself in the strategic genius of one thoroughly engrossing story after another, I was completely unaware of why it should be that I found myself being so drawn towards wanting to know more about a subject which ran so contrary to the teachings of my culture. In being able to watch myself reading my book then I could see that, even though it went against everything that I had been led to believe, there was something in me which I needed to express. It felt very much as though I was being completely swept along by a tide of human struggle which had served to bring mankind to that particular point of its current evolutionary state. To me, it seemed important to know more about why this should be so that I could better understand the world which I found myself being a part of.

It struck me as being such an unimaginably different world in those far distant times, but there again, I had a sense that what people were fighting for then wasn't that much different from what people of my parents' generation stated that they wanted to achieve in their time. Conquering parts of the world appeared to be a grand idea while travelling to far off places and seeing all the different sights must have been really exciting; but what was it all for? I kept asking myself this question in the hope of finding the answers in my book. What impressed me most of all was how one huge army could travel so far and still be fit and able enough to take on opposing forces which hadn't had to endure similar trials and difficulties; such as carrying all their food, supplies and equipment for hundreds of miles.

Knowing as much as I did about farming and providing food then I could appreciate what it must have been like to feed so many thousands of men while keeping them healthy enough to fight and win. I just had to know how they did it and so I read more and more whenever I was able to. I watched myself reading while jotting copious notes in the margins of my book as I did little sums to figure out how so many of the various feats were actually possible. What my numbers revealed to me showed a scale of campaign which my mind just couldn't begin to conceive of.

It was beyond anything the like of which I could ever imagine but for some reason I knew that it was really important for me to gain a much better understanding of the whole subject of battles and the mechanics of war; although I had no idea why. This instinctive feeling made me start to question much of what I observed going on around me, along with many things that I found myself being encouraged to learn. At that young age and being so inexperienced, I could only go by what impressions were forming in my mind through feeling as I did. In this respect it often appeared as though the world I was growing up in seemed to be completely at odds with everything that I had been taught. I well remembered feeling that it was important for me to know more, but I really had no one suitable to guide me or to give me advice; or even assure me that it was acceptable to be feeling the way I did. That proved to be a very confusing time for me and a point in my life where I had a sense that if I didn't pursue what I felt drawn to do then it would mean becoming lost to a world which didn't appear to have a great deal to offer me.

I had no concept at that young age of where this sense of deep unrest within me came from but I did know for sure that I had to follow wherever it led me. I had a need to survive in my social world at that time of my life but I also felt a burning desire to be true to the person who I sensed myself to be; or at least who I saw myself becoming. I also had a feeling, even at that early stage of my life, that before too long I would be able to take care of myself. This was important to me to appreciate as I had the notion that my world was about to change quite considerably. This awareness fostered a growing need in me to become an active part of that change but I could have no idea at that tender age of just how much it would come racing to embrace me and just how deeply caught up in it I would be. My quest for knowledge seemed to be endless and so my books were an essential part of my life at that time. They were my connection to a world which I wanted to know much more about while my mind was like a huge ball of blotting paper which absorbed every drop of wisdom that it could unearth. Knowledge, to me, had become so important that I considered it as being the sustaining source of my developing mind and just as essential as the nutrition which food provided my very needy and quickly growing body with.

That period of my youth proved to be a very memorable one in the respect that I could only imagine just so much of what I considered the world at large to be. I also had precious little idea of what the social landscape beyond my actual horizons was really like, but I did appreciate that I had a yearning to know much more about it as soon as I possibly could. Politics and other matters of weighty importance, however, were subjects that remained completely beyond my level of understanding. Even so, I did seem to have an awareness of there being a need for me to learn as much as I could about such subjects while never questioning why I felt that way. Somehow I just seemed to know how important it would be in the future. There was just so much to occupy my mind in those days and so many unanswered questions that there didn't seem to be enough hours in the day to do all that I felt the need to do.

Without my realising it I had become so engrossed in watching the images of myself, or was it me actually being myself, that it sometimes proved very difficult for me to work out who was who. Feeling all that I did while growing up, as the memories of my family and those days on the farm flooded through me, then it was proving to be an effort to appreciate that a lifetime of experiences had elapsed since those days. For a moment it seemed as though I may be in danger of becoming thoroughly lost in that period of my life. This caused me to panic a little, but then I heard another familiar voice begin to speak. At first I got the idea that someone was trying to wake me from a deep sleep but I could tell that I wasn't asleep.

Somehow I managed to drag my attention away from those memorable days of my childhood and, somewhat distractedly, I looked up to see a lady on the end of the curved bench addressing me. No sooner had this registered in my mind when suddenly the scene in front of me changed to that of a time when I had been a young man and heading off to join the Continental militia. Again I was amazed at the incredibly lifelike quality of the image where, just as before, I could almost be myself while entering the building in which I would agree to becoming part of a budding army. A raw, untrained but willing fighting force that was made up of many like myself who wanted to stand up for a different way of life. I found the atmosphere around me to be a little intimidating in that I felt a certain degree of guilt in going against all that I had been conditioned to believe throughout the course of my upbringing.

At first it almost seemed as though my intention was to commit some act of betrayal with regard to the beliefs of my family. In another respect, however, it felt very much as though I firmly intended to do something really positive about actually protecting their way of life. I knew in my heart that I wanted to secure the future of an idealised way of living, even though it would have to be achieved through violence; something which went so completely against the basic tenets of my Quaker background. Nevertheless, I had a vision just like very many others of my time and I felt ready, willing and able to do something about it. The days of studying were over for me and so it was to be that I would put everything I had learned to the test, even though there would undoubtedly be a strong possibility that my life may lay forfeit to my hubris. No matter, I just had to do it. I had to be true to myself because that's what freedom really meant to me.

Having decided to break the bonds of my conditioned upbringing, I was now about to set about breaking free from the oppression of an increasingly intolerable force which I no longer wanted to dominate my life; or that of my countrymen. Freedom of thought, expression and deed had become something I was prepared to die for and, at that moment, I could feel so strongly how bright and fiercely the flame of battle burned within my heart. I was prepared to do anything to keep that flame alive while carrying it into the future of a world that I had dared to dream could be possible. Alexander I may not have been but his spirit certainly seemed to be providing the fuel for the lantern which lit my path into the ranks of the militia and so sealed my destiny that day. It was one that I will not easily forget.

No sooner had I felt these words reverberating through the determined passageways of my pounding patriotic heart than someone else spoke from the middle of the wooden bench seat. I looked up to see the 'Battlefield Bard' speaking to me and heard him asking me to remember how it had been to feel the way I did at that time. He seemed keen for me to pay particular attention to the compelling emotion, energy he called it, of my being willing to struggle and possibly die for what I believed in. I was more than a little puzzled that he should ask me to do such a thing, but in the respect that I appeared to be pretty much confused as to all else that was happening, then it didn't seem unreasonable to add one more element to the totality of the mystery.

Somehow I figured that all would be revealed in the fullness of time; whatever that may mean, as time appeared to be even more of a mystery from where I found myself to be sitting at that moment. I did however take notice of what had been said to me in that I really could appreciate what I had committed myself to and why I had acted in the way that I did. It also seemed possible for me to get in touch with that motivationally 'fiery' feeling which had burned so strongly in me. So powerfully rousing was this flame that I would have happily gone through anything and given my life in the process just to achieve what I felt justified in wanting. That state of liberation which was so fervently desired; not only for myself but also for those of my countrymen who could no longer tolerate the prospect of a future dictated by a foreign power.

However, I could appreciate that there existed a kind of blinkered single-mindedness to the manner in which I was approaching what I had decided to do. It also became apparent to me that my vision had been focused so sharply on my objective to such a degree that nothing else appeared to be of any consequence or concern to me; not even, most surprisingly of all, my life. It seemed so odd to appreciate this while sitting very comfortably in the midst of such peaceful surroundings. Especially as I could still feel the currents of war swirling so powerfully around in the storm tossed ocean of my entire being. This question had certainly allowed me to get in touch with an aspect of myself which quite evidently existed outside the realms of any conscious process.

Through being able to view my two distinctly different situations in such a contrasting way then I almost wanted to get up from where I was sitting so as to confront my young self. I felt the urge to grasp him firmly by the shoulder while asking him the question of why he thought as he did. It was so confusing to be feeling this way but somehow I sensed the rightness of a destiny which I had set in motion for myself that day. In an attempt to simply accept the past for being just as it had been, without looking for any kind of reason or rationale, I resigned myself to simply watching. What I observed when I did was my pathway becoming patently clear as an unimaginably challenging future beckoned from a very dark and lightning filled horizon.

For what seemed like an age, I sat thinking about the two different images that I'd witnessed while being able to see myself at two memorable junctures of my life. Not only was it highly fascinating but it also proved to be very challenging in being able to compare how my attitudes and convictions had changed from one period to the other. My youthful self had been naively enthusiastic while being an idealist who was comfortably surrounded by the protection of my privileged upbringing. My adolescent self, in contrast, was filled with a passion which seemed to come from a different source while being influenced by the mood of the times.

The country of my birth appeared to be moving inexorably towards war, which went against all that I had been brought up to believe. My roots were with a people who were peaceful and compassionate by nature but here I was heading into a future of conflict, by my willing hand, while being an enthusiastic participant into the bargain. It seemed apparent that my zealous determination had completely overridden the cautious concerns of my sensitive heart. Almost as though someone had taken a picture of my predicament, there was a bright flash in which time appeared to freeze. Through doing so, it allowed me to see something very clearly within the animation of the process. For a brief moment I caught a highly illuminating glimpse of the implications and depths of an internal struggle that I had not been aware was present.

Even though I had only been granted the very briefest of insights into this aspect of myself, it was long enough for me to fully appreciate not only its existence but also the unexpectedly fragmenting nature of its impact on me as well. As you can probably imagine, I felt quite disorientated by what I had been shown as well as feeling the effects of the emotional reverberations which arose from this revelation. I was also more than a little confused, but from within the very heart of this bewilderment a question began to form; although it wasn't yet clear to me just exactly what its proposal was. It seemed to be an important question which offered the tantalising prospect of some kind of comfort if ever an answer would make itself known to me. I listened intently to hear what would be said next.

To my surprise, I suddenly realised that a quite young looking man on the curved seat had begun asking me something which, oddly enough, seemed to be relevant to what I was feeling about my attitudes then and now. Equally strangely was the implication that it also appeared to be connected to my own, as yet, unexpressed question. My mind immediately went into a state of freefall while my emotions were suggesting that they might be inclined to take a walk by the side of the lake at that point in the proceedings. I was very tempted to accompany them. The only thing that seemed to offer me any kind of support was to focus my attention on the question that had been asked while hoping that it would somehow help me make sense of things. Quite honestly I just didn't know what to think, but I did however have a renewed sense of the burden which I had almost forgotten about in my captivation with all that was taking place in front of me. Whatever the level of my fascination may have been, the weight of my emotional baggage seemed to be determined to make its presence felt yet again. Without giving any conscious attention to it, I began to hear the words of the question which had been posed to me echoing around in my mind.

They seemed to be asking me to consider how I had felt and why I had been so determined about the course of my action. It also appeared that I was being asked to look closely at what I had become aware of in my attitudes towards conflict, as well as how my upbringing had influenced me. In particular I felt guided to appreciate and explore how my compassionate nature, the sensitive side to my character, had been encouraged to express itself through the peace-loving beliefs of my culture. I did as I was asked but this only seemed to throw me back into the turmoil of reconciling two states of being. Once again I could appreciate that my emotions were in conflict in that I could see how my determination was paramount, but it had come about at the expense of my youthful sensitivities which were being quite firmly suppressed. I didn't like how I saw this happening but I had absolutely no idea what to do about it.

Before I had time to mull over exactly why I would consider it necessary to even contemplate this issue, I became conscious that the scene in front of me had quickly started changing to one of a much wider landscape. It wasn't long before I began to make out the familiar features of a location which I eventually recognised; although it wasn't one that held any pleasant memories for me. The view in front of me was actually my first sighting of a somewhat featureless place in my homeland where I would receive my initiation into the horrors of battle. I recalled all too well the feelings of apprehension and fear at what was to come, but again my determination to fight for my dream of a freedom-filled future overcame my anxieties. They did so while pulsing the energy of a fervent belief in the rightness of purpose throughout my body.

I was not to be deterred, even by my sense of underlying fear. I remembered someone once telling me that no one had ever died from fear. Those words had come back to comfort me and to carry not only that day but very many other days ahead. Just as those feeling were settling into my awareness, the scene in front of me changed yet again to reveal another very memorable place of conflict; but this time it was in a completely different part of the country. This particular location had required me to wait for a beneficial campaign opportunity to present itself while spending countless hours planning my strategy. All those long days and nights of reading about Alexander and others who had fought many different types of battles were about to pay dividends in the most positive way. This time I was in command where many lives depended on my leadership skills as well as my clear thinking. I could almost feel my determination not to let them down while I gave no thought to anything other than victory.

What I found to be most noticeable about the scene in front of me was the atmosphere of the camp and the men under my command. Everything looked exactly as I remembered it being. However, I could see from what I was observing just how much I had been caught up in the duties of my office while not truly appreciating what was going on around me. Then, to my surprise, I saw a wagon coming through the dell. It took me a few moments to realise that it was bringing my beloved wife to see me. My heart soared at the sight of her presence but what I found really fascinating to observe was the effect that she had on many others who watched her pass by. They smiled at her in what seemed to be genuine affection where she always had her charming smile ready and waiting to be returned to them. I recalled how proud I had felt in appreciating just how quickly her radiant presence could brighten even the dullest of overcast days which threatened to take us ever closer to battle.

Kitty was an absolute treasure and, from my perspective at that moment, I could see how much of a gift she had been not only to me as her husband but to everyone else around me as well. She personified the dream that we all shared while her irrepressibly spirited femininity reminded us all of what we were fighting so hard to achieve. This wasn't an armed conflict which was being waged purely for the conquest of others; or simply out of some distorted sense of revenge, the like of which I'd read about in times past. This was the struggle against the imposition of a culture by an occupying force who wished to enslave our national spirit through denying us our independence. We were fighting against being disenfranchised where the people of my country were standing up for not only themselves but their families and friends as well. Each blow we struck was one which forged another battle-hardened footstep along the pathway towards the realisation of a belief; the creation of an ideal which attested to a better way of life for our children and their children to come. Ours was a 'just' endeavour which necessitated a bitter and bloody struggle where many laid down their lives in the hope that others of like mind would benefit.

Kitty offered a very real reminder of their families back home as well as those who would reap the rewards of their sacrifices along with their children and relatives. This had never been a war of men's minds being filled with ego-driven greed but rather a pioneering battle that was pitched against an occupying force. Somewhat similar in spirit to how our forefathers had faced the often hostile conditions of a new land which harshly resisted their attempts to tame it. The armed struggle had arisen out of a similarly motivated need to establish a national identity. It was our sovereign right to self determination where we would rather die than give up that privilege. Once again I could feel the strength of my conviction coursing through my veins, especially now that I had a wife who I was devoted to and who I wanted so much to provide a wonderful home and future for.

Just as I was about to get lost in this emotion I noticed that the scene in front of me had begun to change slightly while forming into one of a restful night where the stresses of the day were already evaporating. They seemed to flow gently out into the nearby woodlands while being carried swiftly away by the cool waters of the various streams which formed part of the landscape. The men were more relaxed as the campfires burned brightly while the aspect of morale was attended to. As though in response to our needs, the flames of the fires danced energetically in their enthusiasm to repel the darkness as they mirrored the intensity of the flames in our hearts.

As I watched this most evocative of scenes then I became aware of the familiar figure who had always brought so much life and enjoyment to our camps. He was a source of never ending entertainment and wisdom with his stories and songs which invariably inspired all in his presence. He made us all feel alive when times were almost too difficult to strive beyond; while in the better times it was with his help that we allowed ourselves the freedom to hope for what had always been in our hearts to achieve. This particular night he performed for us all while being at his consummate best. He sang and played his instrument for all his worth where many danced and clapped in response. It was a night so typical of many an occasion in those former years of the war where Kitty and I would dance together much to the delight of all who watched us. It wasn't so much that they enjoyed the spectacle of us being so close in the way that a man and a wife are, it was also the wonderful example that Kitty always set. Her fearlessness in support of me, and the cause which we fought for, helped to underline just what it was that we all held so dear to our hearts.

Here, in the midst of the most basic and bloody struggle of humankind, was the softest of gentle females who found herself surrounded, quite literally, by an army of highly appreciative protectors; where she relished every single moment and every admiring glance. Her presence made a statement to the opposing unseen forces that this patriotic battle was being fought not only through the combat of the menfolk but also by the support of their women and children as well. This would never be forgotten even in the darkest of dark times.

History would record it as being an uprising of the people against the mechanistic forces of a foreign government who were only interested in material gains through conquering lands which could be attached to their empire. Kitty said 'no' in emphatic defiance as she danced in the spirit of a land that was shortly to welcome the arrival of her first born child. She wanted that child, and those that followed, to be proud of a heritage which her husband and his men had been instrumental in creating. She wanted it to be known that they had fought to rid their homeland of a scourge which had no interest in the rights of the individual to be just exactly who they wanted to be.

Consequently she danced to the rhythm of the 'Battlefield Bard's' music as she sang along to the words which spoke of love and heartfelt aspirations which would one day bless the land that she was so passionate about. Right at that moment I could not have been more proud of anyone or anything in the world of my acquaintance. I was home to my heart while I danced with the woman of my dreams. We were, dare I say, deserving of our affectionately bestowed title 'bride and groom' and more than happy to encourage its continued inspirational use by our extended 'family'. What more could any man want in this life?

Slowly the scene of the campfires began to disappear as did the magical vision of my dancing with my beautiful wife, while every man present clapped and sang in accompaniment. Gradually, as the vision faded then it began to be replaced with that of a landscape which made me sit up in apprehension. It certainly wasn't a scene that I wanted to recall in such graphic detail but I did manage to appreciate that I was actually viewing it from a different perspective. At that moment I could feel myself still being caught up in remembering those happy times earlier on in the campaign when feelings ran so impassionedly high; as did the hopes of fulfilling our dreams. Being this way allowed me to be much more conscious of my emotional response when it came to recalling my experiences in this godforsaken place. Again, I found myself being able to contrast two very dissimilar states of my emotions and just how much the circumstances of each had served to influence them.

In this instance it was the winter of our ultimate test where the outcome of what we were about to encounter would determine the final course of the war. This would prove to be 'our' time after six long years of struggle where many had fallen in combat to pave the way for their comrades in order that we would triumph from their sacrifice. The place was Valley Forge and the time was the end of another arduous year which had taken us across many states in pursuit of the enemy. We were campaign-weary as our numbers had been depleted after leaving behind far too many of our comrades who had fallen in battle. Not only my men but our supplies were all but exhausted which left us totally unprepared for the circumstances in which we found ourselves.

It was a pitiful sight and one which I could see no justification for in the way that we were being asked once more to give all that we had, and then more, while holding firm to the convictions of our collective dream. My men were ill equipped to deal with the freezing weather while I tried desperately to secure more suitable clothing and to feed them the best way I could. I took it personally while ensuring that every man under my command would be assured of being as well looked after as he possibly could be. I regarded it as being equally important to maintain morale as I did the meticulous preparation of our plans which were needed to bring a certain end to the long years of war; our next encounter was crucial. We were all so very much in need of the final victory where it seemed so unfair that we were expected to rely on just our passion to keep us protected against the harshness of winter. There was still plenty to nourish our souls but our bodies were in desperate need of sustenance and protection against the elements.

My heart was heavy as I once again lived every second of this unforgettably wretched scene but while doing so, for the very first time, I began seeing much more clearly the exact nature of the burden which I was carrying. As I carefully examined my emotional state then I was able to appreciate just how much this dreadful situation had affected me. It was almost as though someone had shone a light into a part of myself which I wished to keep hidden. What I saw quite took my breath away in having peered over the edge of a deep dark well where I had hoped never to look into ever again. I knew what lay at the bottom of it. It was the ocean of my abject sorrow and it terrified me. It was a profound grief which weighed so very heavily on my heart that it felt almost like I would quickly drown if ever I was to wander off course and fall into the nearby lake. I sensed in that instant that there was more than likely nothing which could redeem me at all. Suddenly I found myself being almost overwhelmed by the feeling of the most intense hopelessness and fearing that I would become irretrievably lost as a result.

In the midst of my anguish I heard one of the men on the curved bench speaking and then realised that he was asking me to do something. I responded with a gesture which implied that I hadn't understood and then heard him repeat his request. In a kind of daze I got the idea that he was trying to get me to look at things in a different way, but I seemed not to be at all in the mood to comply. I had become far too immersed in what I was seeing to even think about trying to jump through any emotional hoops like some performing dog. All I could seem to focus on was the plight of this desperately needy body of men under my command where there were very many faces that I recognised.

So many young men just like me when I had been wrapped up in reading all of those amazing tales about the exploits of Alexander and the others. All of them filled with a similar degree of passion but having to suffer so much for what they believed in. How could this be? I kept asking myself this question over and over again. I wanted to know who could have allowed all of this to happen? Suddenly, when no suitable answers appeared to be forthcoming, I found myself beginning to question my faith in a Divine protector while not being able to appreciate that there was another way to view this apparently dreadful predicament.

Had I looked up and to the side of me then I would have seen something else emerging from within the depths of the landscape far beyond the lake. The long valley that seemed to stretch out to the horizon was beginning to come alive with figures who were all making their way towards the meadow. At first there were many different groups of individuals but slowly, as they gathered together while even more appeared, then their numbers grew. What initially could be seen to be scores, soon increased to be hundreds and hundreds where, before long, there were thousands streaming out of the valley. Still I took no notice as I stared intently into the vision of my campsite which had been gripped in the wintry blast of a snowstorm while men huddled around fires in the vain hopes of keeping warm. Even so, our very own 'Battlefield Bard' played on seemingly undeterred by the conditions. His wonderful spirit appeared to be undiminished by even the most adverse of weather conditions that Mother Nature could throw at us. I just couldn't image a gloomier or more heart rending prospect than the one I was looking at.

Little did I realise that fast approaching me across the other side of the field were the first of the men from the procession which was emerging from the valley in the distance. Had I taken any notice then I would have seen the smiling faces of very happy soldiers who were all looking past the point where I was sat towards the scene which had formed behind me. It was a truly splendid sight which would have certainly lifted my spirits had I been able to appreciate it. All that I needed to do was to drag my attention away from something which should have been consigned to a past which I would have been well served to view differently. Unfortunately I appeared not to be in a frame of mind to do this and so the joyous procession of people, which steadily got closer and closer, went unnoticed.

At least that was until I could no longer ignore those almost by the side of me as well as the sound of stirring music which had begun to fill my ears while also seeming to reach deep into my soul. It was certainly infectious through being such a haunting melody; one which I had heard on many other occasions in the past. I somehow knew instinctively who was playing it and so I looked up to see the maestro himself perched on the end of the curved bench while playing his beloved old fiddle. At that moment I couldn't figure where he'd got the name Battlefield Bard from as he was obviously a talented musician as well as a wonderful storyteller. It took me a moment to connect the sounds that were coming from his instrument with the sight of his solo performance; because now it sounded like a whole orchestra had begun playing. Never had I heard anything quite like it. Fortunately it had the effect of lifting my spirits even more than it usually did and for that I was very grateful indeed. It certainly did fulfil a need in me.

After immersing myself in listening to the wonderful melody, I felt as if I was starting to come out of a dream-like state. As I did then I found myself being suddenly caught up in the vision of so many men making their way across the meadow towards me. I just stared in disbelief as I watched ever more of them coming from a great distance while others were already walking past me. Many were dancing in time with the music while even more of them sang, but to a man there was a smile on every single face. I just couldn't take it all in. However, what confused me even more was the fact that nearly all of the men who passed by where I was sitting were looking at me while acknowledging my presence in some way or another. I even recognised quite a few faces although some of them appeared to be much younger than I remembered them. These young boys seemed to know me as well and so everywhere I looked there was just one big sea of happy faces.

Then, as I glanced behind me, I noticed that many were being greeted by loved ones. There were wives and sweethearts as well as brothers and sisters where what had once been a constant flow of men was now a huge gathering; one which appeared to be getting bigger by the minute. I was quite overwhelmed by the spectacle to the degree that momentarily I forgot about my burden; although a certain part of me seemed to know that it was still with me. For some reason it just felt lighter. So many people enjoying such a heartfelt celebration while the music played on as though encouraging everyone's spirit to be uplifted as all cares and woes were banished to another world. Here was a reunion the like of which I could never have imagined possible and what's more it was turning out to be the happiest that I had ever witnessed.

It didn't escape my notice that those who I had considered to have suffered hardships, as well as the most appalling privations, looked to be serenely happy and content; even after all that they had been through. Not only that but they seemed genuinely pleased to see me which was something that I just couldn't reconcile at all in the somewhat overtaxed dimensions of my highly befuddled mind. How could this be? I kept asking myself this question while not being able to deny the truth of what was so clearly unfolding before my very eyes. I simply stared slightly open mouthed with somewhat of a half smile on my bewildered face as man after man greeted me with the same sincere look of gratitude and affection. These were my men, my soldiers, my comrades in arms but they were no longer suffering and what's more they looked to be completely at peace and absolutely wonderfully happy. How could this have come about? What had happened to make it so after all that they had been through and why were they all here? These questions kept repeating in my mind.

I watched for what seemed an eternity as more and more men came streaming out of the valley and then crossed the field to meet with their loved ones; exactly in the same manner as did everyone who had arrived before them. Arm in arm they walked off into the distance as they seemed to move with a communal lightness of step. This they did in response to the ceaseless music produced by the 'orchestra of one' who was now sat quite close beside me. I had no words at all to describe my feelings as so many memories and images seemed to pass lightning-like through my consciousness. The sensations which overwhelmed me as a consequence were becoming so intense that, at one point, I felt as if I was about to lose myself into an oblivion from which there would be no possibility of my returning. That rather scary notion corresponded to the moment I felt a hand alight gently on my shoulder. It came as the most unexpected surprise but its touch was so delightful that I turned to see who had provided me with a much needed distraction.

To my complete amazement I looked up to see a young woman who was holding an infant. The child looked to me as though she wasn't much more than six months or so old. Even so, she was smiling directly at me and for some reason that I was not aware of, my heart absolutely took flight at the sight of her all wrapped up in her pretty clothes. Something in me compelled my arms to extend so as to reach out and immediately take her from the young woman so that I could hold her close to my very needy heart; and that's just what I did before I even realised that I was doing it. I held the smiling child in my grateful arms where I experienced a sense of the most soul-soothing contentment which instantly overwhelmed me. It was utterly amazing. So much so that it rendered me completely speechless.

The feeling I had at that instant could have healed the entire world. The very thought of battle would have been completely impossible to entertain by any man, woman or child as I looked directly into a pair of engagingly delightful light green eyes. They had the most expressive look of unreserved love that I had ever encountered. Somehow I knew that this precious child was very special to me and, as I sensed the absolute truth of this notion, so the smile on her face grew even broader and deeper. I sat holding this irrepressibly happy little soul while countless men walked past me and into the arms of unconditional healing love which was so eagerly given by those who they shared a similarly special bond with.

Holding this precious little life in my arms seemed to stir such strong paternal instincts in the very depths of my being; but when I looked at the men who had accompanied me on my crusade then I realised that I felt the same way about them. The vulnerability of a young life who depended on the nurturing presence of a loving protection seemed not that far distant from the needs of my men. Even though they had grown to the point of being strong and capable of fighting, they were nevertheless just as needy of dependable fatherly guidance and compassionate support. I found myself sincerely hoping that I had provided for their needs in a way which had proved supportive in their times of facing the ultimate price that would be paid in pursuit of their beliefs.

This was something that I had never given any thought to in respect of how deeply I cared about the well being of my men, just as though they were my children. Even in the height of a fury which drove us to battle, I had also been expressing a compassion which had been with me since the day I was born. In the middle of my musings I found myself suddenly feeling very grateful to an upbringing which had enabled me to develop that particular side of my nature. Suddenly I began to appreciate what it was that I had done for my men in providing them with more than just leadership. Never before this moment had I even considered it as being this way. Through holding this little bundle of joy tenderly in my arms, she had guided me to an understanding which I would probably not have arrived at in any other way.

I was so immensely grateful to her and hoped that she could sense my love and appreciation for her healing presence in my life. No sooner had this thought entered my head when her little hand moved so as to grab hold of my finger. It held on tightly while she continued to smile in sheer delight. I felt a tear welling up in me but my instant response was to resist a display of overt emotions. It seemed to be an almost automatic reaction although I had no idea why it should be this way. Immediately I felt a small movement in her hand as she squeezed my finger again which seemed as though she was encouraging me to give in to my feelings. Then she let go while showing me her open hand as though she wanted me to share her joy in feeling that it was the most magical thing in the world. To see such childish innocence was so refreshing but it also reminded me of how I had once been when I too had no reservations about showing my feelings in the way that I felt the need to.

All I knew was that I dearly wished for time to stand still so that I could get some sort of bearing in the Universe while my identity became clearer and then things would make much more sense to me. One look into the unfathomable depths of such sweet innocence, as expressed in the child's eyes, seemed to tell me that my desire for comprehension was completely unnecessary. And so it was. My tear appeared unhindered as did the others which quickly followed and, like the river of humanity flowing along bedside me, I sat holding the object of my affections tightly in my welcoming arms. In doing so my own little emotional river erupted out of me. Never could I remember feeling so overwhelmed by such a powerful current of emotional energy as at this point in my existence.

After what seemed like another lifetime had passed, I felt another hand press on my other shoulder; only this time I sensed a firmer and more encouraging grip. Slowly I dragged my gaze reluctantly away from my young companion so as to see who it was that needed my attention. I turned to see the blurry figure of a man who was looking down at me while smiling in the same way that I had seen so many others do that memorable day. I blinked in confusion so as to get a better view of who it might be and slowly the residue of my tears began to clear. It took me a few moments before I could fully recognise the face of a man who I had known as being a trusted officer and friend, but one who had been so senselessly lost to the merciless grip of the icy weather at Valley Forge. I remembered so clearly how I had mourned his passing and the loss of someone so dear to me. However, right here by the side of me and smiling like a twenty year old, was the face of a truly courageous soul who I never imagined that I would ever see again. I stared at him in disbelief while so much wanting it to be true.

Slowly, as though appreciating my perplexity, he knelt close to me while his hand rested encouragingly on my shoulder. I heard his words filtering in through my emotional upheaval as he proceeded to tell me that this child, who I was still holding as though my very life depended on it, was one that my beloved wife had lost not long after her arrival. We had been graced with a beautiful baby girl, Catherine, who had come to be with us for a short while and who wished to share her love in a way that was uplifting; albeit that there had been precious little time for us to get to know her. My beloved friend explained that she had returned to her home and was now in his care along with the young woman who had handed her to me. He went to great lengths to reassure me that she was being raised in the most loving environment while having been reunited with all those who she loved in turn. I felt more and more tears appearing with each of his compassionate words. At this point I sensed no more need to keep them back.

After pausing for me to absorb all that he had just said, he went on to explain to me that her time with my wife had been valuable for many reasons which would become clearer to me later. For now, he wanted me to know first hand the love which had been mine and which would always be there for me while knowing how grateful she had been to have shared her short journey with my family. Finally he told me that she wanted me to know that I should not blame myself for being absent so much while away fighting the war and that how things worked out was just exactly how they were meant to be. He said that, in her words, there was no blame to be apportioned where only the remembrance of eternal love and gratitude should be contemplated.

I found myself nodding a kind of acceptance without really understanding why I should feel this way. Again I felt a heaviness creeping into my emotional being but looking at that cute smiling face seemed to drive virtually all negative emotions away. There was not a hint of remorse, unhappiness, blame or condemnation in any aspect of her most appealing countenance. All that I could see and feel coming from her was unconditional love and the most heartfelt joy. How could I ever bring myself to let her go after finding her again? I dared not even allow myself to consider it.

To my great relief, both my beloved friend and his wife, at least I presumed they were man and wife, took up their positions beside me so that they could sit close by as I continued to hold this adorable child; my beloved daughter. I just wanted to stay this way forever but I had a feeling that something was about to be decided which would change all that. Whatever it was then I sincerely hoped that it wouldn't come about until I'd had time to relish every precious second of my closeness to this wonderful little being who held my heart in her hands. I had no idea how I could possibly let her go ... again!

- Chapter 11 -

The Choice to Re-Awaken - A Chance to Rediscover Love

I have no idea how long it was before I began to appreciate that the focus of my entire world had been the presence of this precious child who I held so tenderly in my arms. To describe what was going on inside me, as I immersed myself in her captivating closeness, was very much like the feeling which comes from that 'in-between' moment of waking up from a deep sleep. That semi-conscious state of reluctantly relinquishing the dream world while truly appreciating the wonderfully restful peacefulness which had been experienced within it. That essentially ethereal connection with feeling something quite special, almost pre-natal like being able to retreat into the protective cradle of the womb, before understanding that there was yet another day to face. One more animated interval in a demanding existence which would require fortifying the body and mind in order to cope with it.

Yet, you so willingly want to surrender to that truly sublime state which tempts you to linger just five more minutes, or even longer, under the covers if circumstances will permit; which they invariably don't. But this time I was adamant. I didn't want to 'get up' and then have to deal with any more days at that point on my journey. Heavenly euphoria, resting comfortably while wrapped up in such a feeling of the most wonderful love was all that I wanted. My senses were in a state of suspension while finding an undisturbed place to be at peace with myself while the world got along nicely without me. I just didn't want anything to change as though I could almost remember being just this way before; but when exactly that would have been I had no idea at all. My mind was on the verge of seeking some kind of explanation when suddenly I felt something touching me which proved to be quite distracting for a few perplexing moments. I tried to identify it and then came to the bemusing conclusion that it had started to rain.

Immediately I looked up to see not one cloud in the sky but it certainly did feel as though my body was being showered with the very lightest of warm rain. I found it to be a most odd sensation where my first instinct was to cover young Catherine up while protecting her from whatever had caused a change in the weather. When I looked at her however, there were no signs at all of her being affected while she smiled happily in her usual way as though she didn't have a care in the world. I decided to do nothing as it seemed that I was the only one who had noticed it, but the instant that I gave my attention to my own situation then it felt as though the heavens were beginning to open up. What had once been a light shower of tiny warming crystal droplets now felt like a downpour, but it was the most soothing effect that I had ever experienced. So much so that the sensation of its touch seemed like quite the most refreshing of any encounter that I had ever had with Mother Nature's cloud-born precipitation of any kind.

While holding little Catherine close to me, I began to succumb to the overwhelming feeling of being drenched by a wonderful outfall of what felt like water; but obviously wasn't. In doing so, I could imagine myself stood under a cascade of sparkling clear liquid which was descending gently into the deep blue waters of the lagoon which I had been bathing in. Being thoroughly immersed in its fluid embrace, I could feel the stress in my body slowly ebbing away as the restorative waters gently carried off the accumulated detritus of a long dusty journey. It felt so incredibly good to be cleansed of an outer crust which was in imminent danger of being baked hard by the heat of the sun. I could almost see the streaks of discolouration on the surface of the water as more and more sedimentary layers were washed away from my body.

As I gratefully indulged myself in the almost baptismal sensation of this mysterious process, I was somehow able to appreciate that my emotional body was actually the real focus of this energetically purgative cleansing. How I came to know this I wasn't sure but I did feel the presence of some underlying wisdom which existed within the therapeutic nature of this rather strange but powerful phenomenon. Accompanying this insight was the realisation that there were in fact deeper areas of accumulated 'debris' which appeared to be impervious to the effects of this cleansing process.

These cloying residues of trauma seemed to be very well attached, but now that so much of their obscuring coverings were being removed then I was better able to acknowledge their presence. One area of 'encrustation' in particular seemed to be much more pronounced and tenacious than any other, so I began to study it. In doing so I found myself being drawn towards something which caused me to react in a way which was completely at odds with my new found state of peacefulness.

While trying to probe the root cause of this particular emotional lesion I began to sense that there appeared to be a part of me which was actually still in a lot of pain. It seemed to be a kind of malevolent aching like feeling the harsh influences of the same numbing cold that I had experienced at Valley Forge while dulled by the intake of sufficient quantities of alcohol. The pain was obviously still there but it had been lurking just under the surface while awaiting the effects of the wine to wear off. I found myself not looking forward to the moment when it did.

My only protection seemed to be found in closing my eyes while I comforted my precious daughter; albeit something appeared to be prompting me to appreciate that it was in reality the other way around. Somewhere within me an understanding of the fact existed that I was the one being comforted by her closeness, although my mind couldn't seem to make any sense of trying to see it in this way. No matter, I just accepted things as they were at that moment as the prospect of doing otherwise was simply much too overwhelming.

For now, all I wanted was to let the 'rain' continue to pour over me in the hopes that eventually it would wash away even the deepest of disabling suffering from within me. I wished so much that the cascading droplets of purifying comfort would turn into a powerful torrent which absolutely nothing could resist. Suddenly I wanted a small tsunami to come barrelling across the lagoon which would knock me body and soul completely off my feet as it purged me of so much that I felt encumbered by. I wanted to climb back under the covers for that extra five minutes of sleepy luxury but then I knew that I would want it to go on forever. Even as this desire rushed forward to plead for fulfilment, I realised that the time had come to lay aside my burdens. Although, just how I would go about doing this was not clear to me at all.

Slowly I became aware that someone had begun speaking to me and, as I listened in the manner of being only partially interested, I thought that I recognised a certain quality to the voice behind the words. With my curiosity piqued I opened my eyes to see who the voice belonged to as it sounded so familiar. However, the face that I expected to see didn't correspond to what my memories of that particular person had prepared me to see. Those deep rich tones and gentle Southern accent were, to me, so reminiscent of a well respected elder statesman in the Continental Congress. Someone who I had known and admired for a long time.

He had been a valued ally and a great friend whose wisdom I had come to rely on in times when the deeds and actions of those who we trusted to represent us seemed shrouded in doubt. His was a much needed, consistent presence in my life at that time where his example of steadfast integrity had greatly helped keep my resolve in tact; especially on those occasions when I needed to confront my peers. His very existence in our lives was like a guiding beacon of light which helped so many of us navigate our way successfully through even the darkest of hours. To everyone who knew him, friend and foe alike, he appeared to be irreplaceable and so, when the time eventually came for him to relinquish his existence on the earth plane, his absence from our lives had been keenly felt.

He was so sorely missed by those who were closest to him where I felt proud to have been considered as one of their number. And so it was that I looked hard at the face of the speaker but just couldn't make the connection with his voice. I listened and studied as I willed myself to make sense of what I was witnessing. Slowly I began to make out, within the freshness of an appearance which looked to be about mid thirties, the unmistakable behavioural nuances that were so characteristic of this charismatic man. It proved difficult for me to accept this at first, but the more he spoke then the more I realised that it was indeed his inimitable self; although this left me highly puzzled as to why I was seeing him looking so young.

I had never known him at that time of his life but here, in front of me, without doubt was the youthfully vigorous looking image of someone I had come to know and admire in his later life. I was quite taken aback, so much so that I didn't actually register a single word that he said. All I could hear was the comforting sound of his confidently soothing tones but those alone seemed to convey something quite important to me. The closest emotion which I could identify to describe what I felt when I heard him speak would have been that of being unreservedly reassured.

This was certainly something that he inspired in me on those occasions when I had consulted him about issues concerning my men as well as the many challenges created for me by the war effort. He never once let me down or ever said anything which was in the slightest way self gratifying or motivated by pure ego. Neither did he appear to have any kind of hidden personal agenda, unlike very many others who were his contemporaries at that time. He truly was an inspirational presence to many who would have done well to follow his example.

Slowly my mind seemed to be playing catch-up as I concentrated more on the substance of his words. It was then that I began to appreciate that he was in the process of telling everyone gathered around me all about what I had achieved as well as what I had learned from my life's experience. I listened in fascination as he explained to an attentively hushed audience just exactly what the influential factors of my choices had been and how the consequences would certainly have been very much different had I not acted as I did. His explanations were quite compelling where many of his conclusions, and much of his reasoning, surprised me in how he viewed my achievements. He highlighted various beneficial virtues which had been present in many situations, challenges and outcomes that I had never once considered before that point in time. As a consequence I began to pay closer attention to what he was saying as I wanted to hear more.

He continued by pointing out several notable examples from my life that I and everyone else had seen so clearly portrayed in the living scenes of my past. He then described at great length what had happened to create the circumstances surrounding my 'trials' which had eventually led up to the battle of Valley Forge. He seemed to know so much about very many stages of my journey that I was not aware of at the time although I found a few of his assertions to be somewhat difficult for me to accept. I certainly didn't see some aspects of what had taken place in the same light as he did.

Then he began explaining the important significance behind the march of all the young men who had come out of the valley and into the meadow on their way to greet me and their loved ones. It was so interesting to hear his insightful wisdom on this particular subject. Everyone, including me, paid close attention to his words as he contrasted what had been witnessed by us all to that which he had recounted in such detail about my time in the winter camp. Nothing seemed to have escaped his notice where his knowledge of my men was remarkably extensive to the degree that he appeared to know much more about what went on than I did. This was certainly a revelation for me and one which could have challenged my ego had I let it.

As a result, I found myself being quite deeply caught up in listening to an account of my life that was being related in such amazing detail. Especially as it was seen through the eyes of someone who I had no idea, until that moment, had anything but the most politely congenial interest in my military career; or my life in general whatsoever. Not only did I get to listen to his explanation of many things that I had seen and felt, but also I got to hear a surprising amount about quite a few things that I had forgotten. Episodes of my life which had seemed inconsequential but which suddenly appeared to be very important when included in his 'epic' account of the 'life and times of Nathanael Greene'. It was almost as though I was listening to the biography of a relative stranger, but as taxing as some parts may have been, I accepted the truthful and sincere nature of all that had been said.

Then he began talking about the circumstances of that dreadful winter while inviting me to see things from a very different perspective. At first I found this virtually impossible to do but then, as I struggled hard to appreciate his viewpoint, he gently encouraged a remembering of my observing all the men who were so recently paying their heartfelt respects before meeting with their loved ones. He wanted me to understand that what he was proposing had actually been the real outcome of the situation rather than what I had considered it to be. This I just could not seem to do however much I attempted to view it from his perspective. Whatever I did then I couldn't bring myself to associate the stream of happy looking young men with those gaunt faces and tired bodies that I had witnessed dragging themselves out of the freezing snow while heading into their final battle.

No matter how hard I tried, my mind just couldn't seem to get past the longing for things to have been different while creating the feeling in me that I could have done more to prevent what had occurred. I was plagued by my sense of guilt as to why so many of my men had suffered in such a needless manner, only to give up their lives in the process. I had all but forgotten the emotions which had inspired me to join the cause in the first place where the forfeit of a life had seemed a small price to pay for the achievement of our dreams. I realised in that same instant how the indifferent passage of time had changed me through the harsh lessons of experience which it had brought in its wake.

As though knowing what I was thinking, he continued his explanations while I held my daughter closely to my heavy heart. I so much wanted to be able to accept his entreaties which were encouraging me towards a more beneficial way of seeing things. I gently rocked my baby girl as though mentally weighing in the balance all the available 'evidence' in my desperate attempt to make things come out differently for me and for her. I was so overwhelmed by a sense of crushing responsibility that I just couldn't see what he had been trying to get me to appreciate in how everything had worked out according to what he said that each individual had wished to experience; even my daughter. It just didn't seem possible and I couldn't accept it at all.

All these wonderfully brave souls, especially one so young who had deserved much better, who had put their faith and trust in me only to encounter personal disaster. At least that's how I viewed it. In my mind it was impossible for me not to feel responsible for how things had turned out. To my way of thinking it was all my fault and I readily admitted it to myself but as soon as I did then the 'alcohol' wore off and the pain returned while the bitter chill of that winter came back aggressively to haunt me. I just couldn't seem to gain my release from its dispassionately icy grip. Within that state of emotional disarray I hadn't noticed that it was now actually 'raining' quite hard.

The emotion and depth of my grief felt as if it had permanently bound me up in suspended animation with no hope of my release this side of eternity. Everything felt so hopeless which was the precise moment when I felt my daughter's most timely movement in my arms and once again I looked in amazement at her wonderful smile. At that same instant I could immediately see Kitty's sparkling eyes looking back at me, but within that recognition I also sensed the loss of her presence through having been parted from the one who I so dearly loved with every fibre of my being. My emotions felt like they had been caught up in the riptides of some cosmic ocean which had come to enfold me in its midst. I closed my eyes in a feeble attempt to blot out the past but whatever I did then I could feel its unresolved burdens still oppressively present within me. Something had to be done; I surely knew this to be so but I hadn't a clue as to what the solution could be.

There is Always a Plan - Trust that Love Knows what to Do

I stayed motionless while becoming gratefully lost inside the darkness of my visionless world in the hope that I would open my eyes and somehow, miraculously, everything would be fine. Just exactly what this state of 'fine' would be I had no idea but it did seem as though almost anything would be preferable to what I was feeling at that precise moment. I really hoped that, at the very least, it would be comparable to all which I had felt so deeply connected to through my experiences in the garden. However, something told me that this may take a little time for me to achieve.

Quite unexpectedly I detected a distinct change in the air as this thought came to me and I shivered slightly although I had no sensation of temperature in any way at all. I was still very much caught up in my emotions but I did however begin to make out voices which sounded as though they were coming from the area of the curved bench seat. As I listened with half an ear, I could make out a man who was speaking while enthusiastically advocating on my behalf; apparently while telling the others that his idea would bring great benefits. There were a few muted comments from one or two of his companions but he eagerly continued by saying that what had been proposed offered me an opportunity which would be perfect for my needs. He added that it was also something which I deserved to have in the respect of my intentions towards balancing my emotional state; but what he said from that point on eluded me as I didn't understand his words.

I got the idea that a kind of lively discussion followed as a result of what he'd proposed, but my senses were distracting me in that I felt myself as being in the midst of a very familiar place. The greater my awareness of this quite evocative atmosphere became then the more the voices receded into a kind of muffled void; until all was quiet and very, very still. Even the rain had stopped which left me just listening to the sound of my breathing while absorbing everything which this new ambiance generously offered me.

It was an especially welcomed stillness which brought with it a quality of wonderfully peaceful innocence that I had almost forgotten. My first impressions seemed to be urging me to remember it and, as I allowed myself to renew my acquaintance, I also began to recall the surroundings which accompanied this feeling. It was such a delight to be greeted in this way by something so thoroughly comforting. I felt sure that if I opened my eyes then I would, without doubt, see just what I expected to see where, if I were to put my hand out then it would touch the small bedside table which I knew was there to be felt.

The instant I considered doing this it also occurred to me that letting go of the heavy book, which I had been holding in my lap, would mean it quickly toppling over and falling to the floor. The prospect of this happening was unthinkable as the resulting loud noise would probably wake my father up and I had no intention of letting that happen. I hung on to it while anticipating the consequences of having to explain what I was doing up at that time of night. I also certainly didn't want to be questioned about exactly what I had found to be such a compelling read so as to keep me from my slumber and depriving me of my rest.

Slowly, I opened my eyes while peering into the dimly lit space of an environment which was so familiarly supportive of me. The flickering candlelit glow which danced delightedly over all of my things, plus the characteristic smells of my room, seemed to greet me in their usual friendly manner. It was such a lovely environment and one which had shared its sheltering presence with me while allowing me to find my way into a world of infinite appeal. I glanced at all the books lined up on my bookcase where I could immediately see so many fascinating images of far off places unfolding between their pages; so much so that everything appeared to be alive and so real. I began to wonder if I would ever see even a fraction of everything that I had read about and what my experiences would be if ever I did.

Suddenly I felt a chill pass through me as though an icy blast of wind had come racing in through my window so as to grip me in its disruptive power. With it came a disorienting feeling that somehow I had actually lived many of those, or similar, experiences; but the ones that I had were not how I ever fantasised them to be. It seemed as though I was somehow able to exist in each one of them simultaneously while also feeling how I had been affected on each occasion. When I did so, then some of them seemed quite terrifying in comparison to how things were for me in the comfort of my bedroom; while others gave me the most amazing feelings that I didn't even know existed. The contrast of emotions really surprised me but what made the greatest impression on me was the feeling that I had somehow already lived them.

It was so difficult for me to imagine being anything other than how I was at that precise moment even though these memories were persuading me otherwise. They seemed to present me with compelling evidence of having lived a life which had turned out much differently from how I had been led to surmise it probably would from my books. I shivered again at the prospect of something changing me to such a degree that it had caused me to lose so much of how my life had been up to that point on my journey.

I suddenly felt an uncomfortable level of apprehension, bordering on fear, rising in my abdomen but just at the instant when it seemed destined to overwhelm me I caught a glimpse of something out of the corner of my eye. It distracted my attention which was a most welcomed release from how I was starting to feel. I immediately looked out of my window to see what appeared to be someone sat by a fire just a little way off in the darkness. The figure seemed to be just staring into the flames which burned quite fiercely, so much so that I could see the highlighted side of his face and body. From what I could make out, he was wearing some kind of military uniform but it also looked as though it had seen better times; as did he. Just as that thought popped into my head, he turned to look at me and in doing so he smiled.

It was a weary smile but a very friendly one and, for a moment, it seemed almost as though he knew me. His gaze had a lingering fondness about it which made me feel as if, in some way, he was remembering something while looking at someone who he had been close to a long time ago. At one point I thought that I noticed a certain element of regret in the manner of his demeanour as once or twice he sighed while resting his chin on his clenched fist. It was an odd but very expressive gesture and one which gave me the idea that he must be caught up in unravelling some kind of deep dilemma which had probably come about through his being in too many battles.

I was intrigued as I had no idea who he could be, although I had to admit that there did seem to be something vaguely familiar about him, albeit that I hadn't a clue as to why I should think this. Whoever he was, and whatever his circumstances may have been, my heart certainly did go out to him at that moment. Then, quite unexpectedly while studying his fire-lit face, I was suddenly gripped by the strangest feeling that I could actually see right into the entirety of his existence. As a consequence of what I saw, it almost took my breath away. It was the most incredibly intense feeling of travelling every second of his journey from the point at which I felt myself to be at that stage of my life. The sensation proved to be so strong that, briefly, I didn't know whether to run away or to run to him; even though either option seemed as inexplicable as it was unthinkable.

Thankfully the intensity of this encounter began to subside quite quickly and so I was able to regain my composure a little, along with my ability to breathe once more. Even so, its effect on me seemed to reverberate deeply in the heart of my very being. For what must have been quite a while I just sat very still as my mind tried to figure out what had happened. To have been able to see so much which was so incomprehensible, and in such a short space of time, left me feeling a little shaky as my world began to assume a considerably less secure facet to its nature.

As a consequence I felt the need to investigate what was happening to me and why. Not being one to run from a challenge, I decided to ask the only one who appeared to have any answers as I was determined to better understand my experiences so as to settle my emotional state. Even at that late hour, and in such a strangely dark setting, it didn't cross my mind to be cautious and neither did it occur to me that the man would be anything other than friendly towards me. I seemed to be quite confident that he would be more than willing to provide me with whatever it was that I wanted. Although how I came to know this wasn't clear to me.

So I gently set my book down on my bedside table while preparing myself to go outside as my curiosity was now in full flow. Slowly I stood up while being careful not to put too much weight on the place where I knew the board underneath the mat would creak in a very recognisable way if I did. In looking down to locate its exact position I suddenly noticed something else which caught my attention. The big woollen rug, which had always been by the side of my bed, appeared to have a very recognisable pattern on it. I was puzzled by this as it seemed somehow familiar, although I couldn't understand why I hadn't taken any real notice of it before that moment. It was a strange design, like a big symbol of the sort that I thought I'd seen in one of my books; but it wasn't at all displeasing in its appeal.

Something about it gave me the impression that its presence was actually a really good omen, almost like it represented a sign that my fortunes were about to change for the better. Whatever it meant I had a strong suspicion that something unusual and exciting was about to happen, which certainly was a most welcomed feeling indeed. I paused for a few minutes just to study its intricate design a little more closely but then I turned my attention back to the man in the soldier's uniform who I had observed sitting by the fire and looking so pitiably sorrowful. No sooner had I looked at the fiercely burning campfire than there was a bright burst of light as though something powerful had exploded in the middle of the flames. It almost blinded me for an instant but within the intensity of that light I could clearly see an image which caused me to be drawn emotionally into the very heart of it.

Somewhere deep inside me there seemed to be a response to the familiar sight of the old family house and especially the area where my bedroom was situated. The memories which came flooding back were so full of childhood magic that I found myself suddenly yearning for them to return once more. Everything looked just as I remembered it being where I could almost imagine my family sleeping peacefully as they awaited the arrival of a new day. What proved to be the most heartrending thing of all for me was to see myself as a young boy stood looking out of the candlelit bedroom window. Even more engaging was the way he gazed out into the darkness and for a while of studying him I had the oddest notion that he could actually see me.

I well remembered that look which I always had whenever the future and my part in it became the subject of my earnest contemplation. That far distant prospect of maturing into inconceivable adulthood wherein lay a journey to a future which seemed just as exciting as it was uncertain. I could almost feel how my mind would chatter away incessantly at me while trying to anticipate a world that I knew only from what I had read in my books. My enthusiasm for study could in no way make up for my naivety, but it was all that I had to guide me in a community of endeavour which demonstrated little interest in anything outside of their immediate sphere of concern.

So how could I have known what awaited me outside the boundaries of a sheltered environment which knew nothing of life's potential and, what's more, who was there to teach me? My heart seemed to well up with a multitude of emotions as I wished so much that I could just put my protective and journey-weary arm around that young boy. Oh what I would have given to have been able to tell him all that was in front of him on the pathway which awaited his choices. But then, what would I have said? How could I have prepared him to avoid the many pitfalls that he was set to encounter on his chosen route? Even more importantly, what would I have advised him to do when it came to the subject of listening to his heart when discovering his true love, his twin flame?

What would I have deprived him of if he had anticipated the meeting of his other half, the one who would be instrumental in precipitating his passions for so many things? Why would I want to undermine the magical mystery of love's immediacy in how it creates those incredibly precious moments at the most unexpected of times? How could I possibly tell him about this and so many other things quite beyond his imagination or understanding that he would have to discover for himself?

All I knew was that I wanted to protect him in the same way as I wished to protect my own children, but as much as I dearly loved each one of my offspring I accepted that they would have to make their own way in life. I was so torn by this feeling of allowing things to happen as I knew so well what was in my heart at that innocent stage of my life. I just wanted to keep it that way while not having to deal with the heaviness which would be placed upon it through witnessing what mankind is capable of. But there again, in highly redeeming contrast to this destructiveness I sincerely wished him to know the incandescent love of his beloved twin flame; as well as experiencing the devotional love of his precious children.

No words that I could offer him would be the slightest bit meaningful at that point on his journey where only his courage and self determination were to guide his footsteps. They would lead him towards those places where he was set to experience a realisation of much more than his dreams as well as how the light of his soul would inspire so many in their hours of darkness. I could not bring myself to wish that this be altered in any way whatsoever. So I watched him looking longingly out of the window while appreciating that he had no idea about the pathway which awaited him. It was one that he needed to walk without my intervention, however well intentioned this notion may have been. I accepted that whatever had been, all that had happened, every encounter whether exceptionally gratifying or very challenging, had been just as it should be. It could be no other way.

Slowly the vision of the house began to fade from my view as I gazed deeply into the spectacular sight of the big ball of flame as though it were the first time that I'd ever witnessed the miracle of a new dawn. There was something about that deep red fiery hemisphere peering up over the horizon which seemed to be so completely mesmerising. Its appearance heralded a new day and one that would be unique, just as was the crimson messenger in the sky whose radiant light sent the shadows scurrying away from the landscape. However, this day seemed to be presenting me with a view of the world which I was not accustomed to. To my mind, the hazy skyline didn't look anything like the rolling countryside of my familiar surroundings at all.

Instead, what I could see gradually coming into focus was some kind of quite sharp and angular looking landscape that seemed to be slowly appearing out of the sun-reddened darkness. The effect was quite surreal which made it appear as though dawn was breaking rather rapidly over an environment which defied my imagination to interpret. My fascination began to overtake my apprehensions as I started to make out more of the detail as well as the seven figures who were seated on the curved wooden bench. I hardly took any notice of them as I found myself being more interested in concentrating on what was coming into view all around them; but what I saw quite overwhelmed me.

The harder I looked, the more I appeared to be unable to take in what I was seeing. My heart pounded powerfully as I worked hard to control my emotions, but slowly my curiosity got the better of me as I began to look around at the landscape which now confronted me. Gone were the surroundings of my family home or the tranquil garden with the lake. These had seemingly been replaced by what looked like some sort of township, although I had never seen anything even remotely similar before. It was so strange and alarmingly dense with streets that looked like they were covered in something black and hard. Carriages, with no obvious form of pulling power, were moving about all over the place. I stared wordlessly in all directions as my mind raced while trying to take in what I was seeing.

I drew comfort from directing my attention to the semicircular seat which the seven familiar figures, who had been with me in the meadow, were sitting on. It was good to see their faces once more and it was especially comforting to see them all smiling most encouragingly at me. This realisation helped to calm me down and once again my trusted friend started to speak. To my relief I heard him begin to describe in great detail what I was witnessing while I listened in stunned silence to his explanation. It proved to be something of a challenge to take it all in but he told me that I could enter into this experience, this new world, if I so wished and why I might want to.

He explained that in doing so it would allow me an ideal opportunity to lead a life which would entail my having to work through the emotions that I had apparently been so reluctant to give up. I tried to focus on all that he said as I knew that it was important, although I could feel my mind racing just to keep up with the almost unimaginable. He continued to expand on what he could see that I was having difficult in comprehending by telling me that while I experienced life in this environment I would gain a new appreciation for many things through making different choices. This, he said, would then help me to gain an awareness of not only my present emotional predicament, and hopefully bring about a healing, but I would also get to appreciate other important aspects of life as well. He expressed that the circumstances were perfect for all that I needed to do and would offer me the greatest opportunities to advance my spiritual journey.

I wasn't at all convinced and neither was I about to become a willing participant as I really didn't much like the idea of the world which I saw unfolding in the light from the ascending sun. Not only that but I didn't even know where I was. The instant that thought entered into my mind I heard someone say 'Canada' which did nothing to inspire me at all. I knew very little about the country except that it was reputedly bitterly cold in winter and, from what I could see of it at that moment then it looked quite unfriendly and not at all what I had been used to.

My wise friend was quick to reassure me that it would prove to be just what I needed as would be the family that I would be raised with. I was still not impressed. In fact I found myself being almost on the verge of protesting, but somewhere deep inside me a small still voice was encouraging me to carefully consider what had already been proposed while getting more information. I listened with half an ear while figuring that it might be wise to hear whatever else he had to say on the subject; so I paid more attention. No sooner had I arrived at this conclusion than someone else, a lady this time, began speaking while explaining quite a lot about what she described as my 'journey potentials'.

She talked at length about a great many things that I could possibly encounter in the environment which awaited me, as well as having to deal with and learn from so much that would be offered in the circumstances. It suddenly began to feel like more struggle to me, which was definitely not what I wanted at all. It was at this point that I felt a strong urge to return to the meadow as I had no interest in taking up the opportunity that they were offering me. My mind couldn't seem to grasp any of the positive aspects which had been suggested, and so graphically elaborated on, as coming from what they were proposing. I began to feel a sense of hopelessness creeping in to suffocate me and I was not at all happy about it.

Then the entire world in front of me changed to become one where I could see a grown man who, someone kindly told me, was my future self and who was just about to enter a strange building that looked as if it served food. Again, I had never seen anything like it but it appeared as though I wasn't in the least bit perturbed about going inside and even seemed like I was anticipating a pleasant experience. My interest perked up a little as I wanted to know what would happen next.

I watched with baited breath as I saw my future self suddenly stop dead in his tracks while studying a very attractive lady who looked like she was taking food to many of the people who were sat at the tables and waiting to eat. This confident and well dressed man, who I had been assured that I would be, seemed to regard the lady in what could only be described as a state of awe. Someone from the circular seat informed me that this was called love at first sight and that I should remember it from how I had experienced it with Kitty. I did and it certainly was wonderful to feel that way again. Suddenly my interest became highly tuned to the degree that I wanted to see more. Much more!

I studied the man carefully as he stepped inside the building and then made his way towards one of the vacant tables. As he did so then I noticed that the lady carrying the plates of food also looked at him with what seemed to me to be almost a fixed stare; but in a very pleasant way. She hesitated as the man sat down and for a moment all I could see in the building was just the two of them. There didn't appear to be anyone else, but what I slowly began to realise was that the amount of light which came from both of them actually put everything else in the shadow. It certainly was a powerful light which appeared to get brighter by the minute where, at one point, it almost seemed as though it would illuminate the whole town.

Someone else spoke. On hearing their words my heart literally jumped out of my body with absolute delight. All that I heard said was '*It's Kitty, you get to be with her again*'. Nothing else needed to be said. I was sold, I needed no more convincing, I wanted the ticket to whatever train it was that I had to get on so as to be in that place; and I didn't care what I had to do to get it. The thought of being with her again would make anything worthwhile and at that very moment I knew where my destiny lay. I had already made up my mind to do whatever was necessary without considering any reservations that I might have, or any other reasons that I might not want to do what had been described to me. I just had to be with her again and I didn't want her to be where she was without me.

All my objections and reservations seemed to evaporate at the very idea of us being together again. I was still studying the scene intently while I heard people discussing and explaining things about my difficult times of growing up. Then someone mentioned something about going through a healing process to address the overwhelming grief that I still carried with me but my eyes were on Kitty; or whatever her name was in how I saw her this time. To me she still looked like the most beautiful woman in the world and so I was determined to be the man who shared as much of that world with her as possible.

Never in my wildest imagination did I ever anticipate encountering what I was about to experience, but before I could ask any questions there was a very bright flash which hurt my eyes. I later learned that it came from the huge ceiling mounted lamps in the delivery room. I had begun my journey towards meeting my beloved Kitty again and that was all that mattered to me. Someone gave me a sharp smack on my rear end which sent me into a flood of tears as I screamed out in indignation while trying to work out what the hell I'd done to deserve such treatment. I heard the rich deep tones of a familiar voice say *'such is life my dear boy!'*; and so it was to be.

Ronald Phillip Darling had arrived and was more than ready for another wonderful adventure. Kitty had been waiting in the wings to shortly step into the role that would bring the two of us together. The stage was set while the cast rehearsed their parts. The audience remained silent in anticipation of what would happen next while a group of seven very interested individuals looked on with love held foremost in their compassionate hearts. The forthcoming performance, however, would prove to be a highly memorable one.

- Chapter 12 -

Of All the Restaurants in All the World

From the very moment I walked into the restaurant and caught sight of that irresistibly cute smiling face looking in my direction then I knew for sure that I was in trouble. I have no idea of exactly what caused me to be so certain in such a short space of time but I will never forget the feeling of something powerful, within the very depths of my being, which came rushing up to swiftly saturate my senses. It just seemed to burst into my conscious world while almost making me shiver in a most delightful way through experiencing the sheer energy of it. For what must have been a few seconds or more, I almost froze to the spot where I stood; but in that tiny fragment of eternity I seemed to relive many lifetimes of memories which I had no idea even existed until that actual instant.

Being a married man with a family, I had never been one to 'play away from home' but I could tell without doubt that if I took one more step into the restaurant then I would inevitably have to act upon what I found myself feeling when I looked at her. There was just no way that I could ignore the intensity of my emotions. Although, I did get the idea that I might possibly be able to play it cool while somehow resisting a level of temptation which almost overwhelmed me. On the other hand, I found myself also needing to deal with an accompanying feeling of guilt; but I didn't even want to go there. So, for better of worse, I chose to ignore it as much as I possibly could under the circumstances, although I had the distinct impression that it wasn't about to go quietly without first having its say.

Before I had time to stumble blindly into this whole moral bear trap of an unscripted drama, I did however manage to appreciate that I would not be in the least bit successful in denying the strength of feeling I had for this lady; even if I'd wanted to. For a brief panic-filled instant, which lasted less than an adrenaline charged heartbeat, I actually considered turning back to the door and then running away as fast as I possibly could. My feet, however, were not in any kind of mood to listen to such a completely nonsensical reaction and stayed firmly planted on the ground like they'd suddenly taken root. Apparently they weren't paying any attention whatsoever to my overanxious thoughts. Instead, they were heeding the urgings of my enchanted heart which seemed to be taking over complete control of the whole situation. My heart was telling me, in the most compelling persuasiveness of its irresistible language, that it wanted me to get to know this strikingly attractive lady who had so quickly captured its full attention.

As a consequence I found myself facing a dilemma where there appeared to be only one course of action which would satisfy the needs of my innermost feelings to the exclusion of everything else. I didn't seem to have any option other than to jump feet first into the 'deep end' while trusting to what I felt most strongly motivated to do. After all, what did I stand to lose by doing it?

From how I viewed my situation at that moment there certainly appeared to be quite a lot which could actually be gained. As this intriguing idea settled into my consciousness I realised that I was more than a little excited by the prospect of stepping into an adventure that would very probably lead me towards a part of my unexplored self that I had not been in touch with before. Not only that, but it would also more than likely bring me much closer to an answer which a dormant question had been posing for quite some time. I had a shrewd idea that the outcome may force me into making a decision about where my true affections lay, although I found myself flinching slightly at the prospect of what I might discover in the process.

As this thought swept through the shuttered corners of my over-analytical mind, I sensed a very bright flame burn in response which seemed to illuminate much more than I felt able to fully comprehend. My emotional lava stream appeared to be in desperate need of reaching the soft caresses of the sea so as to cool it off and then settle into a state of comfortable solidity once more.

Time seemed to stop still as I became acutely aware of my surroundings and just exactly what I was about to step into. As strange as it may seem, I couldn't help noticing how very peaceful this moment presented itself as being in that nothing I had ever encountered before could compare with it. While completely wrapped up within its captivating effect then all I could seem to see was the glowing face of an angel. This heavenly vision, which had suddenly and unexpectedly enriched my life, appeared to be one that I never wanted to be absent from after having been exposed to its magic. I couldn't even bring myself to contemplate the prospect of it not being in my life now that I had discovered it.

The lightness in my heart which came from experiencing her radiance, and feeling my instant attraction to it, was just so incredibly refreshing. So nurturing to a part of me which desperately wanted to be filled with a type of sustenance that I wasn't about to discover on any menu; certainly not one that I would find on my chosen table. Until that moment of realisation I had no idea of just how hungry I felt or that only one person on the planet appeared capable of satisfying my needs; both physical and metaphysical.

At least, I hoped to God that she would otherwise I was most certainly going to be lost into the void of unimaginable yearning and interminable emptiness; a permanent wanting of something very precious. Never before that moment had I appreciated the existence of such a burning desire within me which needed to be fulfilled. I just couldn't bring myself to contemplate continuing in that state even though I hadn't been aware of any kind of lack or urgent need before that time.

Out of that thought arose an instant of acute anxiety where my resolve almost seemed to be in danger of wavering. Until, that was, I caught sight of a wonderfully appealing glint in her eye. Immediately my apprehensions evaporated as I was suddenly captivated by her presence and especially the softness of her hair which seemed to accentuate the delicate shape of her neck. Besides my finding this aspect of her femininity so appealing there also seemed to be a certain familiarity to its influence. This encouraged me to walk directly up and touch her and then wrap my arms around her in the manner of embracing a long lost love. It seemed such a natural thing to want to do but somehow I resisted the temptation as my mind raced in to intervene while wanting to know if I had suddenly taken leave of my senses.

Something irrepressible inside of me felt compelled to tell it, in a manner of the utmost certainty and peacefulness, that I most sincerely had and that it was such a delightfully pleasing state to be in; one which I hoped never to return from. My mind was not in the least bit impressed while trying to pretend that it didn't know me. I felt it wander off into a dark corner so as to sulk and pout but I just didn't care. I had been far too taken up with indulging myself in this totally new sensation to even consider pandering to the tantrums of my petulant mind.

I knew instinctively that what had been presented to me was actually the opportunity to choose my destiny anew. A chance to change my life to truly suit myself after having lived it for so long while accommodating others in the way that I had been conditioned to believe was necessary. In front of me I could see a tantalising opening onto the pathway of passionately expressive freedom but, through being so unaccustomed to experiencing it, I felt the need to hang on to something vaguely familiar for reassurance. My mind was still in the midst of a deep sulk and had no intention whatsoever of offering any helpful insights, suggestions or advice. It was totally unused to not being listened to while threatening never to return in the process. I decided to ignore it.

For the very first time in my entire existence I felt as though I was about to do something that I, me as myself, Ronald Phillip Darling wanted to do for no other reason than because it made me feel incredibly good to do so. The fact that it made no sense whatsoever, while even threatening to upset just about everything which I had worked so hard to achieve, seemed totally inconsequential at that moment. There was no denying the incredible excitement which I felt at the prospect of what may come by doing just what my intuition told me would be right to do. I experienced such a heady feeling which completely defied all logic, but looking at my waitress angel I just knew that everything would be absolutely perfect if she agreed to become a significant part of my life. It was so unbelievably crazy to feel this way but I wasn't about to deny an emotion that had become so important to me in such a short space of time. It felt very much as if I would be doing a huge injustice to myself if I simply ignored my feelings and so I resolved not to. There was no turning back for me from that moment on.

Whatever my choice would bring me, then so be it. I was anxious to find out what would happen next. My immediate destiny awaited me where all that appeared necessary for it to be fulfilled was simply walking across to sit at a table and then waiting to be served. In doing so I would be allowing the Divine plan to unfold as unseen forces in the Universe rushed in to shape my future according to my wishes. It had to be. It was my time to be myself and to allow true love, if that's what would come from my choosing, to finally find a place in my heart which so needed it to return in the degree that I desperately wanted it to. I was thirsty for a passion that had almost been forgotten to me but it was obviously present in some mysterious part of my makeup which could somehow influence my decisions. I listened. I drew a deep breath and smiled at my angel. I was ready.

I wanted to eat but much more than this I needed the unique nourishment which only she could provide. I headed for my table while saying a silent prayer. Please God let this all work out right for me. Someone was listening as, in far off places beyond my imaginings, forces began to move which would bring about all that I had ever asked for and more. I had no way to know what would come and neither should I have known as this would only have altered how life expresses its incredible magic.

If there had been a way for me to have been granted advanced knowledge of what my decision to enter the restaurant would cause to happen, then I might well have chosen not to go there in the first place. This would have meant abandoning my opportunity to find true love and probably missing out on it altogether in this lifetime. Without being able to experience the amazing sensations that had lifted me up into another level of consciousness at seeing my angel, then how could I have known what to expect and how it would have enabled me to alter my perception so radically. Trying to imagine it beforehand would not have been even remotely like how it proved to be in reality. Being so completely absorbed in the experience allowed me to make choices in a way that just thinking about it could never hope to replace. For the first time I could really appreciate why life is all about really 'living' what it brings us in the respect of showing us so much of what we very often can't see as being who we really are.

I would later come to learn a good deal about how this amazing process works with regards to how our choices really need to be made from the heart; while allowing ourselves to experience the consequences in the fullness of how they are presented to us. This would prove to be a very important lesson for me and one which would require my letting go of the need to 'think' in my usual logical way. In the process of getting to better understand how to do this, I would also learn about how important it is to accept whatever consequences come from the choices we make; to see them as simply being the outcome of our actions without wishing to apportion blame, or anything of that nature, to anyone else. By truly owning our experiences we have the most to gain by doing so while we strive to fully appreciate the valuable lessons which they bring us in the process.

Right at that very moment, all I knew was that I just wanted to be as close to my angel as possible; and for as long as she would allow me to be. Exactly how this would happen I had absolutely no thoughts about at all as my mind just didn't seem to understand what on earth was going on. The cosmic kitchen was now open while waiting for me to place my order according to the most sincere desires of my heart. I watched in a kind of breathless way as she moved gracefully towards my table while a little bolt of lightning shot through me. In that same instant I was in heaven and excitedly anxious about the prospect of my angel coming to serve me. This meal would be absolutely the most memorable ever, as well as being worth every penny of whatever it may cost me.

Dazed Reflections after the Lightning Strike

Sitting at that table and waiting for my meal to arrive seemed to be the slowest that time had ever passed in my entire life. While picturing the city landscape in my mind's eye, I found myself wondering how on earth I had ever managed to end up here in the first place. After my seemingly never ending trek across Canada and America, which had culminated in my arrival at Lansing, how was it that I came to pick this roadside restaurant out of all the others on the planet? I mused over how circumstances of unimaginable complexity had conspired to lead my footsteps to this special place at this particular point in time. I couldn't begin to fathom how one small change along the route may well have taken me in a completely different direction. This to me summed up the sheer magic and mystery of life which I always found so fascinating.

From my altered point of view, at that stage of my journey, it seemed like another lifetime ago that I had been uprooted from my home on so many occasions. This had created a longing in me to find a place to finally settle while being accepted into the heart of a friendly social community. Suddenly none of it seemed real any more where all of my many experiences felt as though they were out of some kind of a dream. One that I had just woken up from while sat around thinking about all the strange happenings that had occurred to me. It settled really oddly into my consciousness but somehow I knew that this was my reality, although I couldn't for the life of me seem to work out what I'd done while living it; or even why. Everything at that moment appeared to be open to question. Suddenly I was inexplicably drawn into examining a whole host of very vivid memories.

One of the more emotive ones concerned the time that I had spent at Sexton High School. This had turned out to be the first period in my life that I ever remembered being anywhere long enough to make any real friends. It seemed such a lonely existence to have gone all that time beforehand without having anyone special in my life while not growing up doing the things that 'ordinary' kids did; but then there was my music. God alone knows where I would have been without that! Fortunately for me it was my passport to being accepted wherever I lived and I surely did have a good time being in my band and performing in front of others. This, admittedly, was one thing which I appreciated that not very many other kids got to do.

I couldn't help thinking that High school had been an altogether different experience in the run up to launching myself in the world at large, where I had needed to earn a good living in order to get married. Meeting Nina at Sexton had changed my whole outlook on very many things as I had never been able to have a steady girlfriend before that time in the way that she and I were. It seemed only natural that we should get married after we left school. However, when I looked back on that whole period of my latter adolescence then I had to wonder about quite a lot of my feelings at that time of my life when so many things were competing for my attention.

No sooner had I started to reflect on this quite intense journey into adulthood than almost immediately I posed myself a telling question. Had I ever really known love in the way that a man and a woman can experience it when the 'chemistry' is right and working its powerful magic? Moreover, and more importantly, how could I be expected to know or recognise the spectacular depths of timeless true love having never encountered it before? I was still young and life was an uncharted adventure waiting to happen but I really wasn't prepared for the journey as I had no map to guide me; or so I assumed.

After feeling the way I did at that moment of entering the restaurant, I just had to ask myself what it was that had motivated me to do all that I had done up to that point in my life; and if it was what I really wanted. When it came to the question of my three children then there could be no doubt at all in my mind that they were an essential part of my life; and one which I never wanted to be separated from. They meant the whole world to me but there was also a part of me which had been awakened that day to what my heart had really wanted me to become aware of. So much had seemed to change in me at the very moment when I felt that I had found something very precious which I hadn't even appreciated was missing from my life. In finding it I got the oddest notion that a major piece of my life's puzzle had suddenly fallen into place. However, at the very same instant my whole world had been turned upside down in the process.

I sipped tentatively at my soothing Manhattan as though I was sampling an unknown future while trying to make some sort of sense out of my past. I watched people walking by as well as viewing others around me while considering whether any of them had ever been faced with a similar dilemma to mine. If so, I wondered if it had come upon them as quickly as my situation had. If this was the case then I wanted to know if they had ever experienced any doubts or regrets about their choices which they had made as a result? If they did have any doubts I felt the need to understand how compelling they had been and if they had given into those feelings and why. So many questions but the most enigmatic of all was the need to know how their lives had turned out if they had actually given in to their doubts. Suddenly I became aware of my need to anticipate the future and how this was not a wise thing to do.

Then I found myself wondering about how I was feeling and if any of them had ever needed to think about it like I was doing. I kept asking myself what they would have done if they had found themselves unexpectedly thrown into a complete quandary after meeting someone who had made them look at things so totally differently. All of a sudden there appeared to be many more questions in my mind than there were customers in the restaurant; which made things seem quite claustrophobic in a way that made me feel quite breathless.

This corresponded to the point when a quite disturbing thought came barging its way into my already flustered state while adding an unwanted extra dimension to my moral dilemma. It wanted to know, did people even stop to consider the possibility of making drastic changes in their lives or did they just act impulsively while saying to hell with the consequences in the process? This was not my way of doing things and, at that moment, I found myself being somewhat envious of those who could simply follow their instincts without ever questioning why. It seemed to be a really liberating way to approach life but I didn't much like the idea of throwing myself off the diving board without at least first checking to see if the pool was full of water. I had already gathered enough cuts and bruises up to that point of my journey to last me a lifetime; or so it seemed.

I kept thinking about my family and my responsibilities as well as how it had felt for me when I was growing up. All that I had ever longed for in my youth, I now appeared to have. A nice stable home life and a comfortable environment where I considered my lot in this world to be a reasonably happy one; and where a satisfying love certainly did appear to exist. Or so I had assumed up to the time when I opened the door to the restaurant; but what now? I couldn't un-know what I had become aware of and neither could I silence all the questions that had come swarming in from the cloud of doubt that had moved into position just over my head. My emotions seemed to be in turmoil as I so much wanted to just be surrounded by the sensations that I felt when looking into the sparkling eyes of my earthbound angel. What in heaven's name was I going to do?

At the moment of my deepest reservations about my whole situation and at the point of feeling so needy, my meal arrived. I looked up to see that wonderful smile being aimed in my direction when something just seemed to melt inside me. At the instant it did then somehow I knew that everything was going to work out, although I also strongly suspected that my life would never be the same again from that point on. Yet another change awaited my footsteps along an already haphazard pathway but this time, unlike at so many other junctures in my life, this change felt as if it was actually very much welcomed. I had a strong sense of this new direction almost certainly taking me somewhere that I really did want to go and, as selfish as it may have appeared to anyone else, I suddenly didn't feel in the least bit guilty about it.

Something inside me kept encouraging me to just go with my feelings and to follow what I felt inspired to do. Logic didn't come into it and no amount of meticulous planning that I could ever come up with seemed to be appropriate or even necessary. I searched for a way to express what I was trying to get myself to appreciate and, as though in response to my predicament, one single word popped magically into my head. I thought about it for a moment and then it really hit home to me. In my mind I could almost see the word emblazoned across the rooftops of the city and it was then that I became aware of the fact that I'd never fully understood its meaning before. 'Trust'.

Only five letters in a quite deceptively simple word but to me it suddenly seemed huge by virtue of its implications. I needed to trust. My mind prepared itself to become analytical but I ignored it. Trust had come to find a home in my heart and I felt so pleased to be able to welcome it in with open arms. For the very first time in my life I knew what it was to have faith in a mysteriously instinctive process that my mind could not conceive of. My mental abilities had served me very well up to that point on my journey but here I was just about to abandon all that so as to allow something to happen which apparently made absolutely no sense at all; and yet, oddly enough, it kind of did.

The woman standing in front of me seemed to be able to shine a light deeply into my soul which, for the very first time, allowed me to see who I really was. It quite stunned me to discover so much of what had previously been hidden from my view and to also appreciate the value of what I had found. No more was there to be any concealing my incompleteness in the darkness of the barren hold within my ship of indeterminate destiny. Now I could see that it was possible for me to be the captain, so I wasn't about to give that opportunity up after having been gifted with it. I wanted to take control, but this time the compass that I would steer by was the one which had always resided securely in the very core of my heart. It had always been unerring but I hadn't seen it as being so before that time where my biological computer had previously always calculated the various courses on my chart to a contrived destination of insubstantial happiness.

I had settled for a mental ideal but now I could so clearly see the shallowness of it all. This had to change and it would. I had come alive after so long of being in my sleepwalking state but there were consequences that would need to be addressed as a result of what had happened on that trip. My children were so important to me and I was only too aware of what disruptions to a stable home life could do to a child after all that I had encountered with my parents. I didn't want any of them to go through even a fraction of what I had endured, so I just had to trust that things were going to be okay. There was nothing else to do.

Learning to Trust - When the Need Arises

After everything that I had achieved in my life, I appeared to have arrived at the quite stunning realisation that all the knowledge in the world didn't amount to a hill of beans if there was no wisdom with which to guide it. Being the owner of a successful medial equipment company I was living the American dream after working hard for many years to make my own way in the world of business. I had always been a good provider, just as my father had been for my mother and me, but it wasn't difficult for me to appreciate that I was recreating just the same family environment as he did.

I tried not to beat myself up over it as I could see that I didn't really have any other environment to base my choices on. I had met my wife at high school and then done all the expected things where we had ended up with a nice 'standard' family while ostensibly being happily married. To look back while viewing this as being a mistake was not something that I wanted to consider. In the light of my new feelings, however, I found myself having to reluctantly acknowledge that my previous choices hadn't brought me the happiness that I now felt I needed. There could be no doubt about the depth of love which I had for my children and, in a way, I really did love my wife but now I knew there was more. This 'more' proved to be something that I quite urgently required in order to fulfil a completeness which, to me, could only come from one woman; and I was sitting close within her presence at that very time. I did not want this to change. I just couldn't allow it to, no matter what.

The urge which pulsed so deeply from within my desire to fulfil this newly awakened yearning was actually providing me with the ability to experience a level of trust that I had not previously encountered. I wasn't fully aware of this fact at the time as all that filled up my emotional panorama was the blossoming image of something which almost came with a certain sense of familiarity. This was also accompanied by a comforting sense of 'rightness' which imbued me with a degree of reassurance that I had never achieved before that time. I didn't stop to think about the hows, the whys or the wherefores as it didn't seem appropriate in the context of appreciating that I had no intention of letting my mind get in the way.

All I knew was that having been guided to this restaurant, by whatever means the universe had provided for me to take advantage of, then I wasn't about to throw away my golden opportunity by thinking myself into some kind of remorseful guilt trip. However, on the other hand, there was a niggling feeling in me which kept trying to get its foot wedged in the crack of the opening doorway to 'doubt city'. It wanted to know if this was just some kind of hormone-driven infatuation, which would burn brightly in the benighted flames of mutually fulfilled passion, only to ebb quietly away into the cold light of the dawn; into the daybreak of deception and potential heartbreak where, inevitably, there lurked the risk of being found out. This would then lead to the inevitable fiery procession straight towards the battlefield of recriminations.

The issue of trust had ostensibly made an appearance in a slightly different guise and was gnawing at my conscience while trying to get my attention. However hard I tried, I couldn't deny that this appeared to be yet another facet to the apparently precious gem of trust that I'd just brought to the surface. What to do? I began to wonder if I was about to do the right thing while ignoring any possible consequences. I set off slowly along that storm-swept, meandering pathway to nowhere when I caught myself stepping into a mind-trap. I just couldn't let this happen. I wanted to remain completely true to my feelings insomuch as I had become aware that something was surely very different about them. To me, their quite amazing energies were not only really fascinating but highly persuasive as well.

This certainly wasn't some adolescent infatuation. Neither was it something that I would allow to be diminished in any kind of mental recriminatory process which would deny me from focusing on my new found sense of trust. This emotion was far too strong in me, even though I hadn't a clue where it had come from or why I had been so drawn to take so much notice of it. It felt good, but more than this it appeared to be a special kind of intensely personal feeling that I actually 'owned' which made feel very happy to do so.

In retrospect there seemed to be so much in my world that had influenced me when it came to making decisions and important choices. From how I could see things now, I could appreciate that I had very rarely made my way in life through acting on what I sensed was right for me. Truly right for me; but then, how could I have known? How does anyone know for that matter and how do we get to learn? No sooner had this question been posed than it was answered. They get to feel what it's like to really trust in something and then everything else naturally flows from that point on. You will know it when you know it, just as I found myself doing at that moment.

For the very first time I could appreciate that to truly trust in yourself, first and foremost, is the foundation from which absolute trust flows in all your relationships as well as all your dealings with the world at large. Within that wonderful atmosphere of self motivating trust, not to be mistaken with the misleading diversions caused by arrogant ego, then complimentary trust will always be fostered. What you give out is what you get back. This is a wonderful adage that I was to learn the timeless wisdom of as my life progressed on its new pathway.

I couldn't help wishing that somehow I could rewind the clock so as to go back to some distant point in my past and then start again. What a wonderful blessing it would have been to be able to restructure my life with the benefit of 20/20 hindsight. How differently things would have turned out where what I was about to do now would have been done without any encumbrances; no emotional baggage. However, the reality is that life isn't perfect and nor are we. In fact, I got to see that we are all perfectly imperfect and that's what gives life its infinite varieties, its unique richness, whereby we can sample the extremes which this existence has to offer or any point in between.

My life had turned out perfectly just as it was because of all the things that I had ever done, all the decisions and choices that I had ever made, every mistake and miscalculation that I had ever acted upon. These had led me unerringly to this particular seat in this wonderful restaurant and into the world of my angel. How could I ever consider regretting anything when looking at it in this way? Any circumstances other than what I had experienced would have meant never finding this place and then wandering through the remainder of my life never knowing how profoundly I could really feel about so many different things. I simply had to have complete faith in the power of 'trust' and then to follow where it would lead me. I was ready for whatever may come. I had bought my ticket and now the fairground car was moving steadily towards the first steep incline of the roller-coaster track. What would it be like? How exhilarating would it be? I was about to find out.

The future that I had chosen to embark upon in those few emotionally turbulent moments after entering the restaurant would take me into an adventure the like of which I could not have prepared myself for. My life was about to change in ways that I had no way to predict, but the journey was one which I would look back on with gratitude for having been able to make. It was to live up to all that I had been promised in the way that it afforded me incomparable opportunities to evolve both emotionally and spiritually while in the company of my beloved twin soul. Through walking in absolute trust along the course of my new pathway I would only ever be able to glimpse the sheer wonder of it all while sharing the deep and abiding love of my other half. It proved to be the ultimate leap of faith for me where so much of what I had come to rely on was challenged in the way that I needed to discover aspects of myself which I had no idea existed. Love, truly inspirational love, has a way that when allowed to work its indescribably incredible magic, brings gifts which transcend even the wildest of dreams and aspirations.

To fully understand all that happened to me in the years which followed that memorable moment in the restaurant, it would take an even more spectacular journey with a very wise companion who would show me things that I could never have figured out for myself. In the revealing I would gain an appreciation for a dimension of our earthly existence which I could not so easily have achieved had it not been for all that I experienced with my twin flame. This truly incredible and highly personal journey I would be very honoured to share with you now.

- **Chapter 13** -

Conversations at the Lakeside

There didn't seem to be much in the way of any discernable movement to the surface of the water although I could plainly see the strikingly multi-coloured fish swimming about beneath the crystal clear covering of the lake. I was pleasantly mesmerised for what seemed like quite a while as I reflected on not only the vision of such appealing tranquillity and beauty but also on the sensing of a wonderfully comforting peace which had settled so deeply within my heart. This spiritually uplifting sensation appeared to come from my vividly recalling how exciting it was to be so happy and so in love in those early days. The emotions which these treasured memories stirred up in my soul were quite magical as well as being so apparently fresh in my mind.

I found myself regarding them to be very much in harmony with what I observed taking place within the almost translucent waters of the lake. Here I could see that wherever I looked then nothing could be hidden where even at the greatest depth there came an immediate comprehending of all that was happening as well as a knowing of exactly 'why'. For some reason I began to experience a certain degree of envy in appreciating how simple life would be in an environment such as this. Oh that it had been so clear to me back then, when I had started out on my venture while allowing my footsteps to tread the pathway of a new found trust.

But, supposing that it actually had been that clear, what would life have been like then? And, even more perplexing, what if I had known how things would turn out in the way that they did? What then? Would it have been the same if I had been able to see the whole of my journey, and where it would take me, as well as what I would be led to 'discover' along the way? For the fish in the lake there were no secrets or mysteries about where they would be going or what awaited them when they got there. Everything was known by virtue of the carefree and trusting unity which they enjoyed with their surroundings. Each element of their microcosmic, self-contained, lake-bound world contributed to its overall uniqueness while becoming one within the uncomplicated and predictable 'All'. The fish were part of that totality where nothing existed outside of the present moment for them and where no journey ever needed assessing or reviewing. Life just 'was' and required no judgement. Without judgement there could be no guilt. No guilt, no recriminations and no stress. How wonderful must that be?

My slowly evolving, but somewhat insightful, appreciation for the relative simplicity of their way of life seemed to suddenly throw mine into a sharper perspective. By comparison I began to think that so much of what had happened as a result of my choices had inevitably led me to a kind of predictable outcome. It was so easy for me to see things in this way now but back then, in my time of emotional intuitiveness, when heartfelt trust had been my only compass to navigate by, then it wasn't at all easy. At that time there did appear to have been a certain new found clarity but I was so unaccustomed to viewing things in this way that it took a great deal of courage and determination to act upon what I felt that I could see in front of me. Where this motivation actually came from I couldn't be sure but I had no doubt that something very powerful kept propelling me in the direction towards doing what I felt to be right for me.

Momentarily I took my attention away from the underwater world in front of me and looked up at my wise companion. I was hoping that I might somehow get a little clarification on my need to better understand those times, but he just smiled as though encouraging me to keep trying to find the answer myself. I knew he was right but at that precise moment it felt as though I just didn't have the ability to figure it all out on my own. My life had trained me to understand that if I didn't have the answer to a problem then I would go look it up, or find someone who I could ask. Success in business had depended on knowing things or knowing people who could help whenever needed. Now it was different. I needed to find my own answers but it felt like being back at school again where there was so much to learn.

I returned to studying the magic of the aquatic world within the peacefulness of the lake and watched in fascination while two quite large gold and white coloured fish swam past me. They moved effortlessly and in perfect harmony as though some sort of invisible force existed which joined them together. It was such a delight to see how they appeared to know one another's thoughts and moods as well as where they were heading. They were so gracefully and lovingly together where I could appreciate that neither of them had any intention of ever being parted from the other; I knew this feeling so well. It immediately brought to mind many occasions in those early days when I would eagerly go to the restaurant so that I could get to be as near to my 'dream girl' as possible. Love was the ever present teacher and I proved to be a more than willing student who couldn't wait to attend class. It made me feel young again where life's purpose was renewed and re-invigorated. I watched the two fish intently while almost envying them their closeness, but very much hoping that they could feel even a fraction of what I did in my togetherness with Janet.

While being so completely absorbed in the emotions of that time, I also began to recall how nervous I had been in the beginning when it came to the subject of how best to approach her. Right from the very start I had made up my mind to take it as slowly as I possibly could under the circumstances. I felt the need to be conscious of allowing things to develop at their own pace so that I would be sure not to scare her off. I remembered how important it was to me that I didn't come across as being pushy in any way. At first I found this almost impossible to do as I so much wanted to monopolise her time where each moment proved to be absolutely precious while we chatted about everything and anything. I especially recalled being very pleasantly intrigued, and more than a little flattered, by the fact that she seemed to genuinely find whatever I talked about so thoroughly interesting. Just as I did when she told me so many things about herself and her life as well as what she was interested in.

As my mind became inundated with a whole host of priceless memories, I began to appreciate what a wonderful gift it was in being able to once again live so many of those euphoric days. Those exciting times of mutual discovery and fascination where I had spent as many hours as possible just being in her company. To me, every encounter was thoroughly cherished in what seemed like the timelessness of a long forgotten intimacy which we both wanted so much to renew. In so doing we were also becoming ever closer in our hearts. We had touched the spark of an eternal happiness that seemed delightfully familiar and, as it ignited into a dazzlingly bright flame, we both realised how very much longed for it was in wanting to be reunited with it. It had all been incredibly magical and such a blessing for both of us although we were blissfully unaware of just how much of a godsend it really was at that time.

For what seemed like quite a while I allowed myself to become totally engrossed in all that I was feeling about my life and how a great many things had turned out for me up to that point on my journey. While doing this I got to appreciate that those thoroughly stimulating times with my uniformed angel were also offering me the gift of a unique view from within an extra dimension of previously inaccessible wisdom. It was as though my experiences were holding up a mirror while allowing me to gain a different perspective on not only how I viewed my life in general but also on how I felt about myself as well. This took me a little by surprise at first but the more I thought about it then the more I found myself being immersed in the wonderful atmosphere of our swiftly budding romance.

I smiled as I remembered the way in which I had listened intently to whatever she said as though it was such a natural thing for me to do in how we were so quickly able to confide in one another; just like we had been doing it forever. Some of our conversations I could almost recall word for word as, for some reason, things just came back to me as well as the atmosphere at the time when we were so totally lost in our conversations. In one respect it felt as if I had been with her just yesterday as I could even picture how she was dressed and how she wore her hair. Many things were remarkably clear to me just as was the water of the lake which I found myself looking so deeply into.

In the midst of my reminiscing, I quite unexpectedly found myself feeling an increasing urge to get a more complete understanding of just why it was that I found it so easy to talk to her. What was it, I wondered, that caused me to feel like we had been very close friends since before time was even invented? I hadn't ever experienced such a feeling before that point in my life so how could I have been so sure about it? I certainly was happy to be that way and there was no denying it! But why? Where did this 'knowing', this sensing of a kindred spirit come from and what was it about Janet that was so different? It was fascinating but also frustrating in not being able to understand it. I felt the need to seek the wise counsel of my companion again but I knew what his advice would be, so I continued on with hoping that some kind of illuminating thoughts would suddenly pop into my head. Sadly, all I seemed to get were more questions.

One of the more insistent was the need to know why I had so swiftly felt the somewhat soul-baring need to open up to her in a way that I had never even considered doing with anyone else before that time. I seemed to have done it with almost indecent haste in my eagerness for her to be aware of just about everything there was to know about me. It had all seemed so natural in the way that things were between us right from the very start where each of our together times came to represent the highlight of our day. I remembered how I had really looked forward to them and I know that Janet did too. Everything was tinged with an indescribable element of magic which I really longed to know much more about. I wanted to hold it in my hands and then examine it but the very prospect of doing so led me to feeling like I actually wanted it to remain just out of reach. It was such an odd way to view it but somehow the mystery made it all the more attractive.

In my daydreaming state I gazed long and hard into the crystal clear waters of the lake as those precious times continued flowing through my physical, emotional and mental bodies; just as though I had lived them only a few heartbeats ago. They were incredibly 'freeing' and so uncomplicated but, in appreciating this aspect of our togetherness, I began to examine the true depth of that 'naturalness' in the light of everything else that I had experienced; which began to appear much less so by comparison. Whenever I was with Janet then the world seemed to be a much brighter and far more exciting place to be a part of. But, more importantly, I found myself feeling so refreshingly different with respect to my place in it.

Whenever I was with her then I somehow became a 'complete' person who no longer sensed the need to keep any part of himself hidden. I wholeheartedly experienced being the 'me' who I felt in the very depths of my sensitive soul that I wanted to be; deserved to be, needed to be. Whilst in my angel's magical presence I could actually be the 'me' who I somehow instinctively knew that I had always been; but who, for some inexplicable reason, I could never seem to express so completely before that point in my life. It was such an amazingly fulfilling experience as well as being a very satisfying one at a level that I hadn't even appreciated I could ever achieve before having met her.

Sitting so comfortably in such pleasant surroundings, I gave heartfelt thanks for having been granted the opportunity to be freed of so many inhibitions. Through doing so I had been able to find myself within the enfoldment of a wonderfully healing completeness. Reliving that precious period of my life once again was enormously uplifting for me in so many ways. As I continued to watch the two inseparable fishes swim slowly out of view, so much of the emotions from my together times with Janet seemed to wrap me up in its captivating energy.

While recalling one particular occasion of our chatting so cosily in the restaurant, at the point where our first date was imminent, I could feel so strongly how I had been viewing my world at that time. Thinking about myself while in that era of revealing my true persona, I could really see that my opinions certainly had been shaped by a mix of surprisingly influential emotions. It was quite surprising to appreciate that some of them battled with others for dominance in my conscience which was a process that went on without my actually being aware of it. As a result there were many things that I appeared to be unsure of when it came to considering what I had worked so hard to put together at that stage of my life; and then there was the subject of Janet's life as well. I didn't even want to get into that area of our relationship but I couldn't ignore it in the way that I felt towards her.

I guess that it was just my protective instinct coming out as that was such a natural part of me. So many unknowns but in the midst of them all was a certain indefinable quality, a kind of sureness of purpose, which kept me pursuing our relationship. It felt right to do so but there were many contrary arguments jostling for attention in my otherwise preoccupied mind. Somehow I managed to keep them at bay although sometimes it took a not insubstantial amount of self control to achieve. Again, as I sat quite still while deep in reflective thought, I couldn't help but wonder where I had found the depth of confidence and strength of will to do what I did. After all, I was a relatively happily married man with three lovely children, Leslie, Phillip and Mark, and a comfortable home life that many would envy. But, in spite of this, there I was pursuing a relationship with another woman albeit that in my heart I felt a very strong bond with her in a way which quite mystified me. I had never experienced anything like that sort of feeling before then.

So what could it have been that I found to be so special about her, and our developing relationship, given that it was still early days and we were very much getting to know each other? Even having said this, it appears so inadequate now as right from the very start it felt to me as though I had known her all my life. She was like my, well, like my ... for some reason I just couldn't seem to find the right words to describe the feeling of familiarity that I had about her, even though it appeared to be so powerful. It was at that moment of feeling lost in the confusion of wanting to understand more clearly that my companion came to my rescue. I listened intently as I heard him telling me about how our twin flame energies were inspiring us both to follow our hearts while trusting that what we were doing was what made us the happiest. He went on to say that it had been our greatest joy in being able to be so close to one another and from within this strong desire came the courage to follow that passion to the place where we felt that it most wanted to take us.

Even though I didn't fully understand all that he had said, I did however feel a certain 'rightness' in his words while applying them to all that I could remember about my feelings while living that part of my life. For what seemed like a long while I found myself reflecting on what I had just heard while turning my attention back to the view of the lake. As I gazed deeply into the crystal clear waters in front of me then I seemed to be drawn completely into one memorable occasion of our togetherness while chatting so cosily with Janet at the restaurant. Very quickly I became thoroughly immersed in what I was seeing of our special time together. In doing so I could clearly remember how it felt to be 'walking on air' as I began to get caught up in the blissful intimacy of that occasion. It was the same every time we revealed more and more of our true selves to one another while feeling that each morsel of 'confidential' information was being offered in the way of a treasured gift.

While in the midst of this highly absorbing reminiscing, once again I began to get a strong sense of the fact that there seemed to be a certain very special quality of timelessness which surrounded our togetherness. Whenever we were wrapped up and getting lost in each others company, then nothing else appeared to be wrong with the world or whatever happened to be going on in our lives. That mysterious 'rightness' seemed to spread out like a huge wave which swept all the chaos away while leaving a feeling of peace and tranquillity in its wake. Time stood silently and motionlessly observing as it did. The world stopped spinning while my dream girl and I chatted about anything and everything; we just didn't care where our conversation took us as long as we could be together. It was so incredibly wonderful at that time but, for me, it felt to be equally so in being able to re-live those moments so vividly. My heart suddenly seemed as though it was as light as air while my spirit soared in sheer delight.

Being able to reconnect so strongly with that powerful energy helped me to appreciate that we must have both had a kind of knowing, an inner sensing of something of great importance to us which served to heighten our mutual attraction. Neither of us had any knowledge whatsoever of twin flame energies at that point on our journey but somewhere deep within us there must have been an understanding of their presence. Somehow, without us being aware of it, they were leading us towards faithfully following our hearts and, fortunately, both of us were listening. This in turn encouraged each of us to open up so disarmingly to one another while we quickly fell very deeply in love.

It was a truly spectacular love which we both knew instinctively to be so 'right' although neither of us had any conscious understanding of this and neither did we have any concept of how that special love came to be. It just 'was' and so we gratefully accepted it for being that way. To us, it had been like the very first time that we had known it. It seemed to have a wonderful freshness to it and was so compelling as well as being something so precious that we handled it like a new born baby; a little miracle that was going to grow in our care while we nurtured it at every opportunity. Just like that intangible magnetism which is so characteristic of a tiny new life, it was an energetic bond that weaved its uplifting magic into every fibre of our being. It did so while filling up that place of longing in each of us which we had searched so long for in our deep seated need to be made whole. My surprisingly lucid memories of this preciously affectionate time were taking me further into the emotions which had exerted their powerful influence over me. Without appreciating it, I was now staring more intently at the surface of the lake while avidly observing the delicate tapestry of our courtship unfold in the richness of its loving intimacy.

Everywhere I looked then I could see so many different aspects of how things were at the time of our getting to know one another. Each meeting seemed to have its own unique quality but under it all was the transparency of a flow; a motion, a constant current which swept us along on a journey of natural togetherness. Within this stream of sustaining energy we were being encouraged to remember and to trust as the tide of life gathered us up into its loving embrace while we offered little or no resistance to its wisdom. We just went gratefully and appreciatively with the flow as our journey gradually unfolded.

By now I had become thoroughly lost in my reminiscences to such a degree that I was almost wishing to fully live those moments all over again. It would have been so easy to have gone back to that period so as to savour once more the discovery of what had eluded me for such a long time previously; although I had not been aware of it until I'd met Janet. All I had wanted from that point on was to completely fill my life up with her closeness, her tenderness and her bright light of femininity. The powerful light of love, which shone so attractively from her, seemed to permeate into every shadowy corner of my being; even though I wasn't aware that many of them were actually there.

Not only had I found her but I had also miraculously begun to find myself in the process. Within that quite breathtaking revealing I experienced a level of joy that was decidedly more than a little addictive. It did make me think, however, about just what this addiction really meant to me and if it could have been inspired by a purely physical need. Thankfully this silly notion lasted only a few cheerless seconds in the more remote recesses of my mind.

How, I wondered, could I ever have considered that what I was setting my heart on pursuing could possibly be compared to some kind of hormone-fuelled infatuation; how crazy was that? Even to think in those terms seemed to me to be disrespectful of such a precious gift.

As though to endorse my heartfelt affirmation, a fish suddenly leapt effortlessly out of the water and then plunged gracefully back into it again while casting shimmering ripples out across the entire surface of the lake. Everywhere in the now sparkling tapestry of this once tranquil world appeared to have responded to its leap of joy while sending me the message that I would do well not to bring any thoughts of a disruptive nature into the peacefulness of such loving recollections. Its timely gesture was not lost on me as once again I settled myself into the comforting nostalgia which had drawn me so deeply into not only their magic, but also into their infinite mystery as well.

Even as this was happening then I became aware of the serenity quickly returning once more to the surface of the lake as my sense of happiness filled me up to almost overflowing. Eventually all became still and again I watched in fascination as the captivating underwater ballet continued as though it had been rehearsed and performed for my sole benefit. For a brief moment I thought I heard my companion mutter under his breath that it was actually being staged for the benefit of my soul. I smiled at his wry sense of humour. I had come to have great respect for this patient font of much wisdom who had so kindly chosen to be my close and much valued companion. He was my gracious guide in a mysterious place which held so much fascination for me as well as being one which never ceased to surprise me.

Another fish jumped but this time it almost seemed as though it was a leap of confirmation of what I had been thinking. I smiled even more at the prospect of having what appeared to be a special connection with a creature that inhabited a different world than the one I existed in. To feel that closeness brought with it a mystical sensation of being 'as One' with Nature which in turn allowed me to connect with a much needed deeper understanding of myself. What a wonderful gift this was and what a privilege to be in the midst of an oasis that did so much to restore a sense of the most profound peacefulness within the very depths of my soul. It was just impossible not to be happy in the presence of such indescribably beautiful surroundings and inspiring company. I felt as though I just wanted to stay by the lake forever. Suddenly, out of the blue, I remembered a phrase which seemed very appropriate to what I was feeling.

The words almost spoke themselves to me ... *He maketh me to lie down in green pastures, He leadeth me beside the still waters, He restoreth my Soul ...* Almost as soon as these precious words came into mind I suddenly had an understanding of them the like of which I'd never appreciated before that moment. I couldn't help thinking how incredibly influential and inspiring they were while considering what they truly meant to me. This very moving revelation made me feel as though someone extremely loving and very powerful was breathing into the deepest recesses of my innermost being.

Gratefully the entirety of my eternal 'self' responded like a delicate bud that had been patiently waiting for the first warming rays of a summer sun to encourage it into full bloom. Immediately I experienced a sensation of the most sublime happiness that I can possibly describe. For what seemed like an eternity I allowed myself to simply bask in the sheer ecstasy of that heavenly feeling as I appreciated that it was one which I would have been happy to become completely lost in forever. I seemed to lose all track of time as I drifted along in what felt like the womb of the Universe. It was absolutely wonderful.

Slowly, very slowly, as my attention returned to what I could see going on all around me, I began to become aware of the fact that I could hear the distant sounds of bells. They were the most delicate of musical harmonies that I'd ever heard but there was a kind of pealing, rhythmic quality to them which seemed quite familiar. I turned to look at where they were coming from and then noticed a really picturesque church way off in the distance. It was set into a hillside and overlooking a wooded valley that appeared to extend out from the far side of the meadow. I could see no other buildings near the church but there did seem to be some activity in the grounds by the front entrance. I became intrigued and felt the urge to discover more about what was going on so I got up to set out on the long walk towards the direction of where I thought the road that led up to it would be.

I had no idea what I might find there or even why I was so interested in travelling all the way up to it in the first place. The bells seemed to be calling me onwards so without even stopping to consider the reason for my curiosity, I set course in the direction of the woods as my companion got up to follow me. The sweetness of the air filled my body with its refreshing fragrance as I made my noiseless progress across the soft grassy canvas of the meadow. Within just the space of a few short steps I had reached the area of the garden where I could see that everything was in full bloom. I found it very tempting just to stop for a while so as to take in the sheer magic of its loveliness but something urged me to press on towards my destination.

I was just about to turn away when out of the corner of my eye I caught sight of a slight movement and, when I turned to focus on what it could be, my mind took a little while to play catch-up. Almost obscured by a large sycamore tree I could see that there was a couple sat very close together on what seemed like a very comfortably upholstered double seat. It took me a few moments to realise that they appeared to be thoroughly lost in the most passionate of embraces while kissing in a very expressively tender manner. Their arms were tightly holding one another while they looked to be completely oblivious to the world around them. It seemed as if absolutely nothing else mattered to them at that point in time where, to them, the only other person who existed was the one that they were kissing.

While watching how they were together, as they basked in the radiant warmth of love's passionate embrace, I found myself suddenly being filled with the most compelling emotions that came flooding back in a very stimulating way. Along with these feelings came vivid memories which quite overwhelmed me in how clear they were and how evocative the imagery was. These, I quickly realised, were all born out of my recollections of similar times when I too had been very happy to lose myself so completely in the heady realms of impassioned abandon. Happily I took the opportunity for a stroll down memory lane while feeling very pleased to have been reminded of those very special romantic interludes in my life. It was while appreciating the truly magical intimacy of those times that I became aware of what the couple on the seat must be feeling which then made me want to look away. Somehow I felt a little awkward in watching them as they so fervently expressed their love for one another but, even though I wanted to give them their privacy, I just couldn't help but feel so much of what they were feeling.

The intensity of their world-excluding ardour was obvious to me but more than that I could sense their deep love for one another as well as their yearning for the kind of closeness that only physical intimacy brings. I knew well that level of neediness and how it felt to have discovered it for the first time in my life. Once found, it was accompanied by a sensation that bordered on panic whenever the thought of not being able to be reunited with it after the moment of separating occurred.

Looking at how the woman was holding her man I intuitively sensed her sincere love for him in the way that she quite obviously didn't ever want to be parted from his side. That mysteriously magnetic, but incredibly intimate, sensation had formed such a significant part of my romantic experiences that I was in danger of becoming irretrievably lost in my recollections of those early passionate days with Janet. As a result of feeling this then it seemed to stimulate a whole stream of cherished memories which came pouring into my mind. Like a river in full flood they were continually sweeping through my head and heart where I almost seemed to recapture the entirety of that impetuous time with my twin soul on our journey through courtship.

It was the most emotionally captivating review of those wonderful occasions when we would spend our days looking forward to whatever time we could find to be together. I remember so well how difficult it had been for both of us in the beginning but somehow we managed as there seemed to be nothing that could keep us apart. In the midst of all this it was also apparent that I had to wrestle with my feelings about making excuses to be away from my family and my wife at that time. Being deceitful was not something that came naturally to me but the need to be with my dream girl helped me to overcome any feelings of guilt. Seeing as much as I found myself being able to through my new perspective, while almost reliving so much of what we went through, then it was fascinating to see how obviously determined we both were in our efforts to be together, no matter what. When I came to analyse it then I had little or no idea of what it was that compelled us both to keep seeing each other while wanting nothing more than to be as close as we possibly could be.

In those times I remember that I kept worrying that I might lose her through my expressions of an obvious need but it seemed that the more I showed my true feelings then the more she responded in a positive way. This was such a different and refreshing experience for me and not at all what I had come to expect from a relationship. Once found, I knew that I could never give it up. Just as I was about to lose myself once more in my visions of the past then the couple on the bench seat stopped kissing. For a moment they gazed longingly into each other's eyes and then fell into an even closer embrace. At the instant they did then I felt a little ripple of the most thrilling electric energy shoot up from under my feet as it passed right through me. Then it seemed to leap out through the top of my head. All of the tiny hairs on the back of my neck stood up and I shivered a little as they did. I seemed to be able to actually feel the intense emotions that had been generated by such a passion-filled gesture which made me smile while being so firmly wrapped up in its wonderful warmth.

I studied the lady's face as she rested her chin comfortably on her man's shoulder while he pressed his cheek closely to hers. It was such a seemingly ordinary thing to do but the way that they did it, with such love and affection, was simply magical and so deliciously intimate. I felt my arm stiffen slightly as it would have done had it been holding my beloved Janet. I would have wanted to give her a reassuring squeeze at that point in a similarly intimate embrace so as to emphasise my feelings for her. I could almost feel how she would have responded had I done so and I treasured the fact that I had been able to get to know her so well.

Their tender caresses served to bring up such a strong feeling in me where, almost immediately, I wanted to urge him to whisper in her ear those words that I knew she was longing to hear. Almost before this thought had fully matured in my mind, the man actually did say something in a very soft voice although I couldn't make out exactly what he was saying. "*You were right.*" I heard my companion say. At which point, in my completely absorbed state, I managed to remember that there was actually someone else with me. "*Thank you.*" came the dry response to my having acknowledged his presence.

I smiled a little but then somehow got the idea that he was about to ask me to do something or point something out to me even though I was obviously still very much caught up in all that had been happening to me. For some reason I just couldn't take my eyes off the couple as they embraced each other so lovingly. When I saw the way that he held her so firmly, while almost breathing her in, I found myself being immediately transported back into a memorable situation which was forever captured in my heart. I knew exactly what his feelings were as he revelled in the touch of her softness while trying to absorb every wonderful sensation which the sheer closeness of her femininity inspired in him. It appeared as though his heart was eagerly taking notes on something very important; a state of perfect joy or a level of intimate connection which it never wanted to forget. More than that, he seemed to be experiencing something that wasn't possible to appreciate without her. A kind of longed for familiarity but from where this emotion could have come from I wasn't able to fathom out at that time.

"Look closely at what surrounds them." I heard my companion say and so I immediately did as I was asked in the hope that it would make things clearer for me. Unfortunately it didn't. I could see nothing but the two of them embracing and the background of the lovely garden which they were silhouetted against; but nothing else. In truth, I didn't even understand what I was supposed to be looking for so it proved to be a little frustrating for me as I felt a real desire to understand. I did, however, get the idea that maybe my own emotions were still getting in the way while not allowing me to be some sort of dispassionate observer.

"Don't worry about being dispassionate or detached in any way. Just allow yourself to feel the energy of such intense love while letting it to show you what it wants you to become aware of. Allow yourself to be thoroughly absorbed in the emotions of similar times with your twin flame and how you were feeling about yourself and life in general as a result. Immerse yourself in the desire to bring about what you felt so strongly in your heart the need to create. Search within for a clue as to where that determination came from while relaxing your focus on the couple in front of you. Let go and feel. Let that energy within you direct your vision and then see what comes as a result."

I was about to ask for a further explanation of a concept which I found to be totally confusing but just as I had almost gathered together some suitable words of inquiry in my mind, I suddenly felt the lightest of breezes brush gently around me. It was as if a large flock of tiny birds had passed close by and then encircled me; but there was nothing to be seen. No leaves moved discernibly on the trees and none of the plants or flowers gave any indication of being influenced by anything of that nature, although I could definitely still feel the effect. However, the lady's long blond hair certainly did appear to move just a little which was enough to make her man bring his hand up to caress it. As soon as he did this then I suddenly noticed a slight change at the edges of their outline which was when I started to appreciate that there seemed to be a subtle difference in the quality of the light all around them. *"Look closer."* my companion urged and so I began to focus on the entirety of the scene and not just the two of them. After a few moments of bewildered fascination I was sure that I could see some kind of flowing movement all around their bodies where each of them appeared to have a sort of glow that had merged with the other.

At first I told myself that it must be just a trick of the light but the way I was feeling seemed to encourage me to accept what I could see as being important while allowing it to settle firmly into my awareness. This I did while simply observing the movement of the light while remaining very closely connected to the emotions of similar times with my Janet. The more I did this then the easier it became to see clearly the quite amazing movement of what I can only describe as light energy enveloping them both. It was quite breathtaking to observe as well as almost too much to comprehend.

"All love in action my good friend, all love in action. You are starting to become aware of the twin flame energy in the way that it looks when reunited with its counterpart. The physical and emotional attraction which they feel so strongly is the result of their being so connected within the mutual attraction of their twin soul energies. They are responding to the call of their other half. The completeness which they feel actually comes from the reuniting of a bond that was broken a very long time ago; as you see time that is.

It became separated in order that they may experience life in the many various depths and ways that they wanted to. Now they have come together again and so they will have more experiences while being as one. What you can see around them is a physical representation of the powerful force which underpins the very structure of the Universe. All is love my good friend. Love is All."

My mind raced while trying to take in the quite revelationary implications of what I had heard as well as what I was seeing. I had no idea of anything so subtle and yet so powerful when it came to relationships although I certainly could acknowledge how this could be so after my own experiences with my beloved Janney Kay. I had no doubts at all that she was my twin soul but, until this moment, I had no idea of what it really meant. I still didn't fully understand but things were certainly starting to add up in the way that I was becoming more aware of why I had done all that I had with Janet. As for stretching my mind into the infinite dimensions of a Universe and then making the leap of consciousness required to apply the energy of love to something so vast, well, that was quite a different matter altogether.

The highly intriguing subject of twin souls I could handle, kind of, but what could that possibly have to do with something so seemingly unconnected as the galaxies and the stars. *"Later my dear friend."* I heard him say quietly with more than a little encouragement in his voice. The instant I registered his familiar tone I suddenly found myself wondering what on earth could come next. Then I appreciated that my wise companion always seemed to have a knack of coming up with things that were often quite exciting as well as stimulating. I felt a little thrill of anticipation shoot through me as I became eager to know just exactly what it was that he had in mind. Things certainly were getting very interesting.

Negotiating My Way through an Unexpected Detour

Reluctantly I tore myself away from the scene of the passionately embracing couple but not before I gave myself one last chance to really study the fascinating light around them. It was a joy to see it in action as well as actually being able to feel it for myself. In doing so I found that I could get a much better understanding of what was going on. I also felt very privileged to have been able to share in the experience which it created, so much so that I imagined that I would probably never tire of watching it. There was something so attractive about it and, in a way, something so very familiar in its magnetic quality as well. The very sight of its presence seemed to cause certain stirrings in me at a level that I hadn't previously been aware of. When I first became conscious of this sensation I didn't quite know what to make of it.

My mind wanted to come charging in so as to analyse it but for some reason I just seemed to 'go inside' myself in a way which felt very satisfying as well as wonderfully calming. By doing this I discovered that I could get in touch with a part of me that I didn't even know had been present. It felt as though there was some sort of ancient place within the very make-up of my being which pre-dated antiquity where a storehouse of 'knowingness' lay waiting for me to rediscover it. This proved to be a very moving experience for me and one which brought with it a kind of sureness; but of what I couldn't exactly say. It did feel good though and so I decided that looking further into it would be an excellent idea. This felt like the time for me to do so but, like the Russian dolls where you open one only to discover that there is yet another one nestled inside of it, I quickly realised that I had only been experiencing the topmost level of something which probably ran quite deep within me.

It was at this moment when I got the idea that there was undoubtedly much more that I needed to be aware of. "*Top marks for perspicacity!*" I heard my companion say. Again I smiled but this time my face must have betrayed a sense of puzzlement which prompted my companion to indicate that we should move on. I was sincerely hoping that wherever we were moving on to would lead me towards a place of a much better understanding. My companion smiled as he placed his hand reassuringly on my shoulder. It was a very familiar gesture which said so much and one which I had learned to interpret as meaning 'trust me'. I did and so I started walking in the direction he seemed to be wanting me to go.

The bells from the church continued to ring out while their enchanting tones seemed to wrap me up as the melodies swirled invitingly all around me. It was the most magical experience where it sometimes proved to be difficult to distinguish a direction of the musical chimes. If I hadn't known where the church was located then I could have believed that the entire atmosphere had been made up of the most exquisite metallic vibrations from invisible bells. Even though their sounds were the epitome of delicate softness, there seemed to be an energy to them which appeared to be very powerful indeed. At least it felt that way to me.

I realised that I had become fully immersed in that state of appreciation when I found myself also wondering whether or not I could possibly be the only one who heard them. My companion appeared to be unmoved while the courting couple on the bench seat obviously had other things on their minds. I continued to listen as I noticed that the day appeared to be brighter than I remembered it being just a short while ago; although I had no concept of time or even what day it actually was. No matter, time didn't seem to be important and neither did anything else apart from getting to the church so as to find out what was going on and why. From somewhere in the deep recesses of my mind I got the notion that I knew what I would find when I eventually got there and that even the sounds of the bells had a poignant familiarity to them. However, I didn't stop to think too much about it as the highly active portion of my mind was still very busy processing the many lingering images of the couple's loving embrace.

My companion stepped nimbly up beside me as we made our way towards the wooded area and up across the sloping ground which led us to it. I just seemed to be one walking whirlwind of emotions at that moment but it felt to me as though there could possibly be some kind of resolution and maybe even some answers where I appeared to be headed. Even as I made my way towards the crest of the hill I had no idea of just how spectacularly these answers would come.

- Chapter 14 -

The Landscape of My Heart - The Valley of My Mind

My mind was still filled with the many wonderful images and treasured memories of so much that I had experienced with Janet during those breathtakingly romantic times when we had first met. They had made such a lasting impression on me to the degree that I was quite convinced that eternity would never be long enough to erase even the merest fraction of them. As I immersed myself in the surprisingly fresh emotions of those occasions I listened to the sound of the most stirring music which seemed to be coming from within the depths of my very grateful heart. The crystal clear bells which were casting their delightful enchantment all across the land had the effect of seeming to celebrate every enduring detail of my vivid reminiscences. They also appeared to remind me of the twin flame energy vision that I had become aware of through the insightful words and gentle guidance of my wise companion.

Visualising those flames burning so brightly in my mind's eye, set me thinking about just how much we had ignited our mutual desire to follow the path of true happiness. That state of newly discovered blissfulness which we had felt the urgent need to express while revelling in our 'completeness'. I closed my eyes while allowing myself to fully savour the moment of that treasured step onto the pathway of a new found way of being. As a consequence of this I felt a definite lightness in my every footstep as my smiling guide and I walked more purposefully up the grassy slope. For some reason, that I hadn't been aware of until that very instant, it seemed to be much steeper than I remembered it being before setting out on it. I then realised that I had actually paid very little attention to this aspect of my route towards the church. Before I could give it any more thought, I opened my eyes and immediately found myself quickly looking up at something which had suddenly come into view above me. It took a few seconds before my mind could fully grasp just exactly what it could be that I suddenly found myself beginning to study so intently.

I watched in fascination as the image of what I can only describe as being a big bird of prey swept across a beautiful, clear blue sky while gliding effortlessly above me. At first it was difficult for me to assess its true size as there was nothing anywhere nearby which I could compare it with. By virtue of the way in which it moved so majestically smoothly, I got the idea that it was probably much larger that than anything I'd ever come across before. Its wings appeared to be very much like those of the kind that I'd seen on eagles

169

when in soaring flight, but these had a sort of fascinatingly bright golden sheen which made them look almost mystical. I also noticed that the big bird had the characteristic 'finger' design at the tip of its wings but, rather than being feathers, these were actually shining very brightly almost like crystals which refracted the light. They gave off the most remarkable sparkling effect which I found to be very attractive indeed.

What proved to be even more interesting was the fact that this particular bird, if that's indeed what it was, had the most striking colouring; some of which seemed to trail behind it as its magnificent body and outstretched wings moved gracefully through the air. I watched in wordless awe as it occasionally circled on the rising warm air currents. In doing so it began painting the most stunning violets, purples, pinks and corals, with many other shades in between. This gave the impression of never ending sunsets appearing in different parts of the sky. It was so impressive to see such a display of creative power from this winged artist. Especially one who apparently had the ability to decorate the heavens in such a breathtaking manner, for no other reason than simply the sheer pleasure of doing it.

I was so taken with its state of obvious joy at producing its masterpieces that I quite forgot about my encounters with the courting couple and my memories of my similar times with Janet. I walked happily along with my companion while craning my neck to see ever more of the spectacle directly above me. Before I knew it, we had reached the crest of the hill where I felt as though I wanted to stop for a while so as to take in the total wonder of this most fascinating aerial display. Almost immediately I sensed that my companion had come to stand close beside me and, without thinking, I turned away from gazing upwards so as to say something to him. I really wanted to know if he was enjoying the spectacle as much as I was but in doing this I chanced to look at the view from the top of the hill. This was the point where my mind momentarily froze when, for the first time, I realised just exactly what was in front of me.

I felt something cold on my chin which must have been the result of my jaw hitting the ground beneath my feet. My eyes opened wide at the very same instant as I tried to take in the totality of precisely what it was that I found myself looking at. Mere words could not do justice to what my mind was trying to process as a result of all that my highly active visual senses were passing to it. Stretched out in front of me was what I can only describe as a loch, just like those I'd seen in pictures of Scotland's wonderful landscapes. It was a huge expanse of water which seemed to stretch for many miles where each side was bordered by quite steep-sided, wooded mountains. I found myself stood completely still while trying to take in the enormity of this scene, as well as the absolutely breathtaking scope of Mother Nature's handiwork.

In being so close to such a magnificent example of what our beautiful earth has to offer, I felt somehow humbled when I gazed at the high mountain peaks and the vastness of a body of water whose depths I had no possible way to imagine. I couldn't help but wonder at what had caused all of this to come into being in the first place. Immediately my mind began to wander into the timeless question of how anything, including myself, came to be created and by whom. I dared not even contemplate the question of 'why'. Then I felt a chill run through me as the ruthlessly diminishing spectre of 'insignificance' came to stand close beside me. As it did so then I seemed to instantly lose myself in the incomprehensible vastness of eternity while being sucked into the void. Coincident with this happening, my sense of completeness evaporated as a result of being faced with such an expanse of imposing emptiness which appeared to be nothing less than the gateway into the unimaginable. I stood quite still in momentarily not knowing who I was or just what to do. I wanted to 'be' and yet not to be all at the same instant. I didn't feel fearful as much as I tried not to 'think' because I had no idea what my next thought might reveal to me.

To my immense relief, I felt my companion gently place his hand on the area of my back just over my heart. I cannot begin to describe to you the sense of reassurance and comfort which this gave me. Just to reconnect with another kindred spirit was a feeling of immense value which allowed me to remember that I was not alone. I felt such a sense of deep gratitude that it made my legs go weak and for a moment I sensed the need to just hang on to him. Quickly I recovered myself as I experienced the grounding familiarity of his steadfast and loving companionship. In doing so I was once again swept up in the familiar vitality of that intense flame which I had discovered with Janet. For a brief moment I foolishly thought that it had gone but, in truth, I realised that it was never really any less than it ever had been. All that had happened was that I had allowed my frantic mind to distract me while it sought to contemplate and defend its existence.

While clearly recalling those few intense seconds of mental impotence, I found myself being able to glimpse the constant battle of the human condition. This subconscious state which wrestles with ignoring the limited assertions of a one dimensional mind that constantly attempts to dominate the infinitely wise dimensions of spirit. My mind had no way to comprehend what it was being presented with when viewing the landscape and beyond. It struggled to make a positive connection whereas my spirit was very much in touch with the potential of creation which it knew itself to be an integral and valuable part of. My confounded mind could only embrace isolation, impending annihilation and confusion but I had escaped its delusions by choosing to listen to the still small voice of my inner self. In doing so my sense of completeness began returning for which I was very grateful.

I had no doubt that my companion was fully aware of my quite unsettling experience and so I turned to look at him only to be greeted by that wonderful smile which expressed more in the way of encouragement than any amount of fine words could ever communicate. He patted me gently as I returned his smile and then once again I began studying the view in front of me; only this time I felt quite differently about it. The entire outlook was truly inspiring and, rather than the profound loneliness which it had so recently caused me to feel, I began to get a sense of something else. Something which I couldn't find a way to describe but which made me wonder about the whole subject of creation. My mind had no way to comprehend or even categorise it, but somewhere inside me I had a knowing which needed no explanation or even invited any incisive examination. It just 'was' and I accepted myself as being a grateful part of that highly mysterious but eminently fascinating state. Gradually I found myself studying every absorbing detail of the landscape. While doing so I allowed as much of a connection within me to emerge with whatever it was that I happened to be looking at. This I did in the sincere hope that it would reveal more of its secrets to me in the process.

Some way along the left hand side of the 'loch' I noticed that there appeared to be a quite large gap in one particularly steeply inclined area of the mountains; although I couldn't make out where it could be leading to. The reason for this was that right where the break occurred, a lot of mist seemed to be rising up from the surface of the water. This completely covered the gap where, in certain areas, some if it had spread out across the woods as well as above them. I could see that it also looked to be rolling over the top of the mountains in the most mysterious way while endowing them with an almost surreal quality. The water of the lake appeared to be quite choppy which gave the impression of it being a fairly windy day. But, oddly enough, there was not a breath of air to be felt at the point where I was standing. If there had been a lot of wind then the mist surely wouldn't have existed.

This really puzzled me, among very many other things which I found myself still avidly trying to absorb into my consciousness. Nevertheless, I somehow managed to settle into a state of acceptance while taking in the awesome wonder of the sights. It seemed easier that way as there were so many fascinating and attractive aspects to the landscape which I really wanted to feel a much closer connection with. I surmised that in the grand scheme of things then it didn't seem important to figure out why there were waves when there was no wind to cause them to be there. To me, they were exceptionally pretty and seemed to need no particular reason to exist other than simply that of their obvious enthusiasm for doing so. How could I even begin to question that?

While looking out across the water I couldn't help but marvel at the sheer beauty which it presented me with. Virtually all the wavelets had shimmering golden crests to them which, at times would make certain areas of the surface look like one huge sheet of rippling gold. The underlying blueness of the water merged with it to create the most stunning effect and was nothing like I had ever seen before; or even imagined possible in my wildest of dreams. I was thoroughly captivated by it but I found my attention being quickly drawn to something which my mind couldn't process at all.

What I'd spotted a little way off in the distance was what looked very much like the spire of a church poking up through the surface of the water. At least that's what I thought it was, but there appeared to be something wrong with it. To me it seemed to be kind of tilted off at an angle where I felt that it was almost in danger of crashing down into the golden tipped wavelets and then disappearing beneath them. I studied it for a while, half expecting it to topple over at any moment. At the same time my practical mind was attempting to visualise what held it up and what the rest of the building must look like given the depth of the lake at that point. Nothing made any sense, so I began to wonder if it might be some kind of prehistoric monster which had a head like a crooked stone-built church steeple. Evidently my thought processes were playing tricks on me and I probably needed to get some sleep sometime soon. This felt like it might be a good plan.

To add to my confusion, I could also see beyond the 'monster' that there was the most beautiful avenue of trees but, most bizarrely, they appeared to be right in the middle of the lake. I just didn't understand this at all but there again, there was so much for my mind to take in about the entirety of what I was seeing that a tree lined avenue situated in the middle of a lake seemed to be the least of my problems. I was just about to turn to my companion to ask for some kind of explanation for everything, or at the very least some words of wisdom that would put my mind at rest, when I spotted the lovely church in the woods.

I could see it more clearly now. It was situated a little way up on the right hand side of the lake and once again I became fully aware of the sound of its delightfully pealing bells. Now that I could see the building in more detail then it became quite noticeable to me that the wooded area which I had seen from the meadow was actually part of the large forest on that side of the mountain. The trees stretched down almost to the water's edge but there was a kind of plateau jutting out from the rock surface which made a natural clearing in that area of the woods. This flat patch of land, which looked as though it had been specially prepared for it, was where the church nestled in such complimentary harmony with the landscape. To me it almost looked as though some divine hand had intended that this beautiful building, and the delightful grounds around it, should have been created on that very spot. Everything seemed to blend in with such an inspired naturalness which gave the impression of there being a certain quality of 'rightness' about it, a synergy of purpose where any one aspect complimented and supported the others.

It really was a thoroughly picturesque setting that I would love to have taken a photograph of so that I could have framed it and then placed somewhere in a favourite part of my house. A very special spot where, as I would pass by it each day, I could look at it whenever I felt myself to be in need of cheering up. I thought about how I could achieve this but while I continued to take in more of the view I suddenly noticed something else. Running alongside the lake, in the direction of the church, was a wide pathway which seemed to be made up of some sort of white glistening material. Its effect was made more apparent through being contrasted with the backdrop of the deep greens of the trees where the pathway looked as though someone had literally painted it into the landscape.

Almost parallel to where I was standing there seemed to be someone on the pathway and for a moment I thought that I could see some other smaller figures accompanying what looked like a woman. I couldn't be certain but I did see that this lady, if it was indeed a lady, seemed to be moving off along the pathway while heading in the direction of the church. I quickly became intrigued by this and began to study her movement as well as the direction she appeared to be heading in. At this point I was even more eager to find out what was going on but the abrupt appearance of this notion in me corresponded to the precise moment when I felt a tug on my arm. This, I quickly realised, came about as a result of my companion attempting to lead me off in a slightly different direction. For an instant I almost resisted as I felt the strongest of urges to walk along the edge of the lake.

I wanted to go across to the pathway so as to pursue what I felt sure was someone I recognised and possibly get to know who the others were who were with her. I just felt that it was really important for me to discover her identity and also that I wanted very much to meet up with her; but I just didn't understand why I should be even thinking this way. While attempting to process this emotion I felt a more insistent tug and so I turned to see where I was being encouraged to go. Once more a complete surprise awaited me when I did. I had no idea why I hadn't noticed the boat moored at the jetty by the edge of the lake before that time as it was by far the most ornate looking waterborne craft that I'd ever seen. It looked incredibly grand while the workmanship was something to be admired even from the distance that I was away from it. It looked quite long and slender with a beautiful highly polished, dark wooden cabin situated right in the middle of it where a gleaming silver smokestack had been set on top of it.

The shape somewhat resembled that of a gondola but this vessel was far larger. It was fitted with handrails and cute little portholes along the side while the cabin had pretty curtains set up in the big windows. Overall I would have to say that it was a rather odd looking vessel but in its uniqueness it also had a quite charming air about it. Even so, I had to admit that there was no mistaking its capability in being able to navigate its way in all but the most inclement of conditions that it may ever encounter on the lake. At least I very much hoped that this was the case.

I corralled my fascinations for all that I found myself looking at while attempting to pay attention to what my companion wanted me to do; which I soon realised was to board the vessel. This prospect delighted me greatly and so I eagerly made my way to the walkway which led along to the small jetty. The imminent promise of setting out on the lake in such a charismatic steam-driven boat made my heart beat a little faster. In the back of my mind however, I found myself still wondering about the identity of the lady who I had seen on the pathway that led to the church in the woodlands. So many things seemed to be fighting for my attentions. However, the moment I heard the little steam engine burst into life then I found that I had been presented with something else which needed to be carefully observed, examined and admired.

What an absolute delight it proved to be. A pure fantasy of mechanical wizardry which whirred and purred as it powered the little propellers while we gradually pulled away from the jetty. For a moment or two I indulged myself in its magic as I slowly made my way into the cabin while following my companion. I was still studying the gleaming engine and its pristine looking polished wooden compartment when I stepped over the mahogany bounded threshold and into the upper deck viewing area. I looked around so as to take in every detail of its design and decoration while also delighting in what was obviously a masterpiece of craftsmanship that would have made any owner extremely proud. I was first impressed by the wonderfully cosy atmosphere that had been created by the way it had been skilfully crafted and furnished. Even being as big as it was, there seemed to be an air of subtle luxury about it which made me feel safe as well as being very welcomed. I loved all the superbly carved woodwork which seemed to be everywhere. Even the furniture appeared to be fashioned and upholstered to match.

The big windows made everything seem so light and airy while allowing an almost unhindered view out onto the lake. I moved farther into the cabin while making my way to a comfortable looking seat which I had unconsciously selected while looking forward to settling into it. There was such a feeling of contentment which the cabin evoked in me that I immediately felt at home as soon as I experienced the sumptuous support of my very plush and incredibly comfortable seat. I exhaled in sheer delight as my grateful body settled back into the marshmallow enfoldment of a wonderfully relaxing feeling. This was absolutely heaven.

After a few moments of savouring my sense of bliss, I noticed that we were already making our way out onto the lake. Quickly I looked around to take in the sights from a new perspective but then found myself glancing across to see if I could catch a glimpse of the pathway and the mysterious lady. For a second or two I became concerned through realising that I couldn't immediately see her. Just as I was about to ask my companion, I spotted some movement behind a small group of trees and then realised that it must be her. As soon as I focused on the lady then I felt sure that I could see more figures moving along the pathway with her. It proved to be quite difficult to tell, given the movement of the vessel and the slowly changing view through the tress, but I hoped that my assumptions were correct. I seemed contented in not having lost visual contact with her and so I turned my attention to look in the direction that we were headed.

It really was a breathtaking sight and one which filled me with an amazing degree of excitement as well. Being actually on them gave me the impression that the waters of the lake stretched out forever as the contours of the 'Loch' weaved and twisted their way towards an indeterminate horizon. I looked once more at the waves moving swiftly past the vessel and then noticed that the rippling golden wavelets in front of us would often break across the bow and sometimes send showers of blue and gold spray up over the cabin. It was quite incredible to watch this highly unusual but completely mesmerising performance. Combined with the constant display of the huge bird above us, it made the whole panorama one which defied even the most gifted of artists to have captured it faithfully on any canvas. It really was utterly remarkable, totally absorbing and quite the most thrilling journey that I had ever made.

"You've already made it." I heard my companion say which mystified me greatly as I tried to take in the implications of his statement. I just couldn't understand what he could mean by this but I didn't have long to indulge myself in any misconceptions or conundrums before he spoke again. *"Look there!"* he said as if I might learn something highly beneficial when I did as he asked. I turned to see what he wanted me to be aware of but instead of him gesturing out of the window, as I had anticipated, he was pointing directly at the floor.

For that moment I couldn't imagine what could possibly be so interesting about a floor given that there was so much magic to indulge my visual senses in everywhere I looked outside of the vessel. Not wanting to seem ungrateful I honoured his request and so I glanced down at my feet but in doing so, for the second time, my mouth opened just as wide as my eyes at what I was seeing beneath me. In an instant of complete mental confusion it appeared to me as though there was no floor at all to support me. I was horrified and my heart began to race at what I saw rather than what I had hoped to see.

My instinctive reaction was to climb onto my seat in search of safety because of what I suddenly found myself looking at which presented a direct challenge to how I perceived my world to be constructed. Nothing made any sense to me in that the view below me seemed to be much larger than the floor of the vessel. It almost appeared as though it would have to be wider than the lake in order for me to be able to see what was beneath me. But what seemed to be even more disorientating, to my progressively overworked mind, was that there appeared to be another world flowing slowly underneath my feet. This made me feel as though I was flying rather than sailing across the surface of a long lake. However much this realisation startled me, I just couldn't seem to take my eyes of what I was seeing while attempting to adjust to a quite incomprehensible situation. What's more, and even more puzzling, was that the world which I appeared to be slowly 'flying' over also seemed to me to be highly recognisable; although I had no idea why this should be. This new revelation once again made me inhale quite deeply so as to stop my head spinning completely off its perch.

For a fraction of a second I half expected someone to come into my bedroom so as to wake me up but I knew full well that I had never had a dream of this nature before. Dreams had a different feel to them where it was always possible to separate illusion from reality by the difference in textures. This, however, didn't fall into either of those categories in that it seemed to be totally beyond real. This went way above 3D real and almost into fourth dimensional reality; if I even knew what that would be like! This was some voyage.

"Yes it most certainly was." my enigmatic companion said with almost the hint of a smile on his compassionate face.

"What do you mean ... it 'was'?" I heard myself say without realising that I had actually spoken the words. No answer appeared to be forthcoming. Only the maintaining of an inscrutable smile so I pursued my plea for clarification.

"There you go again with that past tense thing like I've done this all before. What do you mean by that exactly?"

"You'll see." came the cryptically economic reply. He was never one to waste words.

A New Perspective on What had Already Come to Pass

To say that I was totally confused would have been a complete understatement as to the nature of my situation. I didn't know whether to look up, down or out as either direction stimulated an endless stream of questions in my mind; which appeared to have no logical answers. My companion stayed smiling while seeming to urge me towards taking notice of what was passing underneath the vessel. I guessed that this was as good a place to start in trying to make sense of what was happening to me given the apparent lack of any other helpful explanation. I looked down once more and then began to make out very familiar scenes from places that I appeared to know quite well. Not only that, but in viewing them I also experienced certain accompanying emotions which quite took me by surprise.

At this point in the proceedings I didn't think that anything was capable of producing more surprises for me but the day was yet young and I had given up on not wanting any more puzzles to solve. I refocused my attention on the view beneath my feet in an effort to get a foothold in some kind of familiarity that would bring with it a modicum of reassurance. I began to make out landmarks which were quite recognisable and in doing so I was reminded of times past when my life had been shaped by the many different environments in which I had lived. Some of them weren't especially inspiring but others certainly did have a marked affect on me.

Then one particular building came into view which I had no trouble identifying or relating to as I could see the road that it was situated alongside. It looked to be a highway that I knew the layout of very well indeed and one which I had travelled many times in the past. I realised that I was looking down on the restaurant where I had first met Janet and I could have sworn that a little way off in the distance I could even see my car in the parking lot. I studied the view much closer and then became more convinced than ever that it was indeed my old car. Strangely, however, it actually appeared to be quite new in how I could see it at this time. 'Weird or what?' was the phrase which popped into my mind.

"Depends how you look at it." came the reply from a very familiar voice. I felt like I was getting in over my head and I wasn't even in the water yet.

"So don't struggle. Just float." was the only wisdom that came to alleviate my obvious dilemma. This turned out to be the point at which my mind just shut off and went on vacation for a while. I was tempted to follow its example.

"Let's go out on deck for a moment and just enjoy the scenery. There's plenty enough time to do what you need to."

I looked up into the immensely kind eyes of my companion while wondering what he meant by me needing to do something. I wasn't aware of anything that was necessary for me to do, with the possible exception of finding out who the lady on the pathway could be and what was happening at the church.

"There are other more important things which will become clearer as we make our progress across the lake."

I felt myself to be on the verge of asking another question when, for the first time, I began to realise that I hadn't actually said anything to my companion and yet he was able to answer my unspoken thoughts. I drew a breath in preparation for expressing my curiosity but instead I just let it out in an attitude of resignation at what was simply beyond my ability to understand.

"Nothing is beyond your comprehension my good friend. Just allow things to come to you as they will while accepting any and all explanations without judgement. Place no conditions on your desire to fit anything into the narrow confines of preconceived ideas. The lake is encouraging you to become aware of the fact that there is a certain flow to everything. Within that energetic condition then all things are made clear while life unfolds in the most natural way. Simply allow and accept while acknowledging that there is always another way to view things.

Each and every thing which you see all around you challenges a letting go of whatever it is that you feel 'must be' in order to satisfy the conditioning of your mind. This is the time to move beyond the confines of its limited ability. What you are experiencing is not of the mind but of the heart. Listen, observe, contemplate, appreciate and accept. Then integrate it into your awareness if you so desire. Nothing else is required or expected of you."

Without my realising it, my mind rushed into analyse every word that I had just heard but in the instant that it did then I began to see a little of what it was that I had been told. I stopped myself immediately while feeling that I didn't want to 'think' about anything and could almost feel the instant protestations from a part of me which demanded that it needed to 'know'. I wasn't impressed and began moving towards the area of the deck where my companion had suggested that we retreat to. He followed me out onto the open aft area of the deck space where immediately I found myself being surrounded by the sensation of a smell that I apparently hadn't noticed before that moment.

The air seemed so fresh and what's more there appeared to be a certain quality to it which gave me the impression of newly mown grass. It was very subtle but undoubtedly present, the effect of which was to make me feel very relaxed like I had just walked into the garden of my home while preparing to unwind after a long day at the office. I could almost get a sense that someone may even light up the barbeque while some highly pleasant refreshments might appear in one form or another. My whole body seemed to respond to this notion in preparation for the quiet time to come. Suddenly I began to feel much more comfortable with my surroundings where everything just felt better as I let myself ... *"Go with the flow?"* my companion completed my emotional statement to the world at large and I agreed with it wholeheartedly. It was my turn to smile.

Somehow, I had no problems at all in recognising the timeless wisdom of his statement and what he had been trying to get me to see. So I allowed myself to just accept my environment while being a grateful part of it. After all, what was there to be concerned about? Being surrounded by such beauty and mystery proved to be captivating and fascinating in equal measure, whereas being overwhelmed and obsessively curious didn't change a thing. All it did was to distract me from truly appreciating the amazing beauty of what I had suddenly become so much a part of. Going with the flow sounded like a good plan to me and so that's what I promised myself that I would do.

No sooner had this resolve precipitated in my awareness than there was the most amazing call from the sky. I looked up immediately to see the huge bird performing some breathtakingly graceful aerobatic manoeuvres while painting even more spectacular designs on the backdrop to the heavens. It seemed as though it was calling out to me in heartfelt support of what I had chosen to do; but it could just as easily have been coincidental in consideration of everything else that appeared to be going on around me. Somehow I felt myself being encouraged to think that it had actually been a form of communication that I was meant to hear. Just to underline my reasoning, there was another similar sound which came drifting down to me on the most gentle of breezes which brushed lightly across my face.

That action in itself seemed to stir long forgotten memories and once again I found myself scanning the shoreline while looking for the woman on the white pathway. It didn't take me long to spot her and to realise that she appeared to be making good progress along the route towards the church. I started to work out how far it would be before she actually got to the entrance to the grounds when I noticed the long zigzagging part of the pathway. This seemed to wind its lazy way up to the plateau where the church and its grounds were situated. It did, however, seem like a bit of a steep climb and so I began wondering whether it may be too much for her. However, there was a way to go yet before she reached that point so I just let my concerns rest for the moment.

All was quiet where everything seemed so peaceful. It took me a little while for my mind to register the fact that the steam engine had stopped and that we were now motionless in the water. Our progress, to wherever we were heading, had momentarily halted while we bobbed around on the wavelets as they played all across the surface of the lake. Turning from the view of the path I began studying the range of mountains on the left of the lake where my attention was being drawn to the mist-covered gap in them. The scenery was so thoroughly absorbing that I could have studied it all day while feeling blissfully relaxed in the process. Even so, I couldn't help but wonder what it could be that gave rise to the large area of mist as there didn't seem to be an explanation as to why it should be present.

On such a cloudless sunny day then mist rising up over a mountain didn't make any sense at all, but as soon as this element of doubt crept into my mind I was prompted to recall the words of my wise companion. So I just accepted it without attempting to make it fit into any predefined ideas. After all, nothing else did so why should a very pretty wall of sparkling mist be anything worthy of special consideration. It was while in the middle of coming to this state of resignation that I became aware of a sound coming from the direction of the mist. This had the quality of a low rumbling noise and seemed to be quite different to anything that I'd heard before that point in time. It was especially evident now that the masking sounds from the engine had stopped and appeared to be quite powerful in a way that I couldn't associate with something so delicate as lighter-than-air mist.

I began studying the surface of the water in the region of where this phenomenon was occurring and it was then that I noticed the golden crested wavelets racing towards the opening in the mountains. It seemed odd at first but something in my mind was able to connect the dots although I couldn't quite see the picture as yet. "*Think 'cascade'.*" my companion said but instead of making my appreciation clearer, my mind just froze. I had no idea what he could be referring to as I looked at the rising spectacle of the sparkling mist.

"*Energy my dear friend. Think in terms of energy and separation.*"

I must have done a convincing impression of an owl at that moment as I stared at him blankly while not being able to grasp in the slightest what he was saying to me; or in getting my fuddled brain to comprehend what it needed to. Quickly and most mercifully he came to my rescue.

"*Think about it. What could cause something to rise by doing the opposite? What could go in one direction while a part of it went in another?*"

My eyes remained fixed in 'owl mode' while I frantically tried to figure out not only what I was seeing but what more he wanted me to become aware of with respect to this part of the landscape.

"*What does the sound tell you?*"

Without thinking about it I sat down on a very comfortable deck seat that seemed to caress every needy part of my body. I sank into its luxurious comfort as my attention became fully focused on the mist, the scenery in front of me and the sound coming from it. I knew that I should be able to see the answer but however hard I tried then it eluded me. It seemed impossible for me to consider anything going downwards so whatever he was getting at didn't figure in my mind at all.

"*Let go of what you need to see while allowing things to be as they are. Suspend judgement and then let your mind accept a different perspective which does not conform to any kind of conditioning. Give up and let go my dear friend.*"

I smiled in a somewhat enigmatic manner which reflected my apparent inability to do as he asked but there was a determination in me to at least try. I stared at the gap in the landscape while asking my mind to accept the possibility of something descending. A light went on in a dark place and I smiled again but this time it was as a result of feeling pleased with myself.

"*See! It was easy wasn't it? What prevented you from realising that there is a large waterfall just under the mist is the same conditioned 'need' which stops you from appreciating many other things that would have otherwise been as clear to you.*"

All at once I understood to the degree that even the noise that I could hear seemed obvious when I thought of it coming from a large body of water falling into a big chasm on the other side. Of course! That must be where the mist was coming from as well. It was then that I began to wonder what had stopped me from deducing something so obvious before that moment.

"Your mind wouldn't allow you to accept that there could be a cataract in the middle of a mountain range; but why not? Where's the problem? The difficulty has only ever been in what you will accept as being that which fits into your preconceived notions of how things 'ought' to be. Is this not so?"

I had to agree with him but it proved to be a little tricky in taking on board a somewhat simple statement which obviously had quite far reaching implications. In agreeing to his wisdom then I automatically had to accept that there were almost certainly many other things that I hadn't been fully aware of in my life up to that point either. Scary concept!

My attention was still fixed on the scene of the rising mist, but being very conscious of what had just been said to me, I got the idea that there was probably still a lot more to this aspect of my surroundings than I had been able to positively identify up to now.

"And what could that possibly be my good friend? What more could there be that you need to bring to you awareness in all that you are seeing? To achieve a deeper understanding then allow yourself to feel the true nature of what it is that fills your visual and aural senses. Go beyond these limitations while becoming an integral part of Mother Nature's mysterious ways. Allow her to speak to you in a language as yet unknown to your mind. Let your heart be your guide as you become as 'One' with your world."

For an instant I experienced a tinge of frustration at feeling an inability to do what was being asked of me but then I found myself wishing very much that it could be possible. I had a feeling that many more things would become clear to me and, even though I had no idea of where this notion came from, I did actually get a sense that it could very possibly be somewhere that I had been before. A place, a point of knowing, a state of awareness that was not unfamiliar to me but how I knew this could prove to be the greatest mystery of all.

Whatever else, my mind really did register that what I had been asked to do was very important for me to concentrate on. So I set about focusing on nothing but the beautiful scenery while just enjoying its thoroughly captivating spectacle. I felt the urge to become lost in its serenely magnetic presence but more than that I dearly wanted to share in whatever secrets it had to offer me. I relaxed back against the solidly reassuring bench seat which formed part of the tree that I had been sitting under while I breathed in the emotive smell of new mown grass. The view ahead of me had gained my undivided attention which subsequently filled me with anticipation as well as a certain degree of excitement. I just didn't know what I would find or even what would happen to me. It had completely escaped my notice that something already had.

- Chapter 15 -

The Twin that I Am - A Deeper Understanding of Me

Although I couldn't actually see the waterfall I could see the dense cloud of fine mist rising up above where I presumed that the water cascaded over the edge of a steep rock face and then down into the foaming lagoon below. In my mind's eye there was a picture of what it must look like but not seeing it for real was starting to become a little frustrating. I so much wanted to catch a glimpse of the other side so as to watch the golden tipped waters tumbling endlessly down into whatever awaited them. It was easy for me to visualise what a stunning image this would make after capturing it on a large canvas and then having it framed so that I could hang in my study. I watched closely as the wavelets rushed in towards the gap in the mountains only to disappear quickly under the curtain of mist. The noise from behind the sparkling barrier seemed somehow louder now, although I didn't give it much consideration at first as there were other things already competing for my attention. Gradually, though, it became considerably more noticeable.

Just as I was about to give it some serious thought, by posing the question as to why I could hear it so much more clearly, I noticed what I took to be some kind of figure standing at the very edge of the mist. I couldn't be absolutely sure about what I could see as the image was a little indistinct through being affected by the fine spray which seemed to cover so much that was near to the waterfall. The more I studied the vision in front of me then the more it appeared as though the figure was moving and for a moment it looked as though he or she may actually be walking along a pathway. I hadn't noticed any such footpath structure on that side of the lake but there certainly was something about what I could see that looked sort of familiar. It too had a kind of shimmering quality to it which I first took to be the result of its being in such close proximity to the mist. For some reason I began to discount the effect of the water spray while trying not to analyse things so much.

The figure appeared to be moving closer to the waterfall while I focused the entirety of my attention on what was happening. It took me a little while to come to terms with the full implications of what I could make out. But, when I eventually did realise what they were then I felt my heart picking up speed in anticipation of someone possibly falling into the watery abyss. Suddenly I didn't know what to do although not doing anything wasn't an option either. I immediately looked around for my companion in order to ask his advice but then realised that he was nowhere to be seen and neither was the boat that I had been on just a short while ago. This time my heartbeat seemed to accelerate to triple figures. I tried not to panic. Too late!

I jumped up out of my seat like a startled rabbit. I felt like I wanted to run away somewhere but in not knowing where I was then I could have no idea of a direction to even start looking in. I sat back down and pressed myself firmly up against the tree as this seemed to provide me with a much needed feeling of supporting comfort. I focused on my breathing and closed my eyes while half hoping that when I opened them again then I would be back on the boat. My heart thumped loudly but above its panic-laden beating I could hear the sounds of the waves close by and so I was hopeful. Then I realised that my seat was still unforgivingly solid and equally unmoving. I opened my eyes. No boat! Damn it!

As I began frantically studying my new surroundings, in the hope of achieving some sort of calming reassurance, my mind took a little while to accept that I was actually sitting amongst the avenue of trees which I'd seen apparently floating some way off in the middle part of the lake. At first I was totally perplexed by the sudden dramatic change in my location, but as I allowed myself to take a more level-headed view of everything, then my feelings slowly began to alter as well. What became quickly evident when they did was that this place seemed to present me with and odd sense of a certain familiarity; even though it had once appeared to have been in such a bizarre situation. One of the first things I noticed, as my curiosity gradually overcame my panic, was the quality of the balmy air. This was accompanied by a characteristic smell which was so recognisable and one that surely did stir up quite a lot of poignant memories in me. Not all of these, I regret to say, were pleasant ones.

The really strange thing was that along with these recollections I found myself remembering things which felt like they were from some other time. What I saw in the brief flashes, which came tumbling into my head, gave me the impression of a very different period than the life I had lived with Janet. In one of these quite striking visions I could see some sort of big farm or plantation in great detail, almost like I could walk out of my back door and then know every inch of the land that surrounded it. This made a really nice impression on me but the down side was that I had no trouble at all in feeling the backbreaking effects of working this land. The struggle to cope with all that needed to be done made me feel exhausted from just thinking about it but then, as if to remind me of the benefits, I was also able to smell the sun ripened fruits on the heavily laden branches of the trees. There was such a mixture of emotions which accompanied all of this, but in being so closely in touch with them I suddenly found myself experiencing a great sense of loss. It was a horrible feeling which came rushing at me while giving me the impression that someone had placed a huge pile of weights on my shoulders. The effect was unbearable where they seemed in danger of forcing me permanently beneath the very ground under my feet.

Something inside me would not allow this to happen as I reacted to a force which felt as though it wanted to bring my journey to an abrupt and untimely end. I could feel the anger starting to rise in me at the thought of anything getting in the way of what I needed to do. At the same instant I also realised that I had been unconsciously shaking my head a little as the words bursting inside it said in silent protest No! No! No! So I resisted in my determination to do something uplifting, something to regain my sense of freedom and my sovereign right to life; but what? In the midst of experiencing this almost burning resolve I began to sense the stillness all around me. There was something about it which my mind couldn't grasp in any way at all but to a very sensitive part of me it actually felt like the source of great strength. Briefly I stayed wrapped up in its fascination while enjoying the balmy air which flowed gently past me. Then, through becoming conscious of flows and my being in them, something else happened.

Suddenly my awareness seemed to expand so as to embrace the presence of virtually every tree all around me; especially the one that I had settled myself so closely against. I was able to feel their collective spirit of enjoying just being as they were as well as relishing the freedom to express themselves in the midst of such beautiful surroundings. The big oak seemed so self assured as though nothing in the world could ever affect it or even cause it to be diminished in any way whatsoever. The ages old tree stood proudly displaying its stately permanence while delighting in giving pleasure to anyone or anything which it was able to influence. I pressed myself firmly up against its wonderfully solid form in the hope of gaining inspiration from its strength. It seemed such a simple thing to do but it really did make me feel very much better. I sat and looked up into the enormous canopy above me and wondered if I would ever be able to know more about Mother Nature's incredibly creative ways. I sincerely hoped so.

In my desire to be so close to this magnificent tree, I found that I could almost 'be' each branch of it as they stretched themselves out so as to receive the life-giving warmth and vitality from the sun. As they did this then something quite wonderfully exhilarating flowed through my entire body as well. It rushed in with a feeling of the most irresistible joyfulness whereby the heaviness, that had so unexpectedly come to oppress me, simply vanished just as quickly as it had appeared. I was so relieved and highly intrigued by such an amazing sensation, which oddly enough made me feel as though I wanted to express my profound gratitude to not only the oak but all the other trees as well. But then I began to wonder how you actually said thank you to a tree. Whatever else, I certainly was very relieved not to be feeling so dreadfully dispirited but just exactly where this unpleasant sensation had come from in the first place I had absolutely no idea; or did I? How odd to even consider this possibility as there were no images which came with the awful sensation that I'd experienced while in its grip.

I didn't know what to make of it all so I decided to sit for a while and then calmly think about things while seeing what might happen next. I really had no idea of what else to do. Even so, I couldn't ignore what this place evoked in me and neither could I discount the fact that wherever I was then it actually didn't seem to be at all foreign to my mind or even to my senses; as my recollections were clearly telling me. How incredibly strange, not to mention a little scary, and yet how wonderfully reassuring all at the same time. I gave some thought to snuggling up at the foot of the big oak tree while enjoying its enduring protection and then going to sleep for a while. Part of me figured that it might help but another part of me kept pointing out that there was still far too much that I didn't understand and which seemed to be in need of my attention. So I began surveying the whole area much more carefully.

I allowed myself a few moments of enjoying the stillness once again while almost asking the gently flowing air to sweep away the remnants of any unwanted emotional negativity. Briefly closing my eyes I got the sense of being once again connected to everything around me and in so doing the last of the emotional ripples on my personal lake of much needed tranquillity slowly faded away. I opened my eyes, smiled and then continued with my observations. Judging by what I could see around me I was inclined to regard the quite attractive rows of trees as being part of a large orchard, but why I should have thought in this way was highly puzzling. Even so, imagining them to be as such brought with it a sensing of being somehow reacquainted with an old and faithful friend. This thought cheered me up no end and certainly went a long way towards helping me feel much better about where I had been mysteriously transported to.

My heart rate began to settle back to somewhere near normal as I gradually relaxed through becoming more and more acclimatised to this extraordinarily stimulating environment; and especially the spot where I found myself sitting. Although, it was still fairly disturbing to me that I appeared to be completely alone with the exception, that is, of the big bird who was soaring happily away in the sky above me. I had absolutely no idea what could have happened to my companion or the boat which we were travelling so comfortably in until just a while ago. Somehow I got a sense that things would come clearer to me as I recalled the wisdom which I had heard so recently. This had been offered by my personal font of all Universal knowledge who advised me to just go with the flow. I couldn't help thinking however that my companion had omitted to mention that the 'flow' could actually transport you great distances in the blink of an eye. No doubt he had considered it prudent to leave that part out at the time. From where I found myself now sitting I could certainly see the wisdom in doing so because if he had told me then I may not have been so keen to take him up on his advice.

Looking once more at the wall of mist rising from the waterfall I could begin to really appreciate how much closer I was to it and how thoroughly impressive the scene appeared to be from my place under the shade of the beautiful oak tree. I was just about to return my attention to the figure that I'd spotted at the edge of the mist when, at the very instant before I glanced in that particular direction, a huge flash of what looked like lightning appeared. It was so intense, while seeming to shoot directly up out of the waterfall, that it lit up the entirety of the mist. In doing so it created the most spectacular effect through making it look amazingly like a sheet of pure sliver; like one huge shiny surface. It had the most startling impact on me and certainly got my attention after causing me to nearly jump out of my seat. The odd thing was that I realised, after checking to make sure that my heart hadn't leapt completely out of my body, that there had been virtually no noise whatsoever accompanying it; apart from a kind of slight crackling sound which reminded me of the sort of thing static electricity produces whenever it appears.

Even more remarkable though was the fact that, for a fraction of a second, the mist took on a mirror-like quality which allowed me to see some wonderful images in it; albeit that there was precious little time for my mind to process what they actually were. This probably had something to do with the fact that it was pretty much taken up trying to calculate whether those particular images would be the last thing it would ever see! I then noticed that all the little hairs on the back of my arms seemed to be stood up and that I also appeared to be holding myself in a state of mild anxiety. I remembered to breathe at last while recalling that lightning doesn't strike twice in the same place; which somehow I was now interpreting as meaning that it never occurred only once either. I kind of readied myself for the next appearance. I wouldn't have long to wait.

Somewhere in the back of my mind, from behind a slightly open door, there was a rather timid little voice telling me that sitting under a large oak tree, when there was lightning close by, might not be the best plan in the world. I thought about it briefly and then remembered that heavy rain very often accompanied lightning. With no other obvious place to take cover under, the lovely broad protecting canopy of a big old oak tree appeared to offer the perfect solution for sheltering beneath. I decided to stay put and heard the door gently close while the lock clicked firmly into place. I shrugged while telling myself that I was just going with the flow. My companion would have been proud of me. I allowed myself a little smile at feeling a certain sense of satisfaction at having thought this.

I stayed expectantly looking on in absolute fascination, albeit tinged with a certain degree of nervousness, as the entire focus of my world at that moment was the scene of the mist-filled gap in the mountains. I had just started trying to figure out what I'd actually seen during the big flash when, at the very same instant of my thinking about it, the strange phenomenon happened again; almost as though it had read my thoughts. Thankfully, this time it was far less shocking to me, but to my highly intrigued amazement, the effect actually stayed quite a bit longer. I was completely transfixed by the sheer magic of it, having never seen anything remotely like it ever before. Now, right there in the very heart of one incredibly spectacular light show I could actually make out many powerful flashes of electric blue lightning. They seemed to shoot through every part of the mist before it suddenly and miraculously changed to become one huge sheet of silver again.

It was unbelievably impressive as well as quite humbling in feeling myself being so close to such an awesome power which was capable of producing that much of a stunning change in the mist cloud. I just couldn't take my eyes off it and once again saw the images reappear in the shimmering silver surface. In the instant of examining them, as my mind struggled to decipher what I was seeing, I could have sworn that I was able to make out a pathway or a road. It appeared to be running right across the top of the cataract but along with it I could see a more distinct image of the figure that I had observed earlier. This time I was able to determine that it was indeed a woman and, what's more, it looked remarkably like the figure that I'd seen on the white pathway which ran through the woods on the other side of the lake. This realisation totally baffled me but I seemed to be irresistibly drawn to finding out more. But then the lightning was gone as quickly as it had come and once again there was just the big cloud of mist.

Immediately I became lost in recalling the images that had so mysteriously appeared as the world around me dissolved into an unfocused daydream. The tranquillity of my surroundings seemed to be encouraging me to completely abandon myself to my vivid recollections and so I nearly jumped out of my skin as I felt, rather than saw, someone come to sit beside me. My whole body went rigid for a second or two as my mind could offer no explanations as to what demons may have been summoned up by the lightning. The muscles in my neck relaxed sufficiently to let my head twist so as to see who it could be while the rest of me was preparing to climb up the oak tree as high as I possibly could. At the instant I recognised the kindly face of my companion I managed to relax a little but not before another high energy display of silvery blue lightning had erupted and once again lit up the mist cloud opposite me. I suddenly began to feel as though I was at some kind of giant fairground where anything might happen next. A ride on the ghost train seemed quite tame by comparison. I remembered to breathe and kept telling my muscles to unwind while convincing them that we just needed to go with the flow. They weren't convinced!

My companion sat quietly watching for a few minutes as he seemed to be just as interested in what appeared to be happening across at the waterfall as I was. Again the display was equally as riveting as before but this time it lasted even longer. As a result, I was able to see more of what I had caught sight of before and once more it puzzled me. I wondered if he would be able to tell me more about why the big silvery object kept appearing and also about the lady that I had seen. But before I could ask him any questions he got up and then walked to the water's edge just as the lightning display disappeared. I decided that it might be a good idea to join him and so, while leaving the shade of the big oak tree, I stepped out into the bright sunlight. It certainly was a beautiful day but there was something rather aggressive about it which distracted my attention, almost like a winged insect which had suddenly come to harass me. I wanted to shoo it away but it eluded me.

The odd impression which accompanied this state of mild agitation was that of instinctively feeling that I should take care to shade my eyes a little as well as covering my head so as to keep the sun off. I couldn't really see the point of doing either but the sensation of the need to do it keep nagging at me as I tried to push it away. It buzzed on insistently in my ear while being accompanied by vague images which came floating into my mind, but they certainly didn't come with any good feelings attached to them. In fact, I would have to say that they were actually bordering on the quite morbid. I redoubled my efforts to sweep them out of my consciousness as they appeared to have no place in what I was currently experiencing and only seemed intent on going against the flow. This was not what I wanted at all and so I made a determined effort to ignore them as I got closer to the water. I stopped at the point where the land, which formed part of the avenue of trees, sloped gently down in its grass covered unwaveringness to enthusiastically greet the carefree golden blue waters of the lake. Just looking at such a simple scene of natural beauty helped banish all thoughts of a negative nature from my mind and for this I was very grateful indeed.

The first thing I noticed about the water was that it had the same quality to its surface as that which I had observed from the boat. I felt as though I wanted to bend down so as to scoop some of it up. But just as I was about to do so then I suddenly became aware that the noise from the waterfall seemed to be much louder than I remembered it being just a few seconds ago. I looked up and could see the water rushing away from where I was stood and, what's more, it appeared to be moving quite quickly. Imagine my surprise when I looked at where it was heading only to see that I now found myself almost at the edge of where I assumed the cataract to be with the wall of sparkling mist right in front of me.

It felt so close while the speeding torrents of wavelets flashed by me in their haste to leap over the edge of the rock and on into the lagoon below. This, I quickly assessed, was one particular 'flow' that I had no intention whatsoever of going with under any circumstances however profound the wisdom may have been to the contrary. My reactions to the circumstances which I found myself in were telling me that I wanted to rush back to the orchard so as to chain myself to the huge oak tree which had so recently offered me its loving protection. Trees seemed like a good place to hang out right at that moment.

"Be patient and return to your observations my inquisitive friend." said my companion in a voice which betrayed not a hint of concern for our proximity to the waterfall.

"Look closely at the images which you are presented with when the cloud illuminates and then changes form."

On hearing this I instantly found myself holding my breath in anticipation of being incinerated by the next burst of high energy static, which I felt sure was about to arrive at any moment. I suddenly got a sense of having a ringside seat while looking into the heart of some cosmic electric furnace which I hoped very much didn't regard me as being 'fuel'. I found myself holding my breath while my companion looked at me and smiled at my apparent child-like reactions. I didn't care, I wanted to be prepared!

However, when the amazing lightshow did eventually appear, I was struck not by high voltage electricity, as I had feared, but by absolute awe for such an incredibly breathtaking and indescribably beautiful spectacle. While being so completely absorbed by its magic I couldn't help but wonder at whatever had given rise to such a fantastic manifestation of creative energy. Anyone who ever doubted the presence of an almighty being in our Universe should have at least one experience such as this; there would be no denying it afterwards and that's for sure. Take it from me!

As had previously happened, the powerful lightning flashed vigorously within the entirety of the mist cloud which then changed to become a huge and very solid looking sheet of pure reflective silver. To witness this happening at such close quarters was like looking directly into the process of how the galaxies were brought into being at the very beginning of time. I felt like I was on top of mount Olympus while gazing down on the handiwork of creative forces which I had no way to comprehend but which I somehow felt myself to be a very small, but nevertheless significant, part of. It was such an odd sensation but in the midst of it all then I suddenly became aware that 'scale' didn't seem to matter. I haven't a clue as to how I knew this but it certainly was an interesting notion that needed no confirmation from anyone.

Quickly my attention returned to what was happening in front of me. As soon as it did then immediately I realised that there was no sound at all, except for the faintest of electrostatic discharges just like I'd heard before. The mist had lit up in the most energetic way but I could truly appreciate that it wasn't in the high energy bursting fashion of classic lightning. This seemed to be much more subtle and absolutely fascinating; not to mention being totally awesome. What I found to be even more enthralling was that the silver sheet stayed much longer in its form of becoming one giant mirror-like surface. Through doing so it allowed me to study more carefully what I was being shown in the process. Eventually, after still trying to come to terms with such a magnificent sight, my mind began to settle firmly on taking in what it was seeing rather than trying to work out how it had got there in the first place. As such, I was able to make more sense of the images in the amazingly lifelike reflection. This resulted in a moment of revealing recognition when I became aware of what I had been studying so intently just a short while ago on the boat.

There, in the huge mirror, was a reflection of the figure that I had seen on the opposite side of the lake and along with it I could clearly make out the image of the white pathway through the trees. I realised that I was actually seeing what was behind me but it took the forming of a giant mirror for me to be able to fully understand it. I just stared at the whole view while trying to take it all in but then everything vanished. As a result I experienced an equally lightning-like flash of frustrated irritation as I wanted to ask why it had chosen that particular moment to disappear. As though to answer my unspoken question the mist cloud dutifully lit up once more in a way that I could almost have concluded was being performed just for me. The words I heard next were totally unexpected.

"Well, yes, in a way it is."

I turned to look at my companion while raising one eyebrow in the manner of disbelief as I couldn't quite stretch my ego that far so as to imagine that this incredible spectacle had been created just for me. The lightning vanished. My companion elaborated.

"This whole magnificent setting is actually just for you. The waterfall, the mist, the mirror and even the mountains, the lake and the forests are all here so that you can have the prefect opportunity to observe, and then carefully contemplate, something which is very important for you to become aware of."

My face must have betrayed my instant reaction of abject disbelief but my wise friend wasn't sporting his characteristic wry smile this time, so I had no option but to take him at his word; however incredible it may have sounded. I shook my head in a futile attempt to make it not be true while looking around at everything and then trying to make a connection to what I could see, and my importance in it. All I could feel was a certain level of intimidation by such a majestic landscape, leave alone the sheer power of an experience which appeared as though it could vaporise me in a heartbeat if it so wished. How could it be possible for all this to have been created just for me? But much more importantly, by whom? I couldn't recall anyone of my acquaintance who was that well connected! I smiled at this somewhat irreverent thought.

After a moment or two of trying to take in the truly mind-stretching implications of what my companion had said, I turned my attention back to the scene in front of me. As I did so then I realised that the mist had begun to clear slightly, which was when I thought that I could glimpse some of the water falling over the edge of the rock. My immediate reaction was to step back but my companion remained motionless, so I decided to stay put as well. I'm not sure whether my decision to follow his example had been born purely out of trust for my dear friend, my sheer fascination with what I was seeing or just a case of over-inflated bravado. No matter, I had made my choice to stand my ground while hoping that whatever would come as a result may help me better understand my situation.

Before I had time to even contemplate this matter any further my ears perked up as they heard a question coming from my wise guide.

"What is it that you see in front of you, what's going on in this miracle that Mother Nature has created just for your benefit?"

Again I felt a little humbled by the implications of what he'd said but I managed to put my feelings aside so that I could concentrate on what he was asking of me. I studied the scene in greater detail but all I could really see was a vision in my mind's eye of the golden blue waters charging headlong over the edge of a rocky precipice while recklessly racing into the untold depths below.

"Good, what else?"

An interesting question indeed to which I assumed there must be a perfectly logical answer; but what else was there? I could obviously see the outline of what I considered to be a waterfall, with vast quantities of water falling over the edge of it and then disappearing into thin air, but my mind couldn't seem to stretch to imagining anything else.

"What about the mist?"

His question kind of ambushed me before I'd had an opportunity to consider anything further about the scene. However, it proved to be very timely as it gave me a chance to examine things ever more closely. I considered the possibility that the mist was being produced as a result of the water rushing energetically over the edge of the rock, but it did seem to be rising up very high and then sweeping over the tops of the mountains in the process. It was absolutely breathtaking to watch but I didn't see the significance in what it had to do with the waterfall; if anything.

To me it appeared to be simply mist which looked very nice as well as occasionally lighting up like a big mirror when the lightning shot through it. This in itself was definitely not something that I would have expected mist to do but nevertheless, in my mind mist could only ever be a collection of fine water droplets which were suspended in mid air. Much more than this my analytical processes wouldn't stretch to. For some reason this apparent limitation suddenly made me feel quite inadequate in trying to understand something that I just couldn't grasp in any other terms.

"Let it not be a problem for you my dear friend; just listen for a while and I'll explain."

His words were most welcomed as I had reached the point where I was eager to know more about why I had been witnessing this amazing spectacle and hopefully I would also get to know more about just exactly why I was where I found myself to be. I listened expectantly.

"In all that I am about to tell you, please bear in mind that we are dealing with water and energy. Water is energy in itself, albeit that it's an expression of energy in form. Do you understand this?"

I thought about it for a moment and then nodded slightly to indicate that I was fairly sure that I knew what he meant. I guessed that even if I didn't then I'd pick it up along the way as he expanded on whatever it was that he intended to tell me.

"Good. Now then, consider this carefully please. The water, before it reaches the cataract, is whole in that it's one with itself, agreed?"

I nodded again but in truth I was trying to work out what he meant by it being 'one with itself'.

"It's an entity, a unified energy almost with a life of its own. It flows and it takes on new shapes but it's always water isn't it?"

I had to agree with him on that point. Water is certainly always water.

"What about the mist, is that water?"

I looked at the big cloud and had to think for a moment. The answer came quickly although it posed its own question when it did.

"Good, you're right, of course it is but it's just taken on a new form. This water is able to rise up on the air currents after being separated by the energy imparted during the fall. It's the same as the water which is falling but it's parted in the process and so it has a different experience from that which it's temporarily left behind. Do you see that?"

I got the bit about the parting but I found myself struggling with the 'temporary' aspect of his explanation. Before I could ask, he continued,

"It's temporary because eventually the mist will return to the earth and recombine with the source of its origin. It will be whole once again and that 'wholeness' will be having the same experience."

I could see what he was saying but I really couldn't understand what it had to do with me or anything else for that matter. I certainly found it interesting but I was rather hoping to actually learn something from it.

"Be patient just a little longer and you will."

I decided that this would be a good idea and so I relaxed somewhat in anticipation of what was to come.

"Imagine ..." he said while looking directly at me as though he required my fullest attention, *"... that this water represents your soul."*

He paused momentarily in seeing my eyes open quite noticeably as my mind tried to make the desired connection.

"Just let yourself accept this possibility and then consider what comes next. Would that be okay with you to do that?" He smiled at recognising my evident dilemma.

"Good, just stay with me a little longer. Your soul, the water, is experiencing the lake but, while remaining in that state then this is all that it's able to do. It can explore everything that there is to know and appreciate about the lake but that's it. You and I know that there is more to be experienced but the water has no way to do so unless it either changes its form or it adopts a more refined nature of itself which would allow it to escape the lake."

I looked at the rising mist while thinking about his explanation and then it dawned on me that what I could see in front of me was actually another form of water which had partially escaped.

"To a degree that's correct but what's happening in reality is that certain droplets have been released into the air while the others have continued on into the lagoon. Those that have been freed will be able to experience the mountain, the woods and the atmosphere while the others will have a different experience. However, eventually they will recombine and become one again because there is a natural attraction between them."

I stared at him a little blankly as if to ask 'so what'?

"This is very similar to what happens with twin souls."

This was the point at which my mind went completely blank as it tried to grasp the enormity of what he was saying. I immediately went into 'owl mode' again and stared at him in wordless confusion. Suddenly I felt that even the mountains knew more about life than I did and, if this was the case, then how could I even consider myself as being associated with them in the way which had been suggested to me. I felt quite insignificant and quite alone. It was not a nice feeling at all.

Looking Deeply into the Mirror of Oneness

It seemed as though an eternity had passed as I stood looking at the view in front of me while going over a multitude of things in my mind. I found myself attempting to make all manner of connections with what I thought that I had understood about life, as well as the concept of a soul such as I assumed myself to be. I had often heard the phrase 'soul mates' used, but I had never considered the fact that souls existed as one half of a twin. Even though, on the face of it, the whole subject seemed to be so strange to me, there was a certain part of me that urged an acceptance of the principle; in that I seemed to have a deeper awareness which wasn't yet evident at a conscious level. I let the whole subject permeate the stratified realms of my somewhat limited deductive processes just like I'd seen the lightning doing within the mist.

When I thought about it more carefully then it certainly did seem to explain a lot of things that had very often puzzled me about my life. What had previously given me cause for concern, before being fully aware of this new dimension to myself, now seemed to be quite acceptable; given the notion that it could actually have been possible that I had found my twin soul. This was such a different way to look at things and so much outside of my normal way of thinking, but I couldn't ignore the fact that I had never considered my life in light of this aspect being present in it.

It was very tempting to go over so much of my past with this new information but at that moment it seemed as though I could quickly get out of my depth in not having a much better understanding of the whole subject. My nervousness slowly gave way to a feeling of being intrigued and suddenly I felt the urge to know more. I could see what my guide was trying to get at in having me study the water and the mist, but as much as it helped me it also added to my appreciation that there was undoubtedly a whole lot more for me to become aware of. I decided that I needed to ask for a more complete explanation as there appeared to be a great many questions that this new revelation had caused to spring forth into my highly curious mind.

I was about to turn to my companion to ask the first of them when I felt, rather than saw, something change in the atmosphere around me. For some unconscious reason I was tempted to duck down but even before this notion could be translated into positive action, a quite large shadow cast its slightly oppressive presence over both of our heads. Instinctively I looked up just in time to see the highly detailed underside of a huge bird swooping low above us as it headed straight for the large cloud of mist. I shot an anxious glance of bewilderment at my apparently untroubled companion who almost seemed pleased by this most sudden turn of events. I was very confused, but before I had the chance to fully take in what was happening, the powerful lightning exploded once more and again the mist instantly became one gigantic mirror. Immediately it did then I could see an image of another equally large and beautifully coloured bird flying swiftly towards the other, while looking to be on a collision course.

It was all happening so fast that my mind had no way to interpret this situation as my attention became totally fixed on what I was seeing. As the two magnificent birds' trailed multi-coloured plumes behind them, I had no difficulty in understanding that if they continued on in this way then they were set firmly on a mutual path to inevitable oblivion. I found myself wanting to shout out some sort of warning; or at least do something which would help to avert the unavoidable outcome while feeling almost heartbroken at the prospect of these two beautiful creatures coming to such a fatally dramatic end. Then, as this heartfelt emotion welled up within me, just as energetically as the lighting had in the mist, something even more unexpected happened.

Everything seemed to become frozen in time. Not just the birds themselves but the entirety of my surroundings, including my companion. It was as though I had become able to consciously exist in a snapshot of my immediate circumstances. At first I tried to work out if I could do anything to change the path of the birds, but then I began to study the entirety of what I could see in front of me as my awareness expanded to encompass more than the impending airborne disaster. Suddenly I found the scene in the huge mirror to be quite breathtaking in so many respects as it appeared as though there was another lake and another range of mountains behind it; but somehow my mind couldn't separate the image from reality. The one thing which seemed to give me the impression that I had been looking at a different landscape was the fact that the bird coming out of the mirror appeared to be slightly different than the one heading towards it. In being able to study their markings while in suspended flight, I could see the subtle differences in each of them. However, this really only contributed to my confusion as mirrors didn't change the nature of whatever they reflected. Well, not in my world they didn't.

In the complete silence of suspended reality I felt like I was in a museum where a huge display of inanimate objects had been set out for viewing in the grave-yard quiet of a public building. I was tempted to look for a curator to give me some input but I knew that the only one who could be of any help was standing by the side of me, inert and inaccessible.

"No I'm not."

My heart nearly stopped as I heard his voice break into the eerie silence which surrounded me. At that very same moment I felt that I just couldn't stand one more shock to my system. Placing my hand involuntarily on my chest, so as to keep my heart in place, I didn't even have a chance to recover myself before I felt a strong gust of wind swirl all around me; just as I had experienced when the large bird had passed low over our heads. Snapshot mode was over as everything instantly reverted to real-time. Trying to adjust as quickly as was within my capability to do under the circumstances, I could feel the air movement rapidly gathering pace as a significant wind began to erupt while the birds swiftly headed towards one another.

The wind appeared to be increasing in strength almost in anticipation of the inevitable outcome which I was anticipating for the collision destined aviators. I felt myself tensing up as these two beautiful creatures were almost beak to beak where I didn't know whether I wanted to cover my ears or my eyes. Standing and watching helplessly was the only option. The wind was now very strong as things seemed to move quicker at the very last second where their images became virtually one. At this point I felt my ears almost shutting down so as to ward off the inevitable impact noise that the two giant figures would produce as they finally crashed into one another. My eyes were on the verge of closing, but then something totally unexpected happened.

The bird that had so recently passed over our heads appeared to fly gracefully into the mirrored surface of the mist while the other bird seamlessly merged into it. I was only able to glimpse this for the merest fraction of a second before the mirror instantly erupted into a ball of the most intense light. This time I did raise my hand to shield my eyes as the power of its illumination seemed to pass right through me. Virtually at the same time as my hands covered my face there were several streaks of the most blinding lightning which served to amplify the bright light which then spread out like a miniature sun. Even though my eyes were covered, I had absolutely no trouble at all in appreciating the sheer brilliance of this light. It was almost as though it had enlightened every ethereal dimension of my soul.

I stayed perfectly still while immersed in this quite stunning effect as, for that moment, it seemed as though nothing existed outside of my immediate self. Within this realisation I seemed to be able to make a connection to something of an almost divine nature. Unfortunately, before my mind could come racing in to analyse it, the sensation had quickly subsided; but it was one that I would definitely never forget. In greater part this was because of how I found myself being transported into a state of deeper understanding; but of exactly what, I just couldn't be sure. Whatever else, there was no doubt that I felt happier in having experienced this.

Uncovering my eyes I had to blink several times so as to adjust myself to the view in front of me. While doing so I quickly became aware that the birds were gone and so was the mirror while the mist had returned to being as it had always been. Well, almost. This time it appeared as though the strong wind that had sprung up from the bird's passing was starting to blow it towards the top of the mountain and away from the shore. At first there was very little movement but the wind was persistent and slowly but surely the once big cloud gradually started to thin out. In doing so I was able to see treetops starting to appear where I had originally believed there to have been a gap in the mountains. This puzzled me greatly. I continued to watch as the wind gathered strength all around me to the degree that I felt my clothes beginning to flap. Through becoming aware of this I was almost tempted to look for something to hang on to.

The mist continued to rise under the influence of the wind and, to my complete and utter amazement, as it did this then I could see that there was actually more of the mountain range behind it. This unexpected revelation took me a moment or two to get used to, but what was even more of a surprise was the fact that there was obviously no waterfall. In fact, everything appeared to be very much like the other side of the lake with the exception that there was now a swiftly developing large dark cloud over the part of the mountain where I had presumed the gap to have been. I had no way to explain this at all, but more than that, I found myself working hard at reconciling my new awareness on the subject of twin souls in the light of vanishing cataracts and reappearing mountains. This needed a lot more thinking about, but then I looked up to examine the rather odd cloud that was forming high above the mountains. It did this as the wind continued to sweep by me while it gathered up the last of the mist. This was then transported swiftly up as I watched in fascination until every single drop of sparkling water had become a part of it.

Quite quickly the base of the cloud spread out across a large area of the sky. Instead of being the usual grey, uninteresting, oppressive kind that I had been so used to seeing, this one was made up of darker shades of the colours which the two birds had been trailing before they had disappeared into the exploding mirror. This cloud looked to be a swirling mass of quite vibrant colours where the only thing that caused it to look dark was its sheer size and how it affected the light. Before I had time to think about what was happening, the wind around me seemed to reach almost gale force proportions and then, most unexpectedly, it began to rain. Really, really rain. When I say this then please allow the word monsoon to come to mind.

It absolutely poured down with such a force that the lake began to look like one expansive mass of gold and blue glittering jewels as the droplets completely transformed the entire surface. Instinctively I turned while heading for cover and so did my companion where, very shortly, we were both sheltering under the protective canopy of the big oak tree that I had previously been sat under. I watched the rain in humbled amazement as it cascaded down in sheets all over the mountains where every tree glistened and sparkled under its influence. It was as though some divine hand had sprinkled them all with a mass of tiny diamonds. Everything was getting completely soaked in the deluge but mercifully not a drop appeared to be getting through the dense foliage on the sturdy old oak tree; so we enjoyed a quite cosy ringside seat to Mother Nature's stunning performance.

No matter how many times I witnessed her magic at close quarters, I just couldn't seem to get over feeling like a kid who had just discovered a new world of captivating fantasy for the very first time; only this was real. Part of the way down the mountain I could see that the rains were causing small streams to form as the water gravitated back to the lake. These quickly became fast flowing where many began to merge so as to form little rivers which in turn met up to become larger rivers. Suddenly, everywhere I looked there were countless cascades of water pouring off the mountain slopes and rushing towards the lake. It seemed as though the trees would be swept away by their combined force but just as matters appeared to be getting to a crucial point, the winds started to abate as did the intensity of the rain. Even the surrounding light was brighter as the cloud above us began to dissipate where, slowly at first, the storm blew itself out.

In wanting to see more of what was happening, I stepped out from under the shelter of the oak tree so as to look up into the reappearing sky. The large cloud was almost gone where I could now make out its wonderful colours more clearly. While watching the swirling motion of its dissipating form I watched one part of it gather quickly into a vortex and then erupt. As it did this I stared in fascination as a huge bird suddenly burst out from within its midst and once again it began to grace the quickly clearing sky with its majestic presence. At the altitude it was above me then I couldn't be sure if it was the same bird as before, but something gave me the idea that it was; and yet it wasn't. Goodness knows what made me think this, or even how such a notion could have existed in me in the first place. It seemed bizarre, but it also seemed right.

Whatever the reason, I was so pleased to see it again while delighting in watching its renewed aerial performance. This time however, it appeared as though there were even more colours trailing behind it than ever before. This gave the new sky-lining patterns which it created an extra dimension that hadn't previously been present where there was a certain quality to them that complimented the whole landscape. It was so attractive that I became completely lost in the spectacle as well as the atmosphere all around me. The last of the cloud had virtually disappeared while the wind had reduced in its intensity to the point where there was almost no hint of it ever having appeared. The lake had returned to its customary way of being but the big wall of mist was no longer in evidence where, in its place, there was simply a continuation of the unbroken mountain chain. All felt peaceful to the degree that there appeared to be a certain 'rightness' about how everything presented itself at that moment.

"Very well my good friend. What do you make of this feeling and what you have just witnessed here?"

In my captivation with everything that had happened, I realised that I had quite forgotten about my companion. After hearing his question I now found myself trying to look for meanings of consequence in what I had just seen and felt. Nothing really came to mind although I did seem to have many images that were quite vivid and which did have a strange kind of attraction for me. I was about to speak, more to fill in the silence than in any constructive way, when my companion came to my rescue.

"Well, let's start with what you saw happening with our mystical aviating artist, our master of the skies. If you remember correctly there appeared at first to be one and then, when the mirror had formed, you were able to identify its counterpart. Or was it just an image in the mirror? No matter. For the moment let's consider the possibility that it had in fact been a different bird while you allow yourself to recall where it was in actuality.

Yes, it was in the mist. The mist which we previously determined had been created from the water but which was in actual fact still the same water albeit taking on a slightly altered form; a state of being which involved adopting different characteristics. This then allowed it the opportunity to have an experience in a different environment as a result. The bird in the mirror also did the same in that it was another coexisting aspect of the wonderful creature which flew overhead, but it existed in a slightly 'finer' state of being. While doing so it too experienced its surroundings in a particularly unique way. Are you with me so far or would you like a moment to think about this?"

I gave my companion something of a confused look while putting my hand up to my chin in the manner of being deep in thought. He stayed silent in response while I let his words sink in as I tried to stretch my mind towards accepting that the reflection of the bird in the mist could have actually been a different bird; just as the mist was different from the water that it had come from. It certainly proved to be hard for me to see this at first but I figured that if I accepted it in part then maybe I would get a more complete picture from whatever else he would explain.

"Very good my dear friend. That's a very commendable way to achieve an understanding when you allow yourself to open to the possibility that many things are very often not how you have been conditioned to believe they are. Now then; please think carefully about what happened when the two birds appeared to collide. Remember the light which resulted and the intensity of it? This was at the exact point when they apparently disappeared into each other; if you recall. A meeting, a bright light and then they appeared to be gone. Now then, with this in mind, allow yourself to think about the water at the waterfall and how we were able to determine that the 'one' had actually become two.

Something happened which enabled the water to explore a different form of itself. It was given the opportunity to change temporarily so that it could encounter another way of being. Now, think about the storm and the returning of the water to the lake. The mist was swept up over the mountain and into the cold air above which then resulted in it changing form once again. Energy was released, tiny droplets joined to become big drops which could no longer resist gravity as they became heavier. In doing so they fell back to the surface and then returned to the lake where they had originally come from. They were 'one' again but had, in reality, never been anything other than water. There was no more mist or cloud but nothing whatsoever had actually disappeared.

See if you can apply this same process to the two birds. Our lone bird, who hovers over us now, reappeared after experiencing the bright light but it isn't quite the same bird as it was. Or is it? Could there have been two birds or had there always been just one that was actually having two different experiences. Please think carefully about this prospect for a moment or two."

My mind began to race while it attempted to process all of the information contained within the many reappearing images as I tried to grasp what was being explained to me. There seemed to be so many things to consider all at once but the more I tried to make them fit into what I thought I believed then much of it didn't compute at all. I felt the need to just accept at face value what I had so clearly seen, while allowing myself to agree with the somewhat illusive conclusions which came from simply doing this. I found that if I suspended my judgements and preconceptions then I could actually stretch my understanding. In doing so I could allow for the fact that there were two aspects of one form, the bird or the water, which were having different 'adventures'; for want of a better way of putting it.

"Yes that's a perfectly good way to put it my wise friend. Well done. Now, let's you and I get to the part of this whole subject which really concerns you and what's been going on during your life's journey. This is the part where we're hoping to get an 'ah-ha' moment; you know, that time where a little light goes on in your head and suddenly a great many things make perfect sense."

I was pleased to hear these words but at the same time I found myself becoming somewhat nervous. I got the idea that there may be quite a lot that I may become more acutely aware of which I hadn't truly understood before this time. I just had no concept of what to expect.

"Such is life my good friend, such is life. If everyone really did understand it completely then what would be the fun in embarking on this amazing adventure in the first place? Making choices, making mistakes and living the consequence is how we learn; through truly appreciating why we made them is how we get to blossom and grow in the most beneficially spiritual way possible. How can we evolve if we don't have edifying and enlightening experiences; and how can we possibly encounter the incomparable richness of a full life if choices, helpful or otherwise, aren't included as a major part of our journey?

Life isn't about getting it right all the time, it's about getting it wrong as well and then dealing with the consequences. If there was no right then there could be no wrong. One cannot exist without the presence of the other as they are both part of the same thing. Life! It's about taking responsibility for your choices while allowing others to do the same but not judging yourself or anyone else in the process. Tricky or what?"

I felt like I had stopped breathing as I completely immersed myself in all that he had just said. Never had I heard anyone express an opinion of life's trials and joys in such a manner as this. It impressed me to the degree that I couldn't ignore its far reaching implications which then gave me a whole new way of viewing what happens to us and why. This needed much more thought on the whole subject but even before that intention had fully settled into my mind I noticed that something was happening to the water. I was just about to inspect it more closely when my companion continued with more of his explanation.

"Just take a moment to look around you my wonderful friend. Observe well what is being presented to you and then give yourself the space to consider precisely what you are already beginning to get an appreciation for when it comes to the subject of twin souls. Be you ever mindful of the fact that the soul is not confined to that of simply experiencing the human condition. Indeed, the magnificent oak which has afforded us the benefit of its generous shelter during

the storm is also the experience of a soul which chooses to know what it's like to be a tree. Don't think that the human condition is the only way that a soul can express itself in the entirety of the Universe. Far from it my dear friend, far from it!

Look if you will at the mountains on either side of the lake and then acknowledge, if you are able to, a certain symmetry of form. As you take in the sheer majesty of the scenery then you will appreciate for sure that these two expressions of the terrain, which gives rise to the presence of the lake, are but 'one' in the context of the earth. You see two mountain ranges but they are in truth simply a part of the one earth; albeit they are choosing to see life from different experiences or perspectives. The water in the lake is experiencing the mountains, but as we have seen, it can take on a slightly altered expression of itself in order to see things in another way. Never is it anything other than it always has been; just that it chooses to explore its environment in a different way. Now here is the really important part for you to commit firmly to memory.

In doing so there is ever the attraction to become one with itself once again; and so it is in the nature of all things. This mutual attraction, just as the mountains feel as they move imperceptibly slowly in their constant state of change, and as the water experiences in its sometimes brief existence in a separated form, gives rise to the dynamic of life. That pull which keeps us looking for something that we feel a need to find but can't quite remember what it is. That feeling of there being 'more' to a state or mode of being which can often seem inadequate, or somehow unfulfilled, and then seeking out what it might be in order that we can achieve a satisfaction which we are somehow aware exists. Without this magnetism then there would be little in the way of encouragement to do anything in life and so it would be ever the poorer an experience without it.

When the water and the birds were separated then each aspect of itself became charged with an attractive force which consistently called to the other. Each wants to return to its complete state but through experiencing the pull from its counterpart, its split apart, then they get to ride the wave of life in the most exhilarating way possible before coming back together again. The period before they do this may be measured in hours, as in the case of the mist, or lifetimes in the case of the birds and the trees not forgetting of course, ... and most interestingly of all, with humans.

We each are the other half of a twin. Souls choose to come into a human experience knowing that the twin attraction is what assists them in leading a life which is rich in emotional, physical, intellectual and spiritual content. This attraction is an energy just like you saw expressed when the two aspects of the bird were re-united and the attractive force balanced out in order that they could be one again. Think about the power of that energy in how it nearly blinded you and how it felt when you experienced it. Can you appreciate now how that energy exists to propel you through your life and how it can be used to provide the momentum which contributes to how your life unfolds? It truly is a *hugely potent force but one which is little understood and largely ignored in your waking state."*

My companion stopped and just smiled at me as though having offered me a great gift. I wanted to respond in acknowledgment but my head had already begun to swim while trying to take in everything that I had heard. Some of it just seemed to be a leap too far for me but there was no denying the fact that what I had been listening to actually did make a lot of sense; even if it was all so very different from anything that I had ever imagined before. I had never really given the idea of a soul much consideration as I just didn't see how it could fit in with the concepts of a practical life on earth. However, when I listened to a new way of seeing it then I found it hard to understand why I didn't appreciate how really important it was before.

"Let's see just how important it has been to you and how fortunate you have been in what your life has presented you with in the way of opportunities and experiences. Please come to the very edge of the lake with me and we'll see what we shall see."

For a moment I hesitated as I didn't feel that I had one more atom of space in my thoroughly overloaded brain to take in any more information; however helpful it might turn out to be. Fortunately my resistance quickly faded and so I did as I was asked while hoping that whatever awaited me would enable some kind of clearer vision that would set my mind at rest. Once again I looked at the water but this time I realised that it was not as it had been in the respect that there were no more wavelets, although there was still the wonderful golden sheen to the surface. Everything appeared to be as still and as calm as the small lake back in the meadow, even though this was such a large body of water where I would have expected some kind of movement. I stepped up to the edge while not knowing what would greet me but I had come to have absolute trust in my wise friend who quite evidently held the key to a lot of answers that I needed to be unlocked.

In stepping to the limit of the ground where it met the water I was surprised to see that the golden sheen appeared to be so faint that it looked almost transparent; as was the water which I could see right into. It took me a few seconds of staring into its depths to fully recognise just what had come into view and once again it looked as though I was peering into some kind of underwater world. Only this world wasn't underneath any water; it looked to be very real indeed where the surface of what had been water now appeared to be the sky.

Focusing on a completely different perspective, I found myself looking down on a very familiar part of my home town which was an area that always made me feel good. I began to see things which seemed to evoke quite strong memories in me and then something almost jumped up to grab me quite firmly by the heart. I felt a huge flush of an inexplicable energy rush up through me as an image came tumbling into my mind, and for an instant I felt as though I was about to cry. It proved to be the most gripping emotion I had ever experienced and one which I had no idea existed in me until that highly revealing point on my journey.

What I was seeing took me back to a very special time that I had encountered with Janet. Until that moment I hadn't been aware of just how meaningful it was but, for some reason possibly having to do with my new understanding of life, I was now fully conscious of what it had meant to me and how much it really had affected me. I recognised the scene of a place where we had been wonderfully intimate for the very first time and one which I could feel so clearly the energy of even after all these years. It was an intense and magical feeling that seemed to encompass so many emotions that I felt quite unable to express in any language, however eloquent it might be. Something certainly happened to me on that very memorable occasion but never before this moment in time did I have any inclination as to exactly why it should have been so.

Then, in the midst of my absorption, I saw superimposed on the vision of my time with Janet, the meeting of the two birds in the mirrored mist and the subsequent flash of light which followed the instant when they met. As soon as the bright light appeared in my mind, I found myself suddenly being able to experience a similar energy in how I had felt when she was with me. I could sense my arms around her while holding her tightly where something inside me had erupted so strongly while urging me never to let her go. Our intimacy had been so incredibly special but to have her in my arms was a feeling that went way beyond words. She made me feel ... I just didn't know how to express what was in my heart to say. It felt so much as though I was holding someone so familiar to me, so much a part of me, so much a ... "*Part of your soul?*" my wise friend finished my faltering explanation for me.

Yes! That was it! That's what it felt like but I just wasn't able to recognise it as being so at the time. My other half, my twin soul, my ... my ...

"*Completeness?*"

Something inside of me seemed to melt as I heard this word expressed by my companion. At this point my eyes did appear to be getting a little damp around the edges as I savoured every treasured moment of holding my other half so firmly in my arms. She was the essence of femininity in her counterpoint to my masculinity. I loved her softness, her feel and her smell which seemed to melt into my whole being where I never wanted her to be away from me ever again. The energy which I felt flowing through me at that moment was so intense that my eyes welled up with tears. I closed them in response while the visions of our togetherness were so strong in my mind, as were the feelings which were racing through me.

My arms felt as though they wanted to reach out so as to hold her once again and for a moment I could actually believe that she was held firm forever in my strong and needy embrace. All that I could sense appeared to be so real as well as feeling incredibly wonderful. It was all that I could do just to hang on to my inner strength as I let all these emotions flow through me in the same way that I had seen the rainwater coursing down the mountains so urgently in its eagerness to return to the lake. Similarly I wanted to return to my twin soul so that I could feel as I did. It was such a strong force in me which, at that moment, was so easy to understand just how much it had influenced my life. It proved to be quite overwhelming and so I decided that I would give in to the tears as there seemed to be a need in me to let them flow.

After what felt like an eternity, I sensed a firm but compassionate hand on my shoulder and so I attempted to open my eyes after moping up a certain amount of wetness on my face. As I did so then I became aware of a rhythmic humming noise which seemed familiar as well as appearing to be quite comforting. Without being conscious of doing it I sat back into my seat so as to allow myself the opportunity to recover from my experience. I managed to peer out through a somewhat blurry vision to see the highly recognisable sight of the inside of the cabin. It was then I became aware that we were back on board the lovely little steam powered vessel which was still making its steady progress along the lake.

Feeling very pleased to be somewhere that didn't seem quite so exposed, I took a little while to sit with my memories as my tears began to dry. It had been such a moving experience but one which had given me a great deal to think about. I just didn't know what to say to my companion but I certainly could appreciate what an immensely precious gift he had given me and I was so very grateful. I stayed wrapped up in my thoughts and emotions for quite some time as our little craft steamed purposefully on while supporting me in the most loving manner possible. It carried me ever onwards to an unspecified destination on an as yet indeterminate journey. We cruised sedately along through the golden crested wavelets while the church bells filled the air all around us with their enchanting melodies. The huge bird above us continued to paint the sky with its spectacular sunsets as the lake seemed to shimmer in excited response. The entirety of my surroundings appeared to be expressing nothing but joyfulness in the spectacle of their creation as I was transported on towards even more revelations that were to have such a profound impact on me.

- Chapter 16 -

The View from Above - My Life in Levels of Perspective

As we made our leisurely way along the midway course of the lake I found myself being pulled ever deeper into my thoughts. I just couldn't seem to stop going over so much of my companion's amazing wisdom and advice. Sometimes it felt as though there were far too many new ways of looking at things for my mind to cope with but somehow I knew that it was really important for me to keep trying. There definitely was a need in me to arrive at a better understanding of as much as I could; even if there was a part of me which felt threatened by fearing that I might possibly lose myself in the process. Gradually I became completely absorbed in contemplating just about everything that I'd seen, felt and experienced up to that point in time. There seemed to be so much that I'd already become aware of but this in itself presented me with certain problems.

Through having this awareness I could readily appreciate that there was undoubtedly even more that I didn't yet know. I sighed heavily, just as I apparently did each time this realisation pushed its way into my consciousness. I tried not to feel too dispirited as the shadowy portal of this 'unknown' loomed quite scarily on my personal horizon while seeming to present me with an entrance to a room which I had never ventured into before. The prospect of doing this felt like I would then somehow peek into the dark spaces of my ignorance while anxiously wondering what I might find there; or not as the case may be, which was even scarier. I never much cared for gloomy places but my curiosity often got the better of me in wanting to know more although, this time it seemed to have its disadvantages as well. Being aware of not knowing is certainly a precarious place to be when considering what life could have been like had that knowledge and wisdom been available at the very beginning.

But then, I asked myself, quite reasonably in my view, how could I have known something which I hadn't been conscious of the fact that I didn't know? Or, more paradoxically, that it was even available to be known in the first place. I sighed again while mulling over this seemingly impossible question. To think in this way produced a decidedly unsettling sensation in the pit of my stomach which made me feel a little sick. At first I thought that it was due to the gentle rocking motion of the boat but, if anything, this quite soothing waterborne swaying actually helped me. When I brought my attention to this rhythmically calming sensation then it almost seemed as though I had been lifted up while being cradled in the arms of my loving mother. It put me so much in mind of being very young where I frequently enjoyed the gently comforting protection of her loving care.

This timely recollection did at least go some way towards relaxing me but in the same breath I found myself wishing that I actually could be that young again. Oh to be a babe in arms once more where everything, all my worldly needs, would be taken care of without me having to do anything; absolutely nothing at all! Suddenly I felt a sincere longing for those untroubled times where worry, uncertainties, regrets and recriminations were things that I didn't ever have to think about; didn't even know existed. The world was all brand new and I had no idea about what I didn't know; because I didn't know anything! Sleeping and feeding were the main topics of concern and interest at that stage of my life which, in my current state of mind, seemed like an absolutely wonderful way to be. No worries! I sighed again. How deliriously marvellous! I had suddenly become an ardent fan of that particular way of being.

After a while of contemplating this idyllic state of carefree existence my thoughts gradually began returning to my present surroundings; it was then that I became aware of exactly where I was. I looked across to see my wise and unusually wordless companion just smiling at me. Immediately, I knew that he was completely tuned-in to my thoughts on this subject and then guessed, by his silence and somewhat expectant expression, that he'd been waiting for me to work through my emotions. His way of allowing me to think things through, so as to arrive at a more meaningful understanding which came from within me, proved to be very effective; albeit that I often experienced a good deal of frustration in the process. His smile grew a little wider as he raised his eyebrows slightly and, for an instant, he reminded me of an infinitely patient teacher. One who keenly watched his student wrestle with some difficult concepts while being fully aware that he appeared to be making reasonably good progress without any assistance or input up to that point.

This at least cheered me up but, to me, it still felt as though I was stumbling around in the dark while grasping for something to hold on to. I began to feel that an inspirational 'candle' would have been a great help in lighting my way forward right about now but, in my current state of confusion and uncertainty, I wasn't even sure that I could actually find the match to light it with. All of a sudden my confidence seemed to have waned considerably to the degree that I deemed it to be sorely in need of a boost. I could feel my whole body tensing up at this point and so I made a determined effort to relax while rubbing the back of my neck. It felt good to do this but it also crossed my mind that I was doing it as though it might help release a few valuable insights as well. Nothing much happened but I did find myself thinking about what kind of hurdles I might need to overcome. I relaxed a little more and then made a determined effort not to allow myself to feel frustrated at being unable to see what I needed to. Then a thought popped into my head.

My greatest challenge appeared to come from being asked to view much of my life in a completely different way as a result of my new found awareness. From all that I had begun to appreciate through having had so much explained to me, and from what I had recently witnessed, then I really couldn't help looking back at my past from a confused and questioning viewpoint. Then I realised something else. What was proving really difficult for me to do was to stop myself wondering how my life may have turned out had I known about twin souls at any earlier point on my journey. The questions of would things really have worked out differently and would I have made other choices through being conscious of what was going on, kept cropping up all the time. Whenever they did then the inevitable question of 'why?' always followed. I shifted uncomfortably in my seat at not having a clue as to how to answer any of these imponderables.

I kept going over and over this whole subject in my mind although I realised the futility of speculating about any of it when there could obviously be no satisfactory outcome. I tried to tell myself quite firmly that, I had done what I had chosen to do, and that was it. My life had turned out as recorded for posterity in some cosmic archive and there could be nothing of any beneficial nature achieved through raking over the ashes of a fire long since extinguished. As far as I could see, there was precious little, if anything, to be gained in any positive or constructive sense by indulging myself in the cold comforts offered by any kind of remorse, guilt or regrets. Which was just about as much as I would have received from sitting by the hearth where there evidently wasn't even one small ember to warm my needy soul with.

Self recriminations weren't going to change my past or make it appear any different or even more palatable than it already was. The cosmic stone tablet had already been carefully carved so as to record the passage of my earthly presence; along with everything else that had transpired as a result of my choices and actions. The craftsman scribe had long since laid his chisel and hammer to rest while moving on to do other work somewhere else in the galaxy. The consequences of my 'being' were consigned to the annals of immutable perpetuity for all to see; so what was to be gained by speculating as to what might have been.

Whilst in danger of becoming lost in the very depths of my troubled speculations, I heard a very gentle voice step lightly in to the midst of my dilemma and then say,

"You can never change one single microsecond of the past my dear friend but you most certainly can change the way that you think about it. This is very important to bear in mind when indulging yourself in any helpful contemplation of your encounters and experiences on your recent journey. Please consider this carefully while ensuring that you hold foremost in your mind the enlightening

truth that forgiveness is the key to reviewing whatever has happened in the past.

*Forgiveness, my dear friend, is essential to apply to each and every situation which causes you to feel discomfort; whether it may have arisen as a result of your hand or another's. The cause and effect cannot be changed but your way of looking at the outcome and the circumstances certainly can. This makes **all** the difference my friend and so trust that absolute forgiveness will produce the healing that you so long for."*

All thought became instantly suspended in my mind as his words hung in the air like the mist which I'd seen floating over the mountain. For a moment or two I found that I had difficulty in even understanding the concept which he was offering me. I just couldn't bring myself to connect thinking about something in a way that seemed almost unimaginable and then applying forgiveness! No! This was just crazy; wasn't it? I needed to give myself quite a while so as to fully take in what had been said as well as how I could possibly apply it to how I needed to view my life. I rested my elbow on the arm of my comfy seat and then placed my chin firmly in my hand. This definitely required a lot more thinking about! I went over his words slowly. I can change my way of thinking about the past ... but I have to apply forgiveness in doing so. Did he mean that I should forgive others; those who had influenced or impacted my life in one way or another or did he mean me? Should I forgive myself? "*Both!*" came the emphatic reply before I'd had a chance to complete my thought.

Both?! What me **and** everyone else? Surely you're kidding?! Just one look at the expression on his face told me that he wasn't. I almost willed him to say that he was but I knew that it would be a pointless exercise. Me **and** everyone else?! That seemed to be a huge leap in the direction of a consciousness which I wasn't sure I could even begin to aspire to. How could anyone do that?

I found myself staring at my wise guide as my mind struggled to connect these concepts while also trying to figure out what good would even come of doing so if I was successful. For a moment I considered it to be something which I would find almost impossible to do but, there again, I did realise that I was already aware of my ability to change; or at least being able to recognise the need for me to do so. This was encouraging. I caught sight of my companion nodding his approval which I took to be a good sign. I certainly needed all the support I could get at this point as I couldn't imagine being given anything more difficult to do. I told myself that I was adaptable and smart which had always helped me be successful at whatever I set my mind to do; so why not now? I just needed to think positive so I applied myself to the task.

In doing so I couldn't ignore the fact that I had been guided to appreciate so much of what I now regarded as having been lacking in me before this time. So, could it not be possible for me to accept that I really had done my best under the circumstances and then just forgive all the mistakes and misdeeds. Is that how it worked? Could it be that simple? My mind seemed to go into overdrive as it grappled with this entirely new concept.

On the one hand it didn't seem even remotely achievable, but I had to admit that on the other hand there was something coming from a deeper part of me which had a different opinion. This instinctive feeling appeared as though it was urging an acceptance of the fact that it could indeed be much more than a vague possibility. But, if this were true then how on earth do you set about doing this? I mean, like, just **exactly** how do you do this? How does anyone simply re-evaluate or reassess anything in order to let go of a lifetime's worth of conditioning and many painful experiences?

"*Just one?*" my companion added before my thoughts had an opportunity to go wandering off in any more unhelpful directions. My mind blanked out for an instant at hearing his question. Then it recovered sufficiently so as to ask – "*Just one what?*" This somewhat irritable question, which seemed to literally burst into my mind in response, demanded an immediate answer.

"*Just one lifetime? Do you think that you have only been this way for merely one lifetime? Oh dear! Please think again my well travelled friend.*"

On hearing these words my mind really did go blank as it just couldn't begin to fathom the implications of such a statement. I placed my elbows heavily on my knees and then rested my chin on my clenched fists as I stared aimlessly out of the cabin window. I felt totally and utterly lost. My actions seemed as heavy and profound as that of my mood. It seemed that my mind was being led into a world which it simply didn't recognise any more, or at the very least couldn't make any sense of. I sat gazing out at the scenery while not really taking anything in but rather feeling that I had no idea of my place within its existence; within any existence for that matter. I shifted awkwardly in my seat as though in doing so it would help me see things more clearly. Then I began to wonder about just how much I really had learned during all of those highly eventful and challenging years which represented so much of a life lived in pursuit of love and happiness. Now, it seemed, I was being asked to accept that it wasn't the only one ... by far.

In the midst of my inner emotional turbulence I gradually started to focus my attention on the beautiful scenery which continued to move gracefully by outside the cabin windows. I noticed that it did so while being completely unperturbed by anything that was happening within the confines of my highly introspective world. Somehow I guessed that it was actually well aware of my being far too preoccupied with my own 'landscape of many lifetimes' to acknowledge the true value of its charmingly encouraging presence. Nevertheless it waited patiently for me to once again indulge myself in its refreshingly magical splendour whenever I was ready.

I so wished that I could somehow get myself into a suitable state of being that appreciative so as to be able to accommodate it. I tried hard to do just that and then found myself getting thoroughly caught up in the timeless magic of the scenery while once again losing myself in my thoughts as well. At one point I began wondering about how it would be to just exist in such an uncomplicated way while never having to contend with relationships and your part in them. What must it be like not to make mistakes or get hurt or even feel upset? Life seemed so filled with problems and pitfalls that were simply unavoidable; unless you were some kind of saint of course.

After what seemed like quite a while of going over the whole confusing subject of life's dramas and forgiveness, I started to focus on specific examples. First of all I experimented with applying it to myself and then some of the people in my life. Through re-living one or two of the more memorably painful incidents, which were still uncomfortably clear to me, I did get the idea that it could be possible to let go by forgiving. Well, sort of. What did surprise me though was that I began to experience a certain sense of calmness which seemed to come through just attempting to forgive someone; or even myself for that matter. But, whatever I did then, in a practical sense, it seemed pretty pointless and unsatisfying which is when I realised that I still felt more than a little uneasy about things.

Mostly it was because I found myself not really understanding what it actually meant to forgive someone; or myself for that matter. Saying 'I forgive you' or 'Okay, I forgive myself', were merely words; weren't they? When I said them then all I got was a picture in my mind of some religious figure in white flowing robes holding a hand up while graciously absolving some repentant sinner. This didn't feel right to me at all. In fact it kind of embarrassed me to even imagine things being this way.

Evidently this needed much more thought and so I focused on my understanding of the words while disregarding the off-putting images in my mind. When I did this, and thought about the expression more closely, then I quickly appreciated that I really had no clear idea at all as to what it meant in reality. Suddenly I seemed to have an urgent need to know what 'true forgiveness' actually means in terms of an emotional or mental state of being; or in any other terms or state for that matter.

I mean, was it like you excused someone for doing something? If this was the case then didn't it mean that you were really telling them that it had actually been okay, been acceptable, to do whatever they'd done? As long as they didn't do it again! But if they did do it again then would you just forgive them all over again? Because if this is how it worked then wasn't that like saying that whatever happened then it was never wrong? That couldn't be right – surely not! Or was it like what I understood the religious teachings to say in what God did in the way that He forgave his 'children'? If so, then how in the world could a mere mortal ever aspire to do the same thing? It just didn't make any sense to me in whatever way I tried to rationalise it. I let out a long breath of confusion at not being able to see something which I had never once given any consideration to at all as I really thought that I'd understood it.

This was all very strange and quite upsetting. As my mind didn't appear to be providing me with any suitable answers I felt my foothold on reality beginning to slip at this point in the proceedings. This seemed to be happening as a result of my becoming aware of the fact that what had once served to support me in the past, was quickly starting to crumble and shift under the sheer weight of my doubt and confusion. I was getting to feel that so much of what I thought I knew suddenly couldn't be relied on any more. I sensed the fast disappearance of my personal support mechanism and wouldn't have been at all surprised to hear someone say that the boat was sinking either. It was all so unbearably disheartening and one way or another I felt as though I was in imminent danger of drowning.

"Take judgement out of forgiveness and see what you're left with."

I shot a quick glance at my companion to assess whether he was joking with me or not. One look at his kindly face told me that indeed he wasn't and would never be one to make light of such a weighty subject. His words echoed around in my head. Take judgement out of forgiveness? How on earth do you do that? What's more, what did judgement have to do with forgiveness in the first place? I just didn't see the connection. Once more I plopped my chin on my hands while staring blankly down at my feet. I was trying so hard to sort this out in my mind as I really did feel that it was important for me to do so.

Almost before my question could take up any more space in my already overwrought mental processes, I suddenly got to see an incredibly life-like image of myself sitting in my bedroom; I looked quite young and not at all happy. It took me a few seconds to realise that once more I was looking down through the deck of the boat where, right under my feet, a scene from my past was playing out in the most amazing three dimensional reality. Wherever I looked then it reminded me so accurately of just about everything that I'd been feeling while experiencing my life at that time. Even the smells from my surroundings were so familiar as well as being evocative but what I could sense from them made me quite uncomfortable. What seemed to have the greatest impact on me was the aspect of the sometimes intense loneliness which I felt in that period of my life and I didn't like it at all. I didn't like it then and I surely didn't like being reminded of it now.

After all, I was young and relatively helpless in having to depend on my parents for their support; but where, I kept asking myself, had my father been in all this? I mostly only saw my mother in the way of her being a parent to me and it was her who gave me the kind of love that I considered had been necessary for my survival. Why couldn't my father have been like that? What on earth gave him the idea that what he was doing could possibly be more important than his being with me?

"*Judgement!*" was all my companion said as I continued on with my assessment of my predicament while being lost deep in the imagery of a circumstance that I found myself being so completely caught up in the emotions of. I bristled somewhat at his comment while in the midst of feeling how unfair it was to have experienced such a strong sense of aloneness at that age. I wanted more but it wasn't my fault that I couldn't get it. I ... my mind stopped chattering at me as something else within the very core of my being seemed to be asking for my attention. It appeared to be a kind of knowing which, although still a little unclear, felt as if it was encouraging me to accept that, in truth, I had been seeking to apportion blame for my dilemma; and in so doing I became judgemental. This quite startling realisation took me completely by surprise but there was no way that I could ignore it. I paused for a little while so as to catch my breath. This needed more thinking about. Much more!

If I was honest with myself then I had to admit that I was indeed judging and, what's more, I definitely blamed my father for all my emotional pain. I could see how very needy I had been at that age and I could also see that it was obviously easier for me to lash out and attach blame rather than to deal with it myself. However, I still couldn't get to the point of seeing how it wasn't his fault. I just couldn't seem to make that mental leap into a different way of looking at it. No sooner had this obstacle to my understanding arisen than the scene of my lonely bedroom began to move away underneath the boat only to be replaced by another one. I quickly realised that it was some kind of busy workplace but right in the middle of it I recognised my father who appeared to be totally immersed in doing his job. One of the first things that I noticed was how crowded the whole place looked while the noise and the bustle seemed to be making life difficult for everyone who worked there. At least, to me it did. I well knew how it had been to work in that kind of atmosphere and what the demands were like during every hour that you laboured away to earn your dollar. It was exhausting and left no time to think about anything other than your job and what was expected of you.

I watched fascinated as I saw how my father did everything to the very best of his abilities and then I thought about how much his company must have benefited as a result. In doing so I actually felt very proud of him at that moment. It seemed so typical of him in the way that he always did everything so professionally and that certainly was something which I admired about his character. I also had to admit to being very glad that it was a quality which he'd passed on to me. He always gave one hundred percent to whatever he did but, through watching him at work, I was able to appreciate that giving as much as he did inevitably took a lot of time and energy. Something clicked in my mind and as I gained this valuable insight where, finally, I understood why he was the way he was. Suddenly I could see things in a very different light. From my limited view, while sat alone in the confines of my bedroom, then I had no way to know how things really were for my hard working father but I certainly did have the capacity to judge and blame him.

Being so young and inexperienced didn't give me the opportunity to truly understand how life was outside of my home or even how my father felt about me. Nor did I get to see what he'd actually been doing in the way of how he considered himself to be a loving provider. By working so tirelessly to give my mother and me a better standard of living than we had at that time, I could now see it as being his way of expressing his love for us. Unfortunately, all I had seen at that young age was my need for things to be how I wanted them to be which meant my not being so alone. It seemed obvious to me now that 'blame' was tripping me up through my not being able to move past the feelings of those times but, even though I could see the trap, there was still a part of me which didn't appear able to avoid stepping into it.

Blame, judgement, forgiveness. It was apparent that these were all foreign concepts to a ten-year-old but by wrestling with these three factors at this point in time, after having been a father myself, well, I could appreciate how a new view was a strong possibility. Looking back to when I was a boy then I could feel how it was for me then but from my point of view as someone who had raised his own family then I could see it differently. My companion offered me some timely advice.

"If you are able to identify with those feelings of that time then they are still an influential part of you and have not been resolved. It is not possible to feel what has been healed. This is why it is important to apply forgiveness as this will bring about the changes which you need to make so as to allow the past to have no lasting effect on you. When you recognise that your father was simply doing his best in the only way he knew how, then you eliminate blame. This is the first and most vital step towards true forgiveness."

On hearing this I couldn't quite take in all that he had said but I kept going over his words in my mind while applying them to my feelings about my father. His phrase 'have no lasting effect on you' seemed to make me feel somewhat uncomfortable like he was suggesting that by carrying that blame with me then it continued to affect me in some way.

"Indeed it does my good friend, indeed it does. As does every other unresolved emotion that you carry with you. They accumulate and contribute to the sum total of who you are. All your experiences do this; so, if you want to change then start by changing how you view your past. This is very important and forgiveness is the key."

Again I carefully considered his words where, more and more I kept going over the whole subject of blame. To me as a young boy it was acceptable but to me at this stage of my awareness, with three children of my own, then it wasn't. In the first place I could in no way bring myself to attach any blame to my father as this seemed grossly unfair from how I saw things now. He was doing his best and, at the end of the day I really did love him and didn't want to blame him for anything. How could I? He gave me the chance to live this life for goodness sake and without his presence I wouldn't have had the opportunity to do anything. I would probably never have been so successful in running my own business without him so, in a way, he had also been responsible for the well being of my own family. Blame had to go! It was a word which didn't belong with my father at all but I could see how it had got there all those years back and, after what I had just heard my wise companion say, I realised that I was still carrying it with me. I must be otherwise I couldn't recognise it or feel it; as he had said. So what did I do? I couldn't go back and be that ten-year-old again so how could things change? My companion spoke again in his usual timely fashion.

"Allow yourself to appreciate that you are still yourself no matter what age you are contemplating on your journey. By this I mean that the feelings which you had as a ten-year-old still influence you in the way in which you perceive life to be at this point of your awareness. You cannot go back to that time but you can change the way in which those impressions impact you by adjusting the energy which had been created. You, as a young and inexperienced boy, saw injustice and so you blamed. Now you must correct that so as to move beyond it and towards true and meaningful healing."

Involuntarily I scratched my head which seemed to express my level of confusion but, in the midst of it all, then I felt that I was actually beginning to 'join-the-dots'. There was no 'picture' as yet but I got the idea that if I kept going then something was bound to emerge. So, thinking about what else I had heard, I turned my attention to the tricky subject of judgement. By my reckoning it seemed that blame and judgement went hand in hand. Without one there couldn't be the other. I felt it was like the saying that I'd often heard in that there was never any smoke without fire. This seemed quite appropriate. Fire always produced smoke. Without smoke there could be no fire; without blame then there could be no judgement. Amazing! Elementary but still quite breathtaking in its implications. Two down, one to go!

I was beginning to get a much better idea of what my wise companion had been asking me to become fully aware of but I also had the feeling that there was still a long way for me to go before I truly understood. It was, however, becoming clearer to me that what he had said in the first place, about changing my way of looking at the past, actually could be possible. Something seemed to make a shift in my emotional state at that moment of truly illuminating insight where things started to feel a little lighter as a result. As it did so then I took my attention away from the scene beneath me as my mind felt as though it had found a small foothold on the precipice of inadequacy. Once again it began the painstaking climb towards a new vantage point. There was hope.

My thoughts came thick and fast as I grappled with the whole subject of a new way of looking at my past. On the one hand it felt right to search for a way to bring myself a greater sense of peacefulness but on the other I was still faced with my woeful lack of understanding in how to achieve this in a truly meaningful way. It seemed to me that there were so many questions but little point in posing them as, whatever I did then I couldn't turn the clock back; so why worry? If forgiveness was the key then it appeared that I wasn't quite at the point of opening the door just yet in the respect that I couldn't really see where it was. Even if I could have seen it then I didn't know if it would be possible for me to actually step through it. I reluctantly admitted to myself that I certainly felt more than a little anxious about what I might find on the other side. It was all very confusing which resulted in my becoming increasingly unsure of my identity in the respect of who I considered myself to be.

So many things seemed to be slipping away which had supported me for such a long time. They were a part of me, however flawed in their composition they may have been, but at least they felt comfortable and familiar. To think now that some of them may be so flawed as to be positively misleading, in helping me to understand myself, felt quite scary. I did however allow myself the small luxury of appreciating that I really had done the best I could under the circumstances. Also, like my wise companion had said, I accepted that my life would have been less rich in dramatic experiences through my having not made mistakes and applying unhelpful judgements. No doubt it would have been far less 'colourful' if I had done things differently through having had the benefit of some kind of greater insight but where would it have led me had that been the case? Would I have even found myself in this position now and being able to aspire to whatever my patient mentor was helping me become aware of? He wasted no time in responding to this wordless question.

"My dear friend, please grant yourself the latitude to appreciate that this is a subject which will need a great deal of meditation as you begin to gain a deeper awareness of its importance to you. There will be much adjusting to be undertaken in the process and at each step along the way you will discover it to be increasingly easy to apply what you come to 'know' the truth of. But for now let me just add one more ingredient to the solution which comprises your ultimate healing remedy.

In those formative years of your recent journey, your father offered you the opportunity to experience aloneness. This was his gift to you, as well as many others which he graciously offered. Please bear in mind when I speak of this subject that I do not refer to anyone making you feel lonely as this is not possible. Feelings are only ever your own. You experienced loneliness or aloneness in how you considered yourself to have been deprived of the love which you felt necessary for your happiness and continued survival. In acknowledging this you must also accept that had you not known what love is in the first instance then you could not have been aware of its lack in your life. What you experienced as a result of your upbringing was the realisation that you required a 'completeness' where a similar love to your own would be known to you once more.

*To put it another way, you were being placed in a position which allowed you to feel the lack of your twin soul. If you allow yourself to truly appreciate this then it will go a long way towards helping you adjust your view of your past and so facilitate the removal of blame in the process. This is what I am saying about not changing the past but changing the way in which you view it. Can you see a little clearer now how it works and how by doing this, it affects you now, in this moment, as well? Changing how you 'think' about the past **must** change who and how you are in this moment; it has to. You **are** your past!"*

My head was so full of images at this point where my companion's last words seemed to echo around in my mind like the ricochet of a bullet in the Grand Canyon. You **are** your past. You **are** your past. Over and over again I kept hearing this phrase and, as much as I wanted to make it not be true, I just couldn't bring myself to do it. It seemed such a stunning concept and yet how could it not be so? Suddenly, a whole deluge of apparently random thoughts seemed as though they had come chaotically pouring into my mind. They were like the rivers of rain that I'd so recently seen cascading down the side of the mountain. I got the idea that if I didn't do something to give myself a break from all this then my head would more than likely explode. I figured that going out to get a healthy dose of fresh air might be a sensible thing to do. Without even being conscious of doing so, I got up as though breaking through the surface of the water and then placed my hand on my chest where I found myself actually panting a little. I felt like I was in danger of falling over but I quickly adjusted to the rocking movement of the boat and then headed for the door.

Moving out onto the rear deck space of our valiant little craft, I began looking at the wonderful scenery once again; while taking in as much as my already overwrought mind would let me. The views were just as refreshing as the air which made me simply want to breathe everything in. I felt the urge to immerse myself in all that my senses would allow me to experience, but just as I was in the process of resigning myself to simply going with the flow, I became aware once more that the church bells were still ringing.

This seemed to make a connection in me at which point I immediately began to scan the right hand bank of the lake. I wanted to see if I could establish where the figure of the lady had got to and how far she was along the pathway to the church. At first I could see no sign of her but as we journeyed on, and my view through the trees gradually changed, then I thought that I could see where she might be. For a few frustrating times it turned out to be nothing more than shadows cast by the wooded areas which were partially concealing the pathway but, just as I was about to give up, I suddenly felt sure that I spotted some movement which I found myself hoping would be her.

My eyes were fixed on the place where I felt she was but there were still too many trees in the way for me to be absolutely sure. Then, slowly, things began to clear and my heart skipped a beat as I realised that it certainly was her but, curiously, she wasn't alone. At first I found it difficult to make out exactly what was going on. Then I got the idea that there were some children with her and that they were all well on their way towards reaching the picturesque church on the plateau. This intrigued me greatly but the more I looked then the more I became convinced that there had been something very familiar about the whole group. This was the point when I started to get the idea that the little church would hold the answer to this mystery. In appreciating this I found myself feeling somewhat anxious to get there although I realised that our progress across the lake would undoubtedly be quite slow, but that's when I saw the bridge.

It was quite a way off in the distance and past the avenue of trees but, from my current position, it did look like it could actually be connected to the land where all the trees were. What puzzled me the most though, was the fact that this bridge didn't appear to have an ending to it and also looked to be of a construction that I couldn't fathom in being so far away from its location. It was then that I got the idea that I might be able to make the little engine go faster so that we could get to the bridge more quickly. I felt a certain surge of anticipation as I imagined myself making my way across it and then heading up towards the church.

I was so lost in my thoughts and desires that I nearly leapt off the deck as my companion said from behind me, "*There's no rush.*" When my heart had finally settled back into my chest I wanted to say that I disagreed but it was at that very moment I got the idea that there was something else on his mind. He evidently had an agenda of his own but I couldn't help feeling a kind of urgency in wanting to get to the church. However, chugging serenely up the middle of a very beautiful lake wasn't going to get me there any time soon; not in my estimation anyway.

I did have to admit though, that time was evidently a very slippery commodity given all that had been happening thus far. In consideration of what I had so recently been through, I began to re-evaluate my impatience in the respect that my wishes might quickly be granted; and then I could find myself sitting in the middle of an empty church after I next blinked. I felt that my heart couldn't take any more surprises just at that moment so I resigned myself to 'going with the flow'; which appeared to be the watchword of the day.

"*I concur.*" came the noticeably dry reply from my wise friend.

"*Good choice!*" he added encouragingly. It was always very comforting to receive approval from his sagacious self.

We chugged ever onward in our beautifully constructed vessel as the golden crested waves played enthusiastically all around us. They were a delight to watch and something, however long I stayed on the water, I considered that I would never tire of seeing. Wanting to stretch my legs a little I walked alongside the cabin towards the prow of the boat and once again I noticed the lopsided spire jutting out of the water. Seeing it from this distance made it look quite imposing and something which certainly came under the heading of a hazard to navigation.

I reasoned that there must be much more of it submerged than could be seen above the water, as well as being attached to a large building, which would mean that it undoubtedly presented a notable obstruction to our journey. What suddenly became of greater concern to me was that it appeared as though we were headed straight for it. This appreciation corresponded to the moment when a certain degree of nervousness overcame me as I began to question who was actually steering the vessel and why I hadn't thought of it before. This surely was a day for asking questions but I found myself becoming accustomed to the paradox that whenever the answers came then even more questions seemed to arise as a result. Sometimes keeping silent, while letting things be just as they were, seemed like a good option.

I decided to return to the comfort and seclusion of the cabin to relax for while. I had no idea what to expect from this point on so recharging my somewhat tired body seemed like a good idea given the absence of there being anything else to do. I should have learned by now ... never make assumptions!

An Intimate Reconnection with an Eventful Era

No sooner had I sat down in the cabin than I noticed a distinct change in the rhythm of our trusty steam engine. It seemed to be slowing down and, in consequence of this, so was our progress through the water and along the lake. I knew that lakes weren't tidal and so I felt that without power then we weren't going to be able to make sufficiently speedy progress in order to get to the church. This was unwelcomed but, just as I thought about seeing what could be done to rectify the problem, my companion came into the cabin to join me. He sat down opposite me and smiled slightly as though he could well understand all that I was going through and my struggle to gain a new appreciation on so much of what I felt the need to know. I looked into his wonderfully perceptive eyes which, to me, were the ultimate expression of kindness that I had ever come across. Then I found myself wondering what it must be like to see things through his way of looking at the world and if he must have gone through anything similar to me in order to find his way towards it.

"We each have our own journeys my good friend but there are equally as many diverse pathways as there are souls to walk them. Not all of these pathways lead to a beneficial destination and so we may have many attempts to make the kind of progress we each need. My chosen path at the moment is one which I am more than happy to walk as a portion of it runs alongside your own; and so, while we enjoy each others' company, I am honoured to share with you much that I have been guided to learn. In time you will do the same for another who is in need of your unique guidance where, from all that you have learned on your journey, you will pass on your wisdom. I can assure you that when you are granted the opportunity to do this, then it will bring you a level of happiness unknown to you at this time."

This sounded very interesting but I just had to ask,

"But what do you get out of doing this? I mean, why are you doing it in the first place? Don't get me wrong, I'm grateful of course, well most of the time ..." I allowed myself a smile to show that I really was grateful and just attempting a little humour, *"... but you seem to have all the answers so what's in it for you?"*

For a little while my companion remained motionless and quite silent as he just smiled at me where, at first, I thought that I might have asked something which he couldn't answer; foolish me! But then I realised that it was more than likely that he was searching for a way to put his reply into words that I could comprehend sufficiently well. Just before he spoke, I found myself being overcome by the most odd feeling that he was almost looking quite deeply into the heart of my very being. I wasn't scared at all but more intrigued by the fact that someone would be even remotely interested in doing such a thing and I also felt kind of flattered by his genuine interest in wanting to really understand me that well.

"Let me just say this in terms which will be truly meaningful to you. As you are aware, a reward in the respect of some 'thing' which is gifted by another, is meaningless here. You are beyond that now where the advancement and expansion of your awareness is all that really matters. Being of service to another is very helpful in this way and so, in how we find ourselves now, both of us our benefiting from our journeying together. It gives me a great deal of pleasure to help you on your way and this in itself is reward enough for me. Being of assistance to any other soul in any circumstance is always beneficial but you must trust me when I tell you that what comes of doing so is, at present, beyond your current level of comprehension. Service to another in any dimension has 'significant benefits', for want of a better expression, which go way beyond anything which exists within the limiting confines of third dimensional thinking."

"What do you mean by that exactly?" I felt that I needed to ask him.

"That, my good friend, is what you have conditioned yourself to accept so as to live your earthly experiences. It really is a very restricting way to be as the language which has been adopted so as to serve your purposes is far too unhelpful. Its woeful insufficiencies have not allowed you to embrace many of the important 'finer' aspects of awareness that would have made life more, shall we say 'rewarding', in terms of making good progress along your spiritual pathway. Now the time has come to move beyond those limitations my friend and so I am here to help you do just that. Are you ready to take the next step?"

Even though I'd heard him ask me something, I couldn't really respond as I was still in the middle of thinking about what he'd just said to me. It was so foreign to my way of thinking that I felt the need to ask for more of an explanation. *"I'm confused ..."* was all that I could find to say but then managed to add while remembering one particular phrase,

"... I don't understand what you mean about the limitations of language and how I could have got more out of life if I'd known how to say things better. Is that what you're telling me?"

"Not exactly, but please trust me when I say that, in the respects of your language limitations then it's very difficult for me to expand your awareness by using this same medium; that's why I show you what I do. In this way we move beyond words and then you are able to get a much better and more meaningful appreciation for many things which are important for your beneficial progress along this pathway. In this respect your next experience awaits you and so if you are ready we will move expeditiously into it and in so doing, even more will become clear to you. So, are you ready my adventuresome friend?"

I did another brief 'owl' impression but my companion simply smiled while making a gesture which indicated to me that he wanted to direct my attention to the area beneath my feet. I looked down as he wished me to but, after I managed to get over the initial shock, I quickly became drawn into something totally unexpected; all my questions about language suddenly evaporated as this view needed no description.

Right there, laid out in quite stunningly larger-than-life imagery, was another episode of my recent journey which I could see in the level of detail that drew me completely into the feelings, sensations, anxieties and aspirations of that time. It had been a period in my life that I didn't particularly want to re-live and neither was it one which, if it had anything to do with the subject of forgiveness, did a single thing to encourage me at all. I couldn't for a moment begin to relate it to any sense of self forgiveness or in applying it to anyone else for that matter. The emotions which I felt were so real and ones which didn't appear to allow for any space that would accommodate forgiveness. Maybe I was just trying to be too analytical so I tried to step back as much as I could while working hard at not judging things. This felt like a superhuman effort which left me wondering if I might get a little help. Looking up to see if this was possible, I could tell by the expression on my companion's face that things were about to become even more interesting. Having realised this, I figured that it would probably be a good idea to prepare myself for yet another lesson but this time I had to admit to being a somewhat reluctant student. It had never been my way to shirk hard work or commitment whenever it was necessary to get something done, but there were some tasks which stretched my resolve to the limit. This imminent 'adventure' appeared to fall into that category.

My biggest problem seemed to be that of knowing the trials and the outcome, or at least I thought I did, and so I was anxious to put that whole time behind me. I wanted to consign the 'chronicles of Ron (1971-1981)' to some dusty shelf in the basement of a highly remote cosmic vault. Even as this wish was slowly withering on the vine of unfulfilled fruition, I got the impression that my infinitely resourceful guide had other ideas.

"Trust, my dear friend; simply trust while striving to suspend your judgement, just as you are wisely working your way towards at this moment, and then see how things look and feel as a consequence."

I really did pay attention to his advice but right at this precise point in time I didn't feel at all confident about being successful at doing what he asked of me. After all, even before I'd got drawn completely into this scene, just as I had with all the others which my trip on the boat had been presenting me with, I was already in the process of judging it. I considered this not to be an auspicious start. Not good at all.

No sooner had this notion entered my mind than I felt a jarring sensation like the boat had run aground. I got the idea that it was trying to shake me out of my mood but little did I appreciate that the bow had actually just made contact with the half submerged steeple which I'd been studying earlier. I looked up to see my companion with an expression on his face which was almost saying – 'well, I wonder what this can all be about?' Now I was even more confused than ever. At the same moment of the boat shaking, I thought I could hear the call of another bell; but this one appeared to have the mournful tone of one that was far out to sea and moored to a buoy. I could certainly associate myself with that situation as I felt like I was getting well out of my depth.

For some reason which I'm at a loss to explain, I felt the irresistible urge to look to the side of me and out of the cabin window without having any kind of a clue as to what I might see. It took me a second or two for my focus to change as I found myself looking at the right hand bank of the lake and then immediately noticed the shimmering white pathway through the trees. My mood changed a little as this came into view but then, while being happy to have something else to distract my attention, I spotted the woman; she appeared to be looking across in my direction. My mind seemed to do a few summersaults as it played catch-up but, before it fully registered anything, I realised that I could also make out five or six more figures which looked like children standing next to her.

To my absolute surprise they all started waving but I couldn't imagine for the minute what they could be waving at. There didn't seem to be anyone else on the lake, that I was aware of, but if they were waving at me then why? Were we sinking? Was there some disaster about to befall us? It seemed unlikely but then I realised that the lady appeared to be smiling and, what's more, I got the distinct impression that she was smiling at me. I felt my heart lighten considerably while realising this at which point something stirred deep within me where I found myself being overcome with a feeling of something spurring me on. For a minute I actually got the idea that the whole group of them were cheering me on, as though I was taking part in some sort of sporting event where they had come along to support me.

For what seemed like quite a while I kept looking at them as I found myself enjoying what I took to be their expression of encouragement. They all appeared to be so happy as if they were anticipating something exciting which was about to happen but it was the look on the lady's face which attracted my full attention. It had the effect of making me feel as if I had been in someway renewed, even uplifted a little by what I could sense coming from the manner of her smile. It was thoroughly delightful and so very welcomed. Somehow, as a result, my situation didn't seem to be anywhere near as gloomy as it had struck me as being just a few minutes ago.

What proved to be even more intriguing was that I could have sworn I saw a kind of small spherical light which had formed just above her. For a moment I thought it might be some kind of reflection in the cabin window but then I realised that it wasn't. I could see it hovering briefly while illuminating her. It was only there for a very short time before flashing brightly and then disappearing but, when it did so then to my great surprise, it came directly at me and then shot right through me. It had the effect on me like I'd stepped into a lovely warm shower as my whole body responded to its wonderfully energising influence. There was also something about the light which seemed very familiar, even in the short time that it existed, but I couldn't be certain as to exactly what it could be. No matter, whatever it was then it really did seem to have the most positive effect on me and for that I was very grateful indeed.

Although I didn't have an understanding of why any of this had been appearing on my personal horizon, I certainly did feel very comforted by the presence of the attractive looking lady and her children; at least I assumed they were hers. Not only did I feel markedly better but there was something in me which seemed as though it wanted to go across and join them but again I had no idea why this should be. As I allowed these new feelings to settle deep within me I noticed that she appeared to be gathering her flock together and then shepherding them gently off in the direction of the church. I watched as long as I could before they all disappeared behind a thickly wooded area which inconsiderately hid them from my view. Even though they were out of sight, I could still sense the emotion within me which she and her children had stirred up. Now, it seemed as though I was much better prepared to deal with whatever my companion wished me to study. In fact I found myself almost looking forward to it, oddly enough.

Once again I looked down into the highly memorable world of my past which stretched out in such breathtaking reality beneath the vessel. It was so amazingly engaging that I almost felt myself to be in danger of actually falling into it. The feeling, as best I can describe it, was similar to that of standing on the edge of a very high structure while being convinced that at any second you were going to be completely consumed by it; after plunging ever downwards at high speed. I had always wondered, if that happened, what would be the very last thoughts which would pass through my mind as I did. What would be my last earthly feelings or recollections as I broke the sound barrier before becoming a teeny-weeny little crater in the earth's mantle? All very interesting to contemplate but yet another question that I didn't want to add to the already long queue which was waiting to be attended to. I concentrated on the scene beneath me.

What first got my attention about all that I found myself looking at was the sheer scale of what I could see going on in a most memorable episode of my past. Everywhere I looked it appeared as though particular periods of my life were playing out all at the very same time. Whichever one I chose to study I could clearly see what I was doing or what had been taking place at that time. So many recognisable places, occasions, people, incidents, emotions, challenges but when I really thought about them then I began to appreciate that they had all occurred after Janet and I had set out on our journey of togetherness. Those were the times when we had chosen to adjust our lives so as to bring our pathways together along with those who wished to come with us. That particular chapter of my life also included the eventual breaking up of my home in order to create another. This was indeed a very difficult time for me as well as a highly challenging one.

While going over so much in my mind, I found that my attention kept being drawn to the quite imposing structure of a very large church which was somewhat recognisable; although I couldn't immediately identify it. Nor did the area it was situated in seem familiar but there did appear to be something about it which kept making me want to know more; as well as why I seemed to be so interested in it. The whole place appeared to have a quite haunting quality to it which gave me the oddest of feelings that I knew it really well; but how could that be? How very strange. For the time being I contented myself with taking in many of its various features but, for the life of me, I still couldn't imagine what kept attracting me to it. Nothing at all came to mind, which was a little frustrating so I decided to look around at the many other things which I had no trouble in recognising. Going from scene to scene I began carefully studying virtually everything that appeared to be happening in this quite amazing landscape. It was almost too much to take in which made me aware that I could quite easily become totally mesmerised in the process, so I remembered to breathe and just allow myself to go with the flow. While doing this, I seemed to also experience going through a whole raft of emotions which resulted from my being almost pulled completely in to every circumstance that I cared to concentrate on.

One of the first things I noticed was just how many occasions there were where I wrestled with what to do about my marriage and how it would affect my family. Those certainly were very stressful times where so often the upset was really hard to deal with. Then I could see instances of other times where I was worried about my business and how life would turn out for me. I recognised one or two occasions which were times when I wondered if I even wanted to do it any more as it seemed that I had to question just about everything in my life. So many crossroads which I found myself coming up against but nowhere to turn for advice. Reliving all this so clearly and so intensely made me realise more than ever just how really testing this whole period had been for me. It was one where I certainly had to do some serious soul-searching and that's for sure. However, I felt glad that when it came to the important decisions then I'd listened to my heart; although, in truth, I didn't appreciate that I was doing it at the time. Neither did I know where I found the courage to make some of the more difficult choices that I did, but I must have known somewhere deep inside what the right thing was when it came to crunch time.

Wherever I looked around the landscape I could see ever more instances of those times which made me feel like I was living a ten year roller-coaster ride at breakneck speed. At one point it almost appeared to be more than I could handle, but something kept me looking. To my surprise, I began to realise that there were actually just as many really enjoyable times as there were challenging or difficult ones. It was getting more intriguing by the minute. Even though I was all too aware that there certainly were trials over this period of my life, I was beginning to see something else going on that was almost, for want of a better expression, leading me forward through those tough times. As I studied the many different aspects to my journey then I began to see certain patterns emerging in how I made my choices. Being able to observe myself, then I got a much better idea of why I did what I did and also what contributed to my confidence in making my decisions. It was so strange to watch it all happening while knowing the outcome, but it gave me a most unexpected insight into myself in the most revealing way. As a result I became increasingly absorbed by not only all that I observed taking place but also by all that I was feeling at that precise time. It was absolutely fascinating for me to be able to look at one particular occasion after another while being so completely immersed in the events as well as the mood of the moment.

Through being able to re-live so much of what happened in those eventful years after having first met Janet, it gave me the opportunity to see things somewhat differently. Having gained this new perspective in such a concentrated and intense way, I began to get the impression that there was more to the pattern of my doing things than I'd first realised. It was just a feeling rather than it was a knowing of any kind but I had no doubt that there was something going on. This intrigued me greatly because I had never even considered it in this way before, although it certainly was easy to see how determined I had been to make a life with someone who I had completely lost my heart to.

I felt sure that this must have been what kept me going but, in the instant that this thought arose in me, I could have sworn that I could see tiny spheres of brilliant light flash in every scene. Wherever I chose to look into those incredibly life-like images of past times then I was sure that beautiful little orbs of white light kept popping into view. They were so brief in their appearance, just the merest of glimpses, but even so they certainly did have a truly wonderful effect on me. It kind of made the whole place look like Disneyland but this was much more than just visual as I could actually 'feel' it. I loved it but I couldn't figure out why it was happening or what it meant. My wise companion chose that particular moment to lightly clear his throat and so I looked up to see him wearing his customary wry smile. I got the idea from this that I hadn't appreciated something fairly obvious and that actually, I had missed out on whatever it was that I needed to be aware of. Whenever he had this look then I could be sure that he would inevitably be patiently waiting for me to come to that 'ah-ha' moment and so, never one to refuse a challenge, I was determined to discover whatever it would turn out to be on this particular occasion.

Resting my elbows on my knees and cupping my face in my hands, I looked at so many things that I appeared to remember so clearly as well as quite a few that I didn't. Wherever I looked then it was as though there was something going on that I remembered doing at the time. However, the more I studied each situation then the more I became aware that I could see things from a much different point of view. There were situations which I became thoroughly engrossed in where I observed myself getting into some tight spots. While knowing the outcome of each predicament, it proved to be really difficult for me not to want to interfere by pointing something out which could have made things a hell of a lot easier or caused less upset than it did.

It wasn't just a case of having 20/20 hindsight, which we all wish we had when reviewing past choices and events in our lives, this was much more than that. I realised that I could look objectively into many circumstances and then question whatever I had been encouraged or motivated by which had then led me to make the choices that I did. What was it, I found myself wondering, that kept me on that path towards making a life with my Janet while undoing much of what I'd worked so hard to create up to that point on my journey? There were more flashes of light coming into my peripheral vision but I took little notice of them as I wrestled with so much of what I was observing about my choosing to move towards a completely new way of life.

I looked down at my feet while asking myself just exactly what had guided them to take me where they did. I mean, whoever stops to even consider this kind of thing? It seemed a little silly to think in this way because, after all, they were just following orders in doing whatever they were told to do; but then I had to ask myself precisely where those 'orders' had originated from and why? What subtle compulsion, I wondered, could have contributed so much to my decisions, conscious or otherwise, and how I managed to find my way towards my ultimate happiness? What on earth could it have been that stimulated my determination and commitment to find that pathway and then to walk it; and where was it that I even got the courage from in the first place?

I found myself staring at the floor beneath me without really 'seeing' anything as my mind got lost down the 'rabbit hole'. My whole world felt as though it had contracted into the unexplored regions of the inner 'me' where I found myself wanting to know just exactly 'where' I was. I had no idea what would come when I asked this question but not asking it wasn't an option. Suddenly there appeared to be a real need in me to understand this aspect of myself at a much greater depth. I got the impression that through my having gained a deeper appreciation of what my motivations were then I would somehow achieve a better understanding of myself in the process. I was quite overcome with a pressing need to get some much needed insight but my answers were about to come in the most bizarre way imaginable.

The Crooked Church of Distorted Concepts

Coincident with my overwhelming desire for more clarity, my poor tired feet began to feel decidedly cold and, when I came to think of it, so did the seat that I found myself sitting on. In fact, it began to feel more than a little uncomfortable. This was promptly followed by a distinct sense of uneasiness in not feeling the gentle swaying of its customary soothing support any more. Added to this, there appeared to be a certain echoey quality to my surroundings along with a complete absence of the distant church bells which had been so present up to that point. All these factors seemed to come rushing in to my awareness like a bunch of unruly children bursting into the kitchen at breakfast time. As a result, I felt a pressing need to reconnect with my immediate world through sensing that something was definitely not right with it. I quickly looked up to see what was happening and once again found myself staring wordlessly at what greeted me when I did. My new surroundings looked back at me while wanting to know what the problem was. By this time I had become somewhat used to suddenly finding myself in strange places but what I could see all around me now left me totally and utterly bewildered; please be assured that I am in no way understating the situation here.

It took me a fair few highly anxious seconds to realise that I was actually sitting in the middle of a long hard pew. This was set about half way down a long row of many other similar pews. They all looked very new and lined one side of a somewhat crooked aisle on the left hand area of an extraordinarily looking and very large church. While trying not to panic, I gazed around at everything while attempting to take in the sheer scale of the building as well as trying to figure out what on earth I was doing in it. The interior appeared to be fashioned in the style of the very old and rather grand European churches, especially those that had come to be known as abbeys or cathedrals. This one gave me the impression that it was big enough to easily house a couple of jumbo jets and, for a minute, I imagined that they could have even taken off given the height of the ceiling. It certainly was an impressive space which kind of intimidated me being the only one actually present in it; or so I thought. Having learned to take nothing for granted I quickly looked around to make sure.

I couldn't see anyone else but, while taking in much more of my surroundings in the process, I began to realise that there was something quite odd about the whole building. I felt the need to study many different things for a time while getting used to the design of the huge nave area and other major features, but what struck me first was the thick supporting columns. There didn't appear to be a straight one among them in any part of the structure and neither did the windows look symmetrical either. All this created quite a bizarre effect but the truly odd thing about it was that everything gave me the idea of having actually been fashioned in that way; or so it seemed, even though it didn't look particularly safe.

At the far end of the long nave there was the typical semi-circular apse on the other side of the chancel, but this one had seven tall windows two of which looked to have been blocked up so that no light could get through them. The other five were filled with stained glass panels that had designs on them which I couldn't make out at the distance I was away from them. I didn't give this any more thought as there was still a great deal more to look at while trying to understand why I should have been suddenly transported to a place like this anyway and why I was apparently completely alone in it.

I glanced up into the ceiling above me but then had to stop my head from spinning as I tried to make sense of the jumbled mass of vaulting beams which held up the roof. The beautifully neat geometric patterns which these types of supporting structures usually made were completely absent which made me wonder how it stayed together at all. This ceiling was anything but orderly in its design and for a moment it almost appeared as though it was moving; like it had a kind of slightly rippling quality to it. Rippling in a kind of fluid motion which reminded me of something but I couldn't quite bring to mind what it could be as ceilings most definitely shouldn't appear to move under any circumstances; well not in my view anyway.

This thought did nothing to improve my confidence in the stability of the whole place and neither did it do anything to enhance its ability to reassure me about being alone while sat in the middle of it. I did have to admit, however, that there was a certain kind of attraction to its uniquely quirky characteristics and, strange as it may seem, it actually did appeal to me very much. I smiled a little when I considered the prospect that the architect might have been a distant relation of Salvador Dali or someone of a similar artistic leaning; 'leaning' being the operative word in the case of certain architectural features that I could see.

No sooner had this particular word made its presence felt in my consciousness than an image flashed through my mind of the spire sticking up out of the lake; then I suddenly realised where I must be. Could it have been possible, I had to ask myself? The answer was most certainly yes. Once more I cupped my head in my hands while looking down at the floor. This time I had no expectations of seeing any different world appearing as I knew that I was already in it. But where had my wise companion got to just when I was most in need of his guidance and encouragement. What on earth was I doing in this place and how did it get me closer to the answers which I felt myself to be in need of finding; or to the church on the hill for that matter?

"What gives rise to this need in you and what reason do you consider that it exists in the first place?"

On hearing these words I quickly looked up to see who was talking to me but could see no one nearby or anywhere else in the far reaches of the big building either. I felt confused. I had half expected to see my companion smiling at me but there was no sign of him. This realisation caused me to panic a little at suddenly feeling quite alone in a very strange place while trying to work out what was going on and who might be hiding in the shadows.

"Why is it so strange to you and why is there this need in you to know so much? What is it that you anticipate will change with the coming of a greater knowing and, in exactly what way do you perceive that your life will benefit with the advent of more information?

For this is all that knowledge is; it simply is only information. But, more importantly, what makes you so sure that this longed for change will be a positive one when it does come. Please be very aware that knowledge in and of itself is of no beneficial use to anyone when not accompanied by the guiding light and infinitely protective patience of great wisdom?"

I listened carefully to the words which appeared to be coming from all around me. While trying to make out what had been said I was also attempting to cope with the persistently disconcerting feeling that I couldn't see anyone speaking them. For one terrifying moment I found myself considering the distinct possibility that I was actually being addressed by the big guy upstairs. As soon as the enormity of this notion hit me then I didn't know whether to fall on my knees while clasping my hands in humble reverence or just say 'Hey! How are you boss?' while hoping that He didn't turn me into a frog.

I quickly opted for the fingers crossed approach while offering a friendly hello but just before putting my plan into action I noticed a slight movement in the pulpit way up in front of all the pews. Almost hidden by one of the crooked pillars was a figure who I could see resting his hands on the lectern. I tried to see who it could be but I wasn't inclined to make any sudden moves in light of my predicament coupled with the fact that I considered any movement whatsoever might bring this whole precarious construction tumbling down around me.

"Only if you wish it so my brother."

The words seemed to completely envelop me while echoing off the walls and every other surface of the building. I was just about to ask what in heaven's name I had to do with it when more words emerged so as to almost blend in with those that had only just faded away.

"You see, oh seeker of infinite knowledge, this construction is, in large part, of your making and so you may do with it as you wish. You can choose to put it 'right' or you can make it even more misshapen to the point where it will no longer remain standing if that is your true desire."

Once again I looked all around me while taking in the sheer size and scale of this strange but eminently impressive church as I tried to make some kind of credible connection in my mind. I glanced at the tall misshapen pillars which seemed to reach up towards the stars while supporting the oddly fashioned roof. A roof that I had to admit, even in its unusual design, was actually still quite a marvel of construction and form. The walls looked to be as thick as the trunk of the large oak tree that I remember being sat under whereas the main entrance doors appeared as though they had needed several similar trees to make them. However hard I tried, I just couldn't seem to associate my somewhat inconsequential self with that of the enormity of such a substantial building. One that I reasoned, logically in my view, would have been totally beyond my ability to construct given a whole boat load of lifetimes.

"We shall see." The words came softer this time and, more intriguingly, they appeared to be of a characteristic tone that reminded me of someone but at that moment I couldn't remember who. Before I had time to give this notion any more thought, my attention was drawn to the area of the apse where the five big vertical stained glass windows and two blocked up ones were set into the curved stone wall. The centre panel was starting to become

brighter which made the others look somewhat dimmer but what was more noticeable was that the individual windows on each side, which had been covered up, seemed positively dark by comparison. It created the oddest of effects and caused me to wonder why anyone would want to block out the illumination which they would otherwise have let in.

As the light in the centre panel grew brighter then I could begin to make out the nature of the design in the glass. There appeared to be lots of symbols which I didn't recognise at all but what I found to be most identifiable was what looked like a large and very beautifully designed eye right at the centre. With the light pouring through it then I could almost have mistaken it for the sun. The more I studied it though, then it revealed itself without doubt as being an eye but one which impressed me as being fixed in a kind of distantly dreamy stare; almost like seeing but not seeing all at the same time. It was quite mesmerising to look at where I found myself wondering what the person it belonged to must have been thinking or doing; or even looking at, so as to create that state of mind. This certainly intrigued me greatly while also capturing my somewhat overactive imagination.

The light grew steadily brighter until it took on the form of a large ray which fell onto the area in front of the chancel and then lit up the wide aisle between the two deep rows of pews. The effect was quite biblical in the way it illuminated certain aspects of the church. It could probably have caused some spontaneous religious conversions had the place been filled with a congregation that was made up largely of 'fence-sitters'. I allowed myself to imagine this happening but then suddenly became more concerned with what would happen next and why I found myself sitting in the building in the first place.

My heart nearly took flight as the first booming notes from a very powerful organ erupted through every molecule of air in the nave. I could easily have believed that this sound would have lifted the roof completely off as a great many of the pipes suddenly burst into life while churning out a melody that was almost identifiable. I sat back in my seat so as to give myself a chance to catch my breath as the vibrations from the thunderous organ appeared to wrap themselves around me like I had been caught up in some melodic tornado. I was almost tempted to cover my ears but it was at the same moment of considering doing so that I saw another window alongside the centre panel starting to become brighter as well.

The ray through this window also shone into the main area of the church but this one seemed to be highlighting the entrance to the vestry and, while studying it, I realised that the door was beginning to open. I held my breath as I had no idea who would come walking through it and what they would say to me when they did. My heart remained pulsatingly unsettled while my sense of unease continued to maintain its heightened state. The organ was in full flow by this time where I could have sworn that the whole building felt as though it was responding to the music. This did nothing to inspire my confidence in its continued vertical existence.

What happened next caused me to stand up out of my seat as two people appeared from behind the now open doorway to the vestry. My action was a completely unconscious one which happened at the moment I realised that a bride and groom were coming back into the main area of the church. It seemed as though they were about to walk back down the aisle and past me while on their way out of the church and on into the adventure of married life. I gave no thought to the fact that there was no one else in the seating areas except me, although standing up felt as though it was the right thing to do under the circumstances.

The couple emerged while looking radiantly happy but I couldn't make out who either of them were as my seating position was quite far away and they had their backs to the light. From what I could make out they did look quite young as well as somewhat familiar. This immediately put me in mind of myself when I got married at that age without appreciating what was in front of me or what to expect. I took a moment to immerse myself in that memory as the music played on and the ceremony continued while I re-lived my recollections of a similar time. No sooner had these thoughts entered my mind than I realised that there was something going on behind me and so I turned to look in the direction of the front entrance. I could see that the doors were now wide open and that people were starting to come in, plus there seemed to be a few unruly children racing down the aisle while performing cartwheels and playing tag. Slowly the pews began to fill up as more and more people streamed in through the doors, even though the newlyweds were making their way unhurriedly across to the front of the centre aisle.

Suddenly I felt rather awkward as though I was intruding on a private occasion and so I got up in order to move across to the side aisle so as to look for an inconspicuous route out of the church. I had never found the space between pews to be the easiest of places to move gracefully along especially when I had to step over kneeling cushions and prayer books littered around on the floor. I managed to tread on one book which sprang up from under my foot and then flicked open to reveal some pages which didn't look as though they belonged in any religious setting. I stopped for a moment to pick it up and then noticed that it was actually a manual on how to operate a piece of sign making equipment which I was quite familiar with. I carefully shut the book and placed it on the wooden shelf while wondering what on earth it was doing in a church.

There was no time to give it my undivided attention as people were already coming into the pew that I intended to leave and so I made my way to the side aisle while still feeling puzzled about the book. What got my attention next was the abrupt end to the organ music which only left the noises of people moving about in the church while taking their seats. That was, of course, until the band started playing which caused me to stop dead in my tracks. I had no idea what to make of it at that moment but couldn't see anything of what was going on from my unsighted position in the side aisle that I now found myself in.

What intrigued me greatly, and got my attention most of all, was the music itself in that it appeared to be highly recognisable as was the lead instrument which carried the melody. I could easily make out the unmistakable sounds of a marimba and, what's more, the style in which it was being played seemed very familiar to me. For a moment I became lost in the whole experience of it as the playing and the well known sounds began to evoke a great deal of memories for me. As much as it proved to be nostalgic, it was also very odd indeed and so I just had to find out what was going on. However, I somehow had to get myself into a position of seeing right into the apse which meant abandoning any ideas of leaving the church. This was not what I wanted but the call of the music proved to be far too strong for me to resist.

I could see that the whole central seating area was now quite full as I moved farther along the side aisle towards the front of the church. When I was almost parallel to the front pew I caught sight of the bride and groom, who I had seen coming out of the vestry, but they were now sat in the front row on the right hand side of the aisle. I presumed that they were watching the band like everyone else although why this should be I had no idea at all. My mind tried to convince me that this was some sort of post-wedding reception where the church doubled as a kind of stand-in venue although I couldn't think of a more unsuitable place to hold it. I had to admit that the acoustics were pretty good though, so that was one saving grace in its favour at least.

The farther along the aisle I progressed then the more difficult it had become to catch sight of the band. Added to this, there was now a third window in the apse which seemed to have lit up just like the other two but this one was shining a ray on my side of the church. It was quite bright and obscured my clear view of the musicians who were situated directly underneath it. I found this very frustrating as they continued to play one tune after another which, amazingly, were all very familiar to me, as were the arrangements; I just had to know what was going on and why.

I was in the process of taking a step out across the space in front of the pews when I almost stumbled over the bottom stair of the small flight of steps which led up to the pulpit. To steady my balance I grabbed the wooden handrail and immediately felt a sensation which reminded me of doing something very similar on many previous occasions. It was like experiencing déjà vu but this particular encounter had a far greater element of reality to it. I paused for a few seconds so as to let my mind settle. In the midst of my trying to orientate myself with a sensation that I appeared to remember so well, then another window in the apse began to grow brighter while the ray from it shone directly at me. I wasn't aware of it happening but as the light increased then I began to feel something else. The touch of the wood seemed so evocatively familiar that it made me want to instinctively climb the stairs, even though I knew they only led up to the pulpit. I did however, get the flash of an idea that I might actually discover who it was that had been speaking to me. So, without thinking I began walking up the well worn wooden steps.

They even creaked a little under my feet just like I remembered other similar steps doing but where exactly they were I couldn't bring to mind. Then I got the strong impression of a very familiar smell that I could have easily believed was coming from a kitchen and which seemed highly memorable. With the feel of the wood and the aroma from the kitchen came the strong sensation of going up a very different flight of stairs and also being quite young when I did it. The emotions which this brought up in me were confusingly mixed but the most overwhelming of them all was the really unpleasant feeling of loneliness. With it came the highly dispiriting notion that I was on my way up to a place of solitude in an environment which I so wished could be very much better than how I knew it to be. My footsteps on each stair felt leaden in anticipation of where they would take me.

Even as this unpleasantness appeared to be in danger of completely enveloping me, I noticed that the fifth and final tall stained glass window had lit up. Just as the rest had and so all five were equally as bright making the apse look like the sun had come to settle in it. The light was very bright and so I shielded my eyes slightly as I climbed to the top of the stairs on the way to my bedroom while I could almost taste the food that my mother had been preparing in the kitchen. It made me feel quite hungry in anticipation. Food was a great comfort to me at that time and so I could almost savour once again my favourite snacks and meals which gave me something to look forward to. I was so engrossed in my thoughts, feelings, sensations and the effects of the light that I didn't expect to meet any obstacles on my way up; but that's exactly what happened. I stopped abruptly as my eyes focused on whatever it was that blocked my way, which is when I became aware that there appeared to be a lectern directly in front of me. Equally confusing to me was the fact that I could no longer see my bedroom which seemed to have vanished.

That was the moment when my attention changed to that of looking at what I could actually see in front of me which corresponded to the exact same instant when my blood turned to water. I became rooted to the spot as I realised that I was now looking out over the whole completely packed seating area where everyone present appeared to be looking up at me. I had absolutely no idea what to do. To add to my dilemma, I also became acutely aware that the band had stopped playing and that there was now total silence in the church. Just to make matters more precarious, I could appreciate that the noiselessness was not the typical hushed silence of a normal church. In this one it was 'absolute' where I could easily have heard a pin drop near the front entrance.

I suddenly found myself wondering whether the floor to the pulpit had a trap door that I could quickly escape through so as to alleviate my complete embarrassment when I spotted something quite odd. As I looked out over the sea of faces in the assembled crowd I thought it strange that I could detect no movement at all. It appeared as though everyone was almost frozen in time but then I did catch a glimpse of someone moving and immediately recognised the kindly face of my wise companion. I realised that he was seated on the end of one of the middle pews, almost opposite to where I had been originally sitting before I got up to leave. I was so relieved to see him while feeling at least there was someone around to support me in my time of greatest need.

He smiled and got up from his seat while I continued to look more closely at the mass of people in front of me and it was then that I really began to take in the actual detail of their faces; where again I found myself being unprepared for yet another quite unnerving surprise. Each person I looked at appeared to be someone who I recognised as being either related to me, had worked for me, I had done business with, was a customer, had gone to school with and much more. So many faces and so many memories but I couldn't begin to imagine what they were all doing in this bizarre situation or in this completely amazing looking church.

While my mind was trying to process something so outrageously incomprehensible, my companion came to stand just under the pulpit at the front of the pew and began to speak. His voice seemed to carry everywhere just as before but it had a wonderful quality imparted to it by the surroundings. This had the effect of making me feel much more relaxed for some reason. I presumed it was because I trusted him and then found myself hoping very much that he would tell me what on earth was going on.

"Please come down my friend and pay your respects to the bride and groom."

Right at that moment I couldn't have imagined doing anything worse as they were sat right at the front of the church and I had absolutely no idea what I would say to them.

"I'm sure that won't be the case when you actually meet them."

I should have known that my thoughts were as clear as words to him. So I reluctantly climbed back down the stairs while feeling that familiar wood under my hand once again and then thinking about a different set of stairs from my childhood. It was a very odd sensation indeed but I was still hungry in anticipation of being fed where thoughts of various culinary temptations caused my mouth to start watering. Stepping reluctantly off the bottom step I turned to make my way across to where he was standing and then towards the bride and groom. I glanced quickly out into the body of the church and could see nothing but a whole mass of people looking back at me. It felt like I was on stage once again and having suddenly been reminded of what that was like, I felt that I wanted to take a look at the band. I did manage to get a quick glance but unfortunately the light coming through the windows behind them put their faces in shadow, although I could see that the line-up surely did look familiar. Yet another thing to ponder in this highly confusing situation.

A few steps more and I arrived at my companion's side while being aware of the happy couple sat in the pew. "*May I introduce you.*" said my friend and so I looked at their faces for the very first time. That was the moment that my mind went into complete overload. My eyes told me who and what I had been looking at but my mind just couldn't accept it at all. I could plainly see that it was me with my first wife but I couldn't get over how incredibly young we both looked. We didn't look old enough to even be out of high school let alone getting married. I just stared while not being able to think of one appropriate thing to say or even what question to ask.

There just seemed to be an empty space where my brain once was. I looked across at my companion in the hopes that he might throw me some kind of a lifeline in the faint possibility of rescuing my fast disappearing sense of reality. I looked back at the assembled mass of people and then around at the church while remembering the words I had heard about it being something to do with me and my creation. I struggled to take it all in but there was a door, somewhere in the recesses of a consciousness that once belonged to me, which didn't appear to want to open. I tried knocking. A voice answered. It was me. It told me to go away and come back later as I was busy having a nervous breakdown.

- Chapter 17 -

The Hidden Illuminations from the Seven Windows

Eventually a modicum of sanity did reappear where I managed to look around at my companion while placing my hand gently on his arm as I heard myself say,

"Did I tell you about this really amazing dream I had? Trust me it was way up there on the scale of weirdness. If ten is high then this one was in orbit. You see, I found myself standing at the front of an enormous church full of people, just like this one as a matter of fact, and they all looked like someone I'd known throughout my life but not only that, I was there with my first wife as well and I was still in short pants but I was getting married and, oh yeah!, they had this brilliant marimba band too. Is this making any sense?"

My companion smiled like a proud father who was enjoying watching his young son take the first few tottering steps towards him after being able to stand up by himself.

"Why are you smiling?" I asked. *"I'm serious, I just have to tell someone about my dream or I'll think I'm going nuts!"*

He looked back at me in the most kindly manner and then sat down in an empty seat at the side of the bride. I couldn't help but look at her and then immediately begin thinking about how things were for us at that time, as well as how I felt about the moment of my becoming a husband. A whole flood of memories came rushing back as I did this which caused a strange sensation to overtake my whole body in almost being able to step back into myself at that time. In doing so I could see how the world looked for me back then, but I could also appreciate how naïve and inexperienced I was in having no real idea about what was in store for me.

In certain respects I found it difficult to understand how I could have thought about getting married and becoming a father when I knew so little about life. All I wanted was to somehow tell my younger self about the many forthcoming pitfalls and how to avoid them so as to protect him; but then I realised that even if I had been able to do this then he really wouldn't have understood it. As I looked directly into his youthfully nervous face I could see that early manhood has its own language which comes with a confidence that tolerates very little in the way of challenges to its certainty of purpose. Whatever wisdom and advice I could pass on now, wouldn't make the slightest difference to how things were going to turn out. One look at his body language told me that the bridge between youth and wisdom is one that can only be appreciated from the vantage point of time; a life lived and then reviewed with the clarity of hindsight. I suddenly shivered quite sharply at this realisation which helped break my mood.

Somehow I managed to settle myself a little while trying not to feel frustrated about what I appreciated was simply not possible for me to do. I looked hard at my younger self while almost willing words of advice to somehow magically permeate his consciousness. This was the point at which my companion spoke in those customary soothing tones of his that I had come to value very much indeed.

"I understand your feelings my good friend but please listen carefully to what I have to say to you now. I want you to allow yourself to focus solely on this instant in time and where you find yourself while in it. Please put aside all else that you may be feeling however persuasive or compelling it may be for you to do otherwise. Do not allow yourself to be distracted by whatever temptations you may feel as your attention must remain here with me and what we will discuss forthwith. This is of paramount importance to you my dear friend as this moment will not come again.

Hear me well when I tell you that what you are presented with in this place and at this point on your journey is a gift of the greatest magnitude which you would do well to cherish. It comes to you with immense love and is a reflection of the same love which you too have given but which has often been seen in ways that have misled you. Now, my very fortunate friend, you have a chance to see anew and, when you do, then something else will be revealed to you in the process. Would you care for me to explain what it is that you have been so graciously granted the opportunity of experiencing? Are you quite ready for this my dear friend?"

"*Yes.*" was all I could manage to say which seemed to be a totally inadequate response to what I had just heard, but my mind couldn't seem to find any other suitably appropriate words at that moment. I did, however, manage to utter my agreement with what I hoped sounded something akin to grateful enthusiasm. That was one saving grace at least.

"Good, very good indeed, I'm so very pleased to hear you say this. I assure you my brave friend that this is without doubt a wise choice which will bring you more than you can possibly appreciate right at this moment. Now, please allow me to take you for a short walk first of all so that we can begin our adventure into a more beneficial perspective. Would this be agreeable to you? Are you ready to take the first step in a new direction?"

I nodded and immediately he started to get up while gently patting the bride's knee almost in the manner of saying 'don't worry my dear, I'll be back soon'. It seemed a most odd thing to do but given my present surroundings then 'odd' seemed pretty much par for the course, so I just accepted it while managing to resist doing the same thing. It certainly was tempting but I restrained myself just in time while remembering what had been asked of me. I shot him a quick glance and then noticed him motion to me that we should walk towards the apse where the bright rays of light were still streaming in through the five big windows.

I did as I was asked while not having a clue as to why we should be heading in that direction. To me it seemed logical that any explanations or answers would more likely be found in the main body of the church than anywhere else. After all, that was where all the people from my past were sat; although I had to admit that none of them appeared to be saying anything.

"I entirely appreciate your reasoning my delightfully inquisitive friend but first of all there is something which I need to show you that is very important for you to be aware of. It is essential that you thoroughly understand this fundamental aspect of your situation as everything else will depend on your ability to apply it to what I will explain later. Come, please, I will show you."

With that said we made our way towards the tall windows where he stopped in the middle of the semi-circular shape, as did I. He then looked up at the centre window panel while pointing at the brightly illuminated eye.

"You see that my friend? What do you make of it and why are there five windows?"

I carefully studied all five panels and then focused my attention on the design of the centre window but nothing really came to mind. To me it was the most unusual piece of stained glass artwork and not at all what I would have expected to find in any church. I was more used to seeing iconic images or re-creations of religious scenes which were meant to be meaningful to those who came to worship or make their connection with the big guy upstairs.

"Quite, but what do those kind of pictorial representations tell you? They are pretty, artistic and no doubt inspirational to some but they really don't impart anything in the way of real wisdom or deeper understanding to the viewer. Let's just take a moment to consider what this window might be telling us along with the others which accompany it. What can you see on the other windows?"

Once again I studied each one of them closely and then realised that they all had similar symbols but that their main central designs were different. I was starting to see a pattern but I found it difficult to get an appreciation of any kind of meaning or message that I could relate to.

"Good, that's fine, you're doing well. Now, look once more at the designs but this time allow yourself to relax your preconceptions while taking a slightly different view of things. Let the symbols lead you to a better understanding of something very basic but very powerful. Pay close attention to the central designs on each panel while bearing in mind that there are five. Why five? What would be the significance of that number? Think for a moment what it could mean for you. I'll give you a hint. What is it that you can see which would

connect all five? While thinking about it then please also give some thought to your current perceptions of life and how you came by them. These windows are like writing in the sky and they have a message for you which is just as big."

Again I began studying the designs on the windows while trying to make a connection with my perceptions but however hard I tried I just couldn't make anything come clear to me whatever I did. I found myself thinking about all manner of things to do with religious iconography but five meant nothing to me at all. I plumbed the very depths of my memory banks in the hope of retrieving something that would help me while focusing on the most obvious of symbols which was the eye.

For a moment or two I considered whether this was meant to depict the eye of Horus from Egyptian mythology and then I thought about Ra the sun god in respect of the light shining through it. Ra had apparently become a major deity by the fifth dynasty but what this could have to do with anything that might be connected with me was totally beyond my ability to comprehend. I felt the need to look for something more basic while ignoring all the symbols which looked a little like hieroglyphics and then forgetting about any Egyptian connections as well. In doing so I was tempted to ask for another hint. My wish was immediately granted.

"Consider this for a moment. How is it that you are able to perceive the windows in the first place? What enables you to know, to be aware, that they even exist?"

I looked at my companion like he had just asked a two year old the question as the answer seemed so obvious. *"Well I can see them of course!"*

Even before the words were out of my mouth, something clicked in my mind and again I looked at the eye. It was quite obvious that I could see the windows and, while doing so, I had become conscious of the fact that there was an eye looking back at me. This gave me my first clue. Now, what else could there be to notice, given that I had started to get an idea of what he wanted me to appreciate?

I studied another panel and then saw the central design had what looked like wavy lines and something which appeared to be an ear of some sort.

"How is it that you can appreciate my guidance and questions in order to determine how you see things. What gives you this unique ability?"

Again it sounded like a simple question but I was beginning to get the idea of how to use it to my advantage.

"I listen to you of course and so the other panel must be something to do with hearing."

If this was the case then I began to closely inspect the designs on the other three and, although they weren't quite as obvious as the eye and the ear, they were identifiable as being connected with the five physical senses. All five windows seemed to represent each of the five unique senses which we possess as humans. But what were the other two windows meant to represent and why were they blanked out so that no light came in through them?

"Very good my astute friend, well done! We will get to that shortly, but first of all we must expand a little more on what it is that you have just become aware of. Indeed you are correct in your assessment of the inspirational message contained within the five stained glass windows. But, we must ask ourselves, what could their purpose be in having been crafted into the structure of this potentially magnificent building and what more can they tell us? When we have the answers to these important questions then we will become more keenly aware of what is taking place in the church. Does that sound like it may be of interest to you?"

I wanted to respond by asking him if the Pope was Catholic but I resisted the temptation. My companion chuckled which was the moment I remembered how easily he could hear my thoughts. My face flushed a little as a consequence but I managed to give him an appreciative smile.

"Please give yourself a little time to carefully digest everything that is being offered to you through being able to expand your awareness while standing here. Let the designs on the windows be thoroughly absorbed into your consciousness while I pose a few more questions that need consideration so as to add even more depth of meaning to our discoveries."

We both stood silently looking at the big panel windows while I slowly studied more of their individual designs. In doing so I couldn't help but wonder what significance, if any, there was in portraying the five physical senses in such a grandiose religious setting. When I looked at it in this way then they seemed to be completely out of place.

"Why do you think that, after going to all the trouble to construct such a huge and eminently sacred building, anyone would want to decorate the main light providing windows with such apparently simplistic designs? What could possibly have motivated any skilled architect or master craftsman to include something so seemingly uninspiring in the most inspirational of settings which exists within the whole church? On the face of it there seems to be little in the way of careful consideration where it could almost be regarded as being the bizarre whim of some fanciful mind. Surely not! There must be another explanation ... wouldn't you agree?"

On studying the huge windows and their impressive stone-clad setting I did have to agree that whoever built this place must have had a good reason for including them in the design. I couldn't begin to imagine how much it must have cost to build this quite majestic structure so there had to be some kind of deliberate intent which made me keen to want to find out what it was.

"Good, now, while keeping these thoughts very much in mind let's you and I return to the area of the nave where we shall see what we shall see."

Turning to walk back towards the chancel it took a moment for my eyes to adjust to the light but the first thing I could make out was the band. I realised that we were now standing behind them but it took me only a few seconds to appreciate the line-up and immediately I knew who they were. I stood just taking in the details of every piece of equipment while every performance I'd ever made seemed to play out in front of me. It certainly proved to be the most exciting feeling in being able to re-live those wonderful times when I was so happy to be able to do something that I absolutely loved doing. I could even hear every instrument as the songs kept coming one after the other where every one of the arrangements seemed to be so fresh in my mind. I just wanted to stand and listen but, more than that, I wanted to go up to my marimba and play it. The need in me seemed to be overwhelming at that moment.

"Just stay with that emotion my friend but while you are so immersed in it then allow yourself to visualise the panelled widows while remembering what they have shown you. Ask yourself how it is that you are able to experience the emotion which you feel now in all that you see yourself doing? What contributes to the way that you come by this sensation of joy? Go through your new understanding of the windows and see which ones are appropriate to apply to this situation."

As soon as my companion had asked the question of me then there was a noticeable change in the light. For a moment I could have imagined that it was some kind of stage effect which formed part of the performance but something encouraged me to appreciate that this wasn't actually the case.

I turned to look back at the big panel windows and saw that the light through one of them had dimmed quite a lot while yet another had become slightly less bright. I looked back at the band while feeling myself playing my instrument and then letting all the sensations of that moment just fill me up. I was in danger of becoming lost in the music while concentrating on my technique and what notes I would be hitting next. I was **so** absorbed in this time of pure joy that the rest of the world would just disappear as nothing else seemed to exist.

"So tell me what you're feeling then. From one musician to another, describe what it's like to do what you're doing. What is it that calls so strongly to the emotional being that you are?"

For a moment I was slightly distracted by his reference to him being a musician which made me want to better understand, but the effect of the performance was so compelling that I went back to it almost immediately. Once again I immersed myself in the whole experience of playing in front of an audience while thoroughly enjoying the music. I just didn't want it to stop but I did manage to think about what I'd been asked to do although it seemed like quite a while before I got around to it. The band played on, I played on while loving the feel of my instrument and how it responded to my touch.

As soon as that word entered my mind I turned once again to look at the big panel window. Sight, hearing and touch were all brightly lit but smell was not so bright in contrast where taste appeared to be quite dim by comparison. Again I looked back at myself and the band while once again being me, the young performing musician, while playing my marimba. It was so incredibly exciting to do this. Over and above my sensation of enjoyment I was still able to see the windows and slowly I began to appreciate that the entirety of this experience had been coming to me through three major senses while my ability to smell contributed as well, albeit in a somewhat lesser capacity.

I reasoned that without being able to see what I was doing then there would have been no performance; similarly with that of my hearing. The quality of my playing would have been non-existent without my ability to appreciate touch and so it was easy to accept that my main emotion came from having all three senses providing me with what I needed. Suddenly I became lost in my thoughts as the music faded to become a kind of background accompaniment. Never before had I given any consideration to how it was that I interpreted my world and how important each of my physical senses were in my being able to do this.

Without the three major senses acting perfectly for me then I would not have experienced the joy of performing in my band. If any one of them had been impaired then nothing would have been the same. My sense of smell certainly did contribute to allowing me to appreciate the atmosphere more fully but I would have been able to manage without it; albeit that things wouldn't have been quite the same. I was intrigued by what I had just become aware of having never even given it a thought before that time.

"You and very many others like you my friend."

My companion's words corresponded with the band abruptly stopping which consequently reinstated the characteristic level of hushed silence that had previously existed everywhere in the church.

"Hear that?" he remarked almost in a whisper.

"Hear what?" I replied, a little puzzled.

"Precisely!" was all he said but then he gave me that enigmatic smile which I knew was telling me to pay greater attention to something. I did and then appreciated that I actually could hear the silence. If I had no hearing then I couldn't appreciate the lack of sound.

"Very good, very good indeed. You are starting to get a true appreciation for what is becoming much more obvious to you. Now, let's move on as there is so much more for you to discover. This really is exciting and I am so grateful to you for allowing me to be the one who leads you on this part of your journey."

Once again I must have done my highly convincing impression of an owl as my eyes opened in surprise at hearing his statement. Never before that moment had I considered the possibility that he would ever be grateful to me for something after so much that he had led me to an understanding of.

For a second or two I felt quite honoured. His wonderful smile told me instantly that he understood and it was then that I appreciated what a true delight it was to be in this man's company. He seemed to be everything that I had ever imagined being perfect about a brother who I would have been able to share so much with. It was an absolutely wonderful feeling indeed and made me feel equally as happy as I had been while playing my music.

"And where exactly did that feeling of brotherly joy arise from my very special friend? Did it come about as a result of your physical senses? Not at all! So how was it that you were able to experience the same joy through feeling it as that which came through playing your music which you did feel? The answer may surprise you."

Before I had time to think about what he had said, he put his arm gently in the small of my back so as to encourage me to walk out towards the nave. I did as he asked and soon we were back in the main body of the church where everyone remained sitting almost like they were waiting for us to return; which of course they were. It was the most odd feeling but slowly I found myself getting used to seeing all the recognisable faces even though there were so many of them. We stopped in front of the raised space which formed the dais while my companion began looking around at the somewhat odd shapes of the huge building.

"Now then, let's you and I put our attention on what we can see of this splendid structure and what it also has to tell us in the same way that the panel windows did. What is it that this truly imposing and most complex structure wants us to know?"

Again I did my party-piece owl impression while looking around at the inside of the church. My mind was just as silent as the atmosphere all throughout the interior of the building. I had no idea at all about what message there could be hidden in the intricate structure of such a huge place of worship. The message from the panel windows I could see, eventually after being given a lot of clues, but what there was about carved stone blocks and ornately crafted wood that could impart any wisdom I hadn't a clue.

"That's quite understandable my friend but let's just take a closer look and then see if this marvellous edifice of your creating will give up its secrets."

Before I could ask a question about the exact meaning of his last statement he continued.

"Firstly let's look at the floor."

I must have raised a puzzled eyebrow as once again he smiled before continuing.

"What we are standing on is the foundation to the structure of this quite substantial building. I'm sure you'll agree that if not for its physical strength and

robust form of construction then nothing else could prevail without its supportive presence. It is without question the mainstay of the building's existence and ever thus it shall be in order for everything else to constitute what you recognise as being a church. The solid structure of its nature also extends up into the walls so as to form the body of the building; the shell, the tangible expression of its visible identity. Are you with me so far?"

I nodded hastily while wondering what would come next, and more importantly, why.

"As you enter the church are you not greeted by the most splendid of sights and atmospheres? Do your physical senses not respond to what has been created by those whose clarity of thought and depth of awareness knew how to construct something of the utmost consequence? All four senses, sight, hearing, touch and smell provide you with an emotional experience as you fall under the influence of the master craftsman's wisdom. What you are seeing my good friend is a message from a gifted soul who designed this place in such a manner that only those who are truly ready to appreciate its gift can receive it. You are at that point on your journey my brother and so it is that you shall unwrap your treasure; if this is what you wish of course."

I found myself feeling a little apprehensive about the implications of his statement but there was no way that I was going to pass up an opportunity like this, so I nodded. While smiling his approval my companion turned to look up at the high ceiling.

"And what do you see up there? Why do you think that anyone would want to build something so high in such a manner as to make it very difficult to construct. What possible reason could there be for creating such an imposing covering in this way and what knowledge must it have taken in understanding how to position all those heavy materials up there in the first place. What was it that the master craftsman knew, what closely guarded secrets was he privy to before even setting out to design a work of such enormous complexity? Does this not seem fascinating to you in itself?"

I had to admit to being more than a little intrigued as I appreciated that in the days when large churches, abbeys and cathedrals like this were built then there were no computers or any kind of modern construction machinery such as the world has become used to. I began to wonder how they even got the stones and timbers to hold together in such wide arches that held up what must have been a very heavy expanse of ceiling.

"How about the steeple? How heavy do you think that is and how much skilful effort do you imagine it took to erect ... but more importantly, why? What does a steeple do apart from hold a few bells? Could there be another reason for it do you think?"

As soon as he said the word steeple then the image of what I had seen jutting up out of the lake came instantly tumbling back into my mind. For what seemed like an age I started to piece together all that was happening to me and where exactly I was. Fortunately, just as I seemed to be in danger of disappearing into a veritable whirlpool of highly distracting internal debate, my companion spoke.

"My friend, please understand that this place is situated in what you will soon come to appreciate is actually the Valley of your Mind and, with a little help and guidance from me, you are just about to find your way out of it. If it is your wish to do so of course."

Through the Portal of a Wider Perspective

My attention immediately pounced on his statement like a fox leaping around while trying to trap a field mouse. At first I had to think about what he had said as I couldn't even link the words together coherently in my consciousness. The Valley of my Mind? What on earth could that possibly be for goodness sake and why would I be in it in the first place? What was more confusing to me about his statement was the inference that I had somehow got lost in it as well. I didn't like the sound of that part of his explanation at all. Not one bit. It all seemed like one conundrum too far and so I was just about to ask for a little more clarification on the matter, well actually I wanted more than just a little, when I noticed that kind of 'patient' look on his face.

I was about to protest but something prompted me to just let the matter go for a moment while waiting to hear what he had to say next. At the same instant that I decided to rein in my inquisitiveness he smiled in appreciation of my attention and then turned to face the front of the church. Placing his hand firmly on my shoulder, and then pointing to the big stone arched entrance to the nave with the other, he began to beam a huge smile. I instinctively turned to see what he could be looking at or wanting me to see but everything looked the same as it always did. Then I heard him say through clenched teeth *"Smy ... ellll!"*

Before I could ask him why the heck he would want me to smile, the huge front doors of the church began to open. As they did so then I could see that outside, a short distance away from the doors, was a smartly dressed lady who stood behind the biggest looking tripod mounted camera that I had ever seen in my life. She was peering through the viewfinder while holding what appeared to be a flashgun unit in her outstretched hand; but this one looked more like a searchlight. I was just about to say something to my companion when again he said through his fixed smile,

"Say cheeeeeeese!"

Before his words were even registered in my mind there was an almighty flash from the 'searchlight' which was so powerful that I had to blink in a kind of defensive response. The light appeared to come racing at me like an explosion and for one moment it seemed to be of such intense brightness that I felt as if I could easily get an instant suntan from it. No sooner had this sensation passed than I got the impression that it had begun to recede just as quickly back to where it had come from but that I was somehow being gently sucked along with it. This proved to be a most disturbing feeling albeit one that I had no option but to give up to.

All of this happened within a fraction of a second but now there was absolutely no sound at all. I considered briefly that I had gone deaf but when I opened my eyes I could see that my companion and I were still holding the same pose although now we appeared to be in some kind of dark room while staring out through a big round plate glass window. What's more, we were now outside the church and looking back at the front entrance but somehow I was able to see not only the whole front section of the building but I could also get a view of the sides as well. This gave me a much greater appreciation for exactly how big it was and I have to say that I was very impressed by the sheer scale of it all.

"Good! Now my friend, please pay attention to what you see." said my companion without seeming to be at all fazed by our current situation and the fact that we appeared to be trapped inside the bowels of some kind of giant washing machine.

"Yes, yes, quite." he said almost in the manner of indulging a persistent child.

"Please my good friend, ignore where you find yourself while concentrating on what tremendous advantages your new situation affords you. Can you not appreciate how extensively and richly you can see while looking through this carefully crafted visual portal? Notice, if you will, that you are able to take in much more than in any other circumstance but bear it well in mind as you do that you are still only using one of your major senses while doing so."

I somehow managed to let go of my extreme curiosity about our new surroundings while starting to fix my attention on the quite unusual view of the church. It wasn't too difficult given the fact that virtually the whole of my visual world was taken up by the impressive building while the rest was in darkness. I couldn't help but appreciate what a unique way of looking at things this brought about as there seemed to be nothing else to distract me and so my mind was able to absorb everything that I had been presented with.

"Excellent, that's just what we want." My companion sounded very pleased and so I relaxed at hearing his words.

"Now then my highly observant friend, let's see what we can see while bearing in mind all else that has already been revealed to us in this most fascinating and enigmatic of man-made structures."

He was still pointing towards the general area of the open front doors when his outstretched hand started making circular motions which encompassed all that we could see.

"Just look at the entirety of this grand design and then notice the way in which it's constructed. Pay particular attention to the solidity of not only the walls but the foundations on which it's built as well. It may seem quite uninteresting at first but allow yourself to appreciate that your eyes see much more than your mind is programmed to accept. Be aware that whatever you see is firstly filtered through your conditioned thought processes which then interprets your visual world accordingly."

I glanced briefly at my companion to contest his assertions as I didn't agree with what he'd said at all but then something, somewhere in the back of my mind, reminded me that he was not one to say things that were without substance. He was a very wise man who had chosen to share so much of his wisdom with me for reasons that I'd never asked and so I had to respect the fact that whatever he told me was for my benefit and mine alone. He seemed to have no agenda other than to help me find the answers to very many questions that I had and even more that I hadn't even been aware that I wanted to ask.

Never once did he force any opinions on me but only ever gave me things to consider, however bizarre they may have appeared at the time, while letting me make up my own mind about what I had become aware of as a result. So how could I question what he had just said? I decided to put my attention back on the church and then see what came to me when I did this although I didn't much like the thought of looking at something while feeling that my vision was somehow being 'distorted'. I suddenly found myself also hoping that the lady behind the camera didn't decide to select the 'spin' cycle any time soon as my brain was coping with just about all the summersaults that it could handle right at that precise moment.

Distorted; this word suddenly began to bother me but in a way that was more deeply meaningful than I could figure. The moment I let it settle completely into my mind then I felt a kind of oddly disquieting sensation in the pit of my stomach. At first I couldn't understand why this should be, but then I began to see myself sat all alone on the pew while looking around the church for the first time. I recalled thinking how strange things appeared in the way that the columns seemed misshapen and the ceiling slightly jumbled up and not how I thought it ought to be.

That proved to be the moment when I made the connection. Suddenly something within my discomfort shifted as a little light went on which enabled me to see things more clearly. Distorted; that was a really good way to describe how I viewed the nature of my surroundings especially when I looked at the pillars and the ceiling. They were distorted. That was it! I can't tell you how it made me feel to appreciate this but it also brought with it another more subtle feeling in me which I found to be quite uncomfortable as well. I was just about to give this more thought when my friend gripped my shoulder in a kind of comforting way which I was very grateful for.

"Patience my good friend." he said calmly while squeezing me gently again.

"All in good time but first let's get an appreciation of what it is that's important for you to see and then more will come clear to you as your 'vision' improves. Please do not let any element of anguish cloud your view as total clarity is the very minimum that you must demand right now. So then, oh most diligent one; back to our study of this mysterious building and what wondrous secrets it's waiting to reveal to us."

The view from the inside the dark room through the special 'window' was certainly very impressive in that it seemed as though I could easily inspect any detail of the church that I wanted to. It was quite fascinating in its own way in that I had never before been able to see so much of a craftsman's work and what an amazing amount of effort that they had put into constructing the building. To me, a church had been just a special building albeit that it did seem to have a different atmosphere when going inside it. I hadn't really given much thought to the aspect of why it was so different and what was behind the design of it.

In fact, now I came to think of it, I began to wonder why anyone would want to build something so grand and so complex as this in the first place. I mean, where did the original idea come from and what was the motivation of the designer if these types of structures had been around for centuries when only basic dwellings existed in those times. What gave anyone the notion to build something so large, so intricate and so different? I had always imagined that it was simply a by-product of religious enthusiasm but somehow that just didn't feel right any more. Suddenly something didn't seem to add up.

"Wonderful! Now you're starting to really see much more clearly my clever friend. You are correct in what you are thinking and how you are allowing yourself to see beyond the limitations of your conditioning. By not taking something for granted any more then you permit your vision to impart a greater depth of appreciation to your consciousness. You become 'aware' which is not the same as 'thinking'. Awareness transcends thought. Thought is very limiting, as you will hopefully see.

Now, let's look once more at the church as a whole while carefully reflecting on the splendour of its existence and its place on this scared spot. For a moment I would like you to consider purely the physical nature of the building. Just look at what you see in front of you and then think of a word that would describe it in relationship to the whole. Any ideas come to mind?"

I studied the church but could only see the structure and the design while still wondering what would inspire someone in ancient times to conceive of and then build something on such a grand scale as what I was seeing. I couldn't really think of a single word which would express my true feelings about it.

"That's fine my good friend, at least you're considering things in a new way and that's a very good start. Now, please just give some thought to a word that I would like to offer you. It's a very simple word but one which will come to mean a lot more to you very shortly. The word is 'body'. Can you just accept that word at face value for the moment until I expand on things further?"

I nodded my agreement.

"What you are seeing is the body of the church. It is, I'm sure you will agree, a very apt way to describe the crafting of the stones which go to make up what you recognise as the church and its foundations. I am also certain that you will consider this to be a quite inconsequential word but, as we shall see when more is revealed to you, that it will come to have a very different significance to you in a moment. Then you will begin to appreciate how your mind limits your perceptions."

I was about to make a comment on what had just been said when, to my slight discomfort, we seemed to start moving. What's more, the motion had a slightly bouncy aspect to it which was most bizarre. It took me a few seconds to work out that we were actually moving towards the front entrance to the church and then, slowly but surely, we were heading through the entrance doors and back inside. I watched in fascination as my view of the outside world began to change. No longer could I see the sides and then less and less of the front until we were entering the big stone archway which spanned the front doors.

Then, shortly after, we were once again looking into the huge interior of the church although I was able to see much more of it and in much greater detail, just as I had when I'd been outside. Now I could clearly see the impressive design of the whole magnificent nave and beyond. From within the almost tomb-like quiet of the dark room, while looking out at the view through the strange glass window, I couldn't help feeling very moved by what I saw. It certainly was having the most profound effect on me. Never before had I noticed the scale and amalgamation of such wonderful artistry and the quite spectacular colours of the designs in such detail. The carvings on the walls and pillars were simply wonderful while the floor was a mosaic of intricate designs that were absolutely fascinating, as well as being highly decorative. Even the beautiful wooden furniture and the gold fittings blended in with the atmosphere to make the whole experience ...

"A what?" My companion spoke gently in the midst of my thoughts and once again I found myself wondering what I was supposed to see over and above what I already was seeing.

"This time, my friend, please let yourself move past the purely visual while allowing a different part of you to speak in respect of what's happening to you. Take a moment before you reply while continuing on with your appreciation of

this wonderful spectacle. What is it that you truly want to say about it without letting your mind get in the way?"

Having heard this request I was almost tempted to press my face up against the glass so as to take in more of the vision in front of me. I dearly wanted to find, without prompting, what it was that I had been given the opportunity to appreciate. This time I realised my keenness to understand things for myself. I looked more intently at the vision that came to me from the inside of the building which suddenly, for some reason, began to affect me much more than it had before. The highly recognisable environment of a church suddenly wasn't that any longer. It appeared to me to be a quite amazing structure that I couldn't begin to fathom how anyone could have thought up in the first place. It was so … so …

"Impressive? Inspirational? Awe inspiring?" my wise friend had obviously decided to give me a clue.

Yes, 'impressive and inspirational' those certainly were very apt words to describe my overall impression. My mind quickly returned to the time when I had been outside where the room, or whatever I was in, began to move towards the doors and then travel inside the church. While thinking about it I could appreciate that no one who was greeted by what they would see, hear or smell on entering this unique atmosphere, could fail to be influenced or moved by it. Suddenly I thought of the big panelled windows once again and their illustrating the five physical senses. A little seismic quake erupted within me as a gradual shift in the tectonic layers of my true appreciation began to take place.

"So, what kind of experience would you say that you are having now? What would be a good way to describe it? Just one word."

There was no denying that I found myself being more than a little affected by what I was seeing as there were so many things that seemed to speak to various parts of me. In fact, there appeared to be far too much to take in all at one time but to think of one word to describe everything that was going on in me seemed to be a task beyond my reach at that moment. It was all too much for my emotions to cope with. Another little aftershock appeared having made that statement so I took it as a definite sign that I was on the right track.

However else I analysed my appreciation of the interior of the church then I couldn't deny how I felt about it in the way it affected me. I was moved by what I saw especially in view of how much of it I could absorb through this special window. There seemed to be some kind of compression to my perspective which brought everything I wished to see much closer and more clearly in view than ever before. In a way it was quite overwhelming to the degree that I was having a little difficulty in controlling my emotions.

"Excellent!"

I turned to look at my companion who was now looking straight ahead while holding his hands out in the manner of expressing some kind of appreciation.

"Just look at the wonder which confronts you. Behold the creation of the master craftsmen of old who wished to influence you in such a way as to bring about such a profound state in your awareness. Look at what this magnificent creation offers you in the way of such contrast to how things are in your mundane everyday world. What a gift this veritable wealth of artistry presents you with in not so much what they want you to see but more in how they wish it to attract your attention and so capture your imagination. Can you appreciate their skill in transporting your awareness into a place of greater peace and inner calmness which transcends that of the chaotic nature of your daily existence?

By virtue of their ancient knowledge and understanding you find yourself in a space where your whole attitude to life is affected and, while you are present in the midst of this sacred artistry, you cannot fail but to be moved by what you experience. Through their skilful fashioning of this environment they speak from across time to a part of you which they had already mastered. These were not just craftsmen my dear friend, they were alchemists who were entrusted with the answers to the greatest mysteries of life and the universe. Can you understand now that what you are experiencing is something which highly impacts your emotional state of being? Is this how you could best describe what you are seeing? Something which is 'emotional'; a quite moving experience?"

There was no denying that it did indeed affect me in this way but I wasn't sure what it had to do with anything in the context of what it was that he had been trying to get me to see.

"That's fine my adventurous friend, just stay with these two aspects of what we have come to appreciate thus far. Remember that outside we became aware of the body and now we are being presented with an awareness of the emotions. Are you starting to see what else may come?"

I was just about to say that I didn't, but before I could answer I became conscious of the fact that the room we were in had begun to tilt backwards. In response I instinctively put my hands behind me while setting one foot back to steady myself but there appeared to be no sensation of gravity and, even as we seemed to be looking at the ceiling, I didn't feel as though I was going to fall. It never occurred to me that there was probably only the infinity of space to fall into as what might be behind me in the pitch darkness was totally unknown. I dared not even think about it.

Looking up at the huge complex ceiling which covered the whole church was a different experience altogether. I guessed that this aspect of the design was something which only received the most casual of glances from anyone who came into the building. In my new way of being able to see it then I marvelled at the manner in which it had been constructed. I just couldn't begin to work out how it had been put together in those ancient times with such limited equipment while being so high off the ground. Neither could I comprehend what was in the mind of the designer in the first place while wanting to create such an imposing and difficult to construct aspect of the building. Why make it so high and so intricate when hardly anyone took notice of it.

"*But you did!*" said my companion in the most encouraging and complimentary way.

"*You appreciated it from almost the first moment you arrived. You couldn't make sense of it but you did appreciate what it took to put it up there and to decorate it in the manner in which it is so beautifully presented. There was no doubt in your mind about what a feat of human ingenuity it is. Would you agree?*"

I nodded firmly as this certainly was the truth of how I saw it.

"*So, which part of you is impressed then? Was it your body or you emotions or what? Did you feel the same as when you were looking at the inside of the church or was it a different experience?*"

This proved to be a good question and one which I found myself thinking about. Obviously it didn't affect my body, and didn't see how it could, but I didn't really feel emotional about the ceiling as much as I had admiration for the way in which it was put together. It appealed to my sense of appreciation for what it took to build it.

"*So which part of you has become aware of this aspect then?*"

I was just about to ask what he meant when I noticed the strange effect that I had seen when sat in my seat. The roof was rippling in an odd way and, as I studied it more closely, I appeared to be able to see right through it.

There seemed to be all manner of wooden beams appearing in complex structures while I could even see workmen above them and some starting to appear on platforms below. Suddenly there was a veritable hive of industry going on where I could also see many artists painting the complex and beautiful frescos which gave the ceiling its unique effect. I found myself being drawn into the enthralling complexity of it all while something in me seemed to be trying to calculate the sheer scale of what was taking place.

"*So your mind is quite captivated by what's going on then? Would it be true to say that your attention is focused solely within your mind at this time and that you are operating purely on a mental level?*"

I had to agree as there was so much to look at which I wanted to get a better understanding of while still trying to figure out how anyone managed to make such a complex structure out of wooden beams and basic tools. Even as these thoughts were whirling around in my head, I could see even more through the roof as greater heights of wooden platforms began to come into view. At first I couldn't understand what they were for but then I began to appreciate that they were enclosing the tall spire which formed the most prominent feature of the church. This truly was a challenge to the craftsmen where all of their skills were needed to accomplish what must have taken them a very long time to complete.

"So why build it then? What do you think would persuade someone who lived in those times to even contemplate putting up such a large structure? Why go to all of that trouble when they could have just finished at the ceiling and hung the bells somewhere else? Was there something else they knew and were aware of or could it have just been a flight of fancy? I have a feeling that there most certainly was a very special reason don't you my good friend?"

Before I had time to answer there was a noise from behind me which sounded like a charge of electricity building up and one which most definitely had a lot of power contained in it. I wanted to turn so as to see what it could be as I felt the hairs on the back of my arms almost standing up with the increase in noise and its effect on me. While in the midst of processing this thought there was a loud echoing click. This was immediately accompanied by something that felt like a very close discharge of lightning whereupon the most enormous flash erupted from somewhere outside the room. The blinding light raced forward and then streamed in through the huge round window while instantly filling the space all around me and then making me feel quite small. For a fraction of a second I had the feeling that it actually wanted to completely consume me but no sooner had this thought entered my mind than it was gone.

Absolutely everything within my vision was obliterated but when it returned then I could see that I was once again standing in front of the congregation while looking at the now closed doors of the church. I rubbed my eyes a little so as to acclimatise them to a different situation but as I did so then my companion began to explain; but at the very same moment I felt like I wanted to sit down as it was all getting a bit too much for me.

"In a short while my friend we will relax but just give me your attention for another few minutes where I feel sure that you will be pleased to have done so. Now, let me just refresh your memory with regards to your recent experiences. I promise I'll be brief as I know that you have been given a great deal to consider and that it seems like a lot to take in all at once. Please don't overtax yourself as there will be another opportunity for us to go over everything in much greater depth; but for now I would like you to keep in mind just four important words. Here they are. Physical, Emotional, Intellectual, Spiritual. Shall I say them again?"

I shook my head as I went over them in my mind. Physical, emotional, intellectual and spiritual. I did it again and then again.

"Good, now, this is very important. Keep these words at the forefront of your mind while I place images to go with them and then I will answer any questions that you might have. Here we go. We are standing at the front of the

church while observing the body of it. We step inside to be greeted by the atmosphere and the environment which affects us emotionally. Then our attention is drawn to the ceiling which appeals to our intellect and which hovers over the emotional and the physical, body that is, and then we see the steeple which points to the heavens. The spiritual.

Can you begin to appreciate that this entire structure stimulates each aspect of that which constitutes the fundamental nature of our totality, the sum of who we express ourselves to be. We, in our experience of being human, have more than just the physical body. There are four distinct aspects of our make-up that we can be aware of through the simple process of careful consideration and observation. We are corporeal, meaning we have a physical body; just as the church does. We are emotional and so have an emotional body which the creators of the interior express through their artistry and design. This part of the church speaks to that part of us as we become influenced by its presence and our proximity to their creative expression.

Then we are intellectual, we 'think' and so the ceiling speaks to that part of us through expressing its complexity which our mind recognises instantly. It makes an association with the intricacies of what 'thought' is capable of creating. There is nothing so fascinating to the human mind as the workings of another mind. This is why there is such an attraction to solving puzzles and riddles. It's the way in which minds communicate with each other. Your intellectual body and your emotional body are just as real as that of your physical body albeit that they are not as obvious to our visual senses. There is no denying their existence as much as there is no way that we can ignore the presence of a spiritual body no matter what our beliefs in any kind of religion are. We are spiritual beings, all of us, but it is only ever the level of our awareness which keeps us from appreciating this fact.

What you are seeing here, my very privileged friend, is the result of a true master's inspirational creation. Someone who understood so well the secrets of our mysterious existence and what it is that is so important for us to be fully aware of. This magnificent building is a masterpiece of communication that speaks so clearly to each individual level of our composite 'self'. Those essential elements of what makes us who and how we are but which so often get ignored to one degree or another and, as such, end up throwing us out of balance. By coming to a building of this nature then we are encouraged to restore that balance by becoming attuned with all that has been so carefully crafted into it and which speaks to so much of what makes us who we are.

What we see here shows us that our whole experience in life is lived through what information we receive by virtue of our five physical senses. Everything that we accumulate on our journey through life has to be interpreted within the confines of having this limited information passed to us. In so doing it has a consequential effect on all four of our bodies, to one degree or another, and so we evolve, or not, as a direct result. For life to be harmonious, so as to bring us the true depth of joy which we so long for, then it is imperative that we *balance the four bodies in order for the greatest degree of harmony to exist. Anything other than this will result in dis-harmony or, to put it another way, dis-ease. This state underlies all illness because that's what illness is. Ill, not good, not desired, not in harmony, not at ease. Can you now see why it is that what you are seeing is so important to the true understanding and appreciation of the human condition my good friend?"*

Now I really did need to sit down as my head felt like it was starting to swim. More than that, I wanted something to hang onto as it seemed as though so much of my 'fixed' world was becoming fluid just like the ceiling. I also seemed to be in danger of falling through a floor which suddenly felt like it wouldn't support me any more. There was just too much for my highly overworked mind to take in. Without thinking I sat down beside the motionless form of my first wife. For one moment I felt like asking her what she thought about all this but then I got the idea that she didn't have a clue about what was going on and so I just sat back against the seat while thinking about how good a nice refreshing drink would be.

Anything would have gone down well right at that moment so without thinking I gratefully accepted what my companion handed me. I drank like I'd just crossed the Sahara while carrying my camel after not having seen an oasis for the last hundred miles. I had no idea what it was that I found myself drinking but it tasted absolutely heavenly and was so incredibly refreshing. It crossed my mind that if this was what the people who attended services in the olden days received then it was little wonder that so many of them went to church. I would surely have been one of their number.

Then I considered that I had never ever had wine which was remotely like this so maybe this variety came from a completely different part of the world. Right at that moment I didn't care where it came from as it was just what I needed. I finished every last drop of it and then smiled a grateful 'thank you' at my ever thoughtful companion. I felt better already. Going to sleep seemed like it ought to come next but something told me that I wasn't about to be getting that kind of rest for a little while yet; and, besides, I still wanted to know what all this had to do with me plus what all the people who were sitting in the church were doing there. Even as I contemplated this notion my eyelids felt like I just couldn't keep them open any more and that even a brief moment or two of having them closed would bring me a much needed sense of refreshment as well as settling my somewhat overworked mind.

It felt good just to shut things out for the moment while relaxing as much as I could against a rather unforgiving seat. I started to wonder if these weren't the creation of some uninspiring minister from times long ago who wanted to ensure that no one in his congregation dozed off in the middle of some tedious sermon. From how things felt to me at that moment I was tempted to say that he had achieved his objective with a remarkable degree of success. With my eyelids firmly shut, I began to imagine myself sat listening to some crashing old bore droning on while preaching to many of the reluctant, and probably bewildered, churchgoers in the present congregation.

I smiled a little at that prospect as I sensed their equal discomfort. My mind started to buzz again and so did my stomach. I blamed it on the drink!

- Chapter 18 -

My Flight along the Pathways of My Choices

The first thing I became aware of was that I could hardly open my eyes but when I eventually did then I felt as though I had been asleep for at least a century. What seemed to bother me the most was the fact that I could have happily slept for at least another couple more but something in the back of my mind kept telling me that a matter of some importance needed my attention. I couldn't recall whether I considered it to be urgent or not but, come to think of it, I wasn't exactly sure where I was or even what day it might be. I began rubbing my eyelids in preparation for opening them in the hope of seeing something familiar that would remind me of where I was. I did just that but what came quickly into my expanding field of vision left me looking totally bemused while blinking repeatedly and wondering if I was still asleep.

"No you most certainly are not my good friend and I am here to help you appreciate all that you are able to see when you have had sufficient time to fully awaken from your refreshing rest. I trust that you are feeling much better now as there is much to do and even more for you to benefit from. Take heart my adventurous friend as this is one experience that you will never forget."

Slowly I got up from my seat and then began walking steadily across the white marbled floor towards the large curved ornate stone balustrade which surrounded the edge of it. I appeared to be high up on some kind of grandiose balcony of the type I had sometimes seen in expensive Italian homes or plush hotels. Those beautiful creations which were so often set on the slopes of picturesque high cliffs while looking imperially out over the Mediterranean Sea; where the sun cast its magic across a natural canvas that any artist could easily have spent a lifetime attempting to recreate. All around me I noticed big displays of flowers which were set in semi-circular arrangements at the base of small exotic looking trees, while several fountains sent jets of water playing over statues of what looked like miniature winged angels. The whole atmosphere was one of peaceful splendour which gave it the feeling of being some kind of oasis in the midst of some very puzzling scenery.

My footsteps seemed dreamlike as did the view that was starting to come into a deeper perspective as I began to see ever more of the huge valley opening out in front of me. Peering tentatively over the edge of the beautifully decorated parapet walls, it appeared to stretch out forever while each side sloped up quite sharply in some places; but I couldn't see the tops of them as there was some kind of light blue and gold sky which they passed through. This created the most striking effect that I had ever seen but more than that, I could also see streams of shimmering light pouring down everywhere which served to highlight thousands of individual parts of the valley.

Whichever direction I cared to look in there seemed to be something different going on. From my high vantage point it was difficult to tell exactly what was happening in each situation but to me, the landscape appeared to be literally covered in all sorts of activity where tiny lights twinkled around every occurrence. To me it looked like Christmas decorations but the ones in front of me were much more impressive while having a quality to them which seemed to be so lively and incredibly energised. I felt the need to look at everything all at once as there appeared to be so much of interest to take in, but the most amazingly eye-catching thing of all was the sight of a big building some way off in the distance. It appeared as though it was actually growing up out of the valley floor while perched precariously on top of a structure that looked to me like an immensely thick and really ancient tree trunk.

The tree-like structure was complete with countless stone coloured roots coming down from it where, at the base, they all spread out into the valley. Here they formed into roads, pathways, tracks and even streets which led just about everywhere and into all manner of different situations. The complexity of all that I could see quite overwhelmed me but I could appreciate that there appeared to be a kind of natural flow to everything while the building in the sky formed some kind of hub; a sort of central focus. I rubbed my eyes again so as to clear the last of the sleep out of them in order to get a better view of what I was being presented with. As soon as I did this then I recognised something familiar about the shape of the big building. Gradually I began to make out what looked to me like the church that I had just been in. Although, from my current position on the high balcony I was able to appreciate that I actually had a side view of it.

I was reasonably certain that I could make out some of the big widows in the apse but then I began to study the roof and it was at this point that I noticed something odd about the shape. It took me a moment or two to realise that much of the spire appeared to be completely missing. I found this to be very confusing after having seen the visions of the workmen constructing a similar structure just a short while ago. Further careful examination of what I could see helped me to appreciate the reason for it appearing as though most of the spire had been cut off. I suddenly realised that a large part of it was actually projecting up through the 'sky', if that's what it was, and so I couldn't see it. My mind was slowly getting back into gear and as it did then I started to remember the image of a similar spire sticking up through the water of the lake. I recalled what it had looked like from the boat and then compared it to what I could see rising up from the church and that's when I figured out that I must be ...

I looked up to confirm my suspicions while examining the blue and gold sky which I could now make out was rippling just like I had seen the church roof doing a while back. My sense of innate reason was telling me one thing while my mind didn't want to listen. I just decided that wherever I was then it had to mean something very important to me. I looked out over the long expanse of the valley stretching out in front of me once again and was completely consumed by what I saw. My companion spoke gently while encouraging me to fully appreciate the significance of the view.

"Everything you see here represents a virtual map of your life where all of your experiences have shaped who and how you are. What you see happening below is actually illustrating all that has influenced your thinking, your views, your convictions and how you have responded in making your choices as a result. This, where you find yourself now my dear friend, is the Valley of your Mind. It represents a living record of all that has been successful in shaping your sense of self and what you have had an impact on by making whatever decisions you did as a result.

All roads lead to the 'monument' of your creation in how you have impressed the evolving nature of your very being upon its appearance. You are the one who has made of it such as it is and now you will see why the building which we have been examining so closely is distorted, as you choose to describe it; or, out of balance, not in a state of ultimate harmonious expression, as I would put it more appropriately. Notice if you will how the structure which holds this edifice up is the very conduit that stems from the 'monument of your mind' which has created whatever you see in the valley.

The influence of this imbalance is what gives rise to your unique experiences through the choices which you saw fit to make as a result. Had it been any other way then you would not be seeing the same view that you are at this moment. Your life and your experiences are how you created them but whatever influences were allowed to sway you in the process will have manifested themselves in the consequences of your actions. This is true for each and every soul who walks the path of duality.

Please do not judge anything that you have seen thus far, or are shortly about to see, in the way of applying terms such as good or bad while appreciating that there are certain limitations in your ways of thinking on this subject. This area of your awareness needs to be 'expanded' so as to bring a greater sense of beneficially proportioned balance to your four important aspects; the physical, the emotional, the intellectual and the spiritual. Remember that they all need to be perfectly complimentary so as to bring the utmost harmony and joy to the being who is you."

I looked down into the valley so as to examine anything which would give me a better understanding of what I was suddenly feeling the need to know much more about. Nothing obvious came to mind although I could see that there was indeed a connection which the church high up on its tree-like perch had with everything in the valley. However, there appeared to be so much going on that it was just too difficult to focus on any one aspect or situation in particular. In surveying all that I could see from my vantage point on the balcony there certainly did seem to be something I had gained a very clear appreciation for. It was the inescapable fact of just how much had apparently happened to me in my life given the vast amount of different activities in all manner of places that I could make out going on.

My companion stepped up beside me and pointed towards what appeared to be some kind of park in the distance. On studying it I could see that there was some sort of special event taking place and quite a few people attending but there appeared to be a family that I recognised.

"Do you not remember that day my friend? The day when life seemed pretty good and you felt that things were working out to your liking in having a loving family just as you had hoped for. At that time your future looked as though it was all mapped out in the respect of where you were heading while watching your children grow up as you made your business more successful and enjoyed life. Even though it wasn't how things turned out, you need to be aware of what you were granted the opportunity of experiencing at that moment when you felt as though life was just how you wanted it to be. Without meeting your first wife then you would not have been blessed with your three precious children and neither would you have shared a part of their journey so as to experience all the joy which they brought you.

Nothing that has ever happened to you can be viewed in any way as being good or bad and neither should you question your decisions or choices. Your wife Nina was your soul mate who chose to share part of her journey with you just as you did with her. Please do not overlook the fact that you both chose to do what you did while, at one level, there existed an appreciation of the valuable lessons which were to be learned through making those choices. In the uniqueness of your special gift to one another you gave each other the chance to share in a magical experience. She also has her twin flame which calls her forward and so she was influenced to make her choices just as you were. In this way you both created circumstances which you were able to grow and evolve from until the point in time where you chose to travel your separate pathways.

It was your time to do so as much as it was hers to experience a different way of life when you parted. Again, please do not fall into the trap of regarding this as being in any way right or wrong. Be very careful not to apply judgement but simply allow it to be just how it turned out to be while seeing the important lessons which came for both of you. She could not have continued on that special journey without your help in providing the circumstances where great opportunities were presented for learning what was most important for her; just as they were for you. There can be no blame attached to any aspect of your journeying together but there certainly can be a great degree of gratitude applied while appreciating that so much came from your togetherness; just as much as that which came from your eventually going your separate ways. To accept what 'was' as actually coming about because of the many different choices that were made, for reasons that are not yet clear to you, is to move gracefully along the highly illuminated causeway of understanding as to what true forgiveness really is.

Forgiveness is not about absolving anyone or excusing them in any way but appreciating that what 'was', what you experienced as the consequences of your choices, occurred for beneficial reasons and that those reasons are very rarely fully understood. All too often the mind comes racing in to apportion judgement and blame while wanting to identify a victim. This futile exercise is of no value to any living soul. Victims infer perpetrators and so divisions are created which is to the benefit of no one by virtue of their highly disruptive influences moving us ever further away from appreciating that we truly are All One.

Think for a moment about your impressions of the church. Consider for a moment how you initially viewed it as being distorted, as you termed it. Then remember our discovery of its significance to the four elemental bodies and then visualise the five windows which depicted the individual senses. Can you appreciate now how it is that we create distortions when we allow the interpretation of our senses to carry misrepresentations and misinterpretations into our four important bodies? What good comes of impacting the emotional body by viewing an event and then judging it through qualifying it in a negative way; all judgement is inherently negative as it only ever serves to create separation. To judge is to compare and through comparison one is set above or below the other. This is unhelpful and misleading and in no way contributes to anyone's beneficial evolvement.

In fact, it leads to stagnation where many other lifetimes are needed to address what has not been learned. To see things in the light of simply accepting whatever occurs as being just another expression of life's experiences, nothing more or less, is to create greater harmony in life. To look back at what 'has been' while applying the same perceptive principle is to apply forgiveness in the most beneficial way. You cannot change the past but in seeing how things were in the way of being non-judgemental then this allows the healing process to bloom just like a precious garden intends to do in the midst of summer. Remember and then carefully contemplate the windows my dear friend while taking into consideration what I have said as you review your life. Consider the fact that what you actually see is only what the limitations of your mind will allow you to appreciate. Look now on things anew and apply forgiveness wherever you feel able to. Enjoy your flight!"

I was so totally caught up in the enormity of what my companion had said to me that I completely missed his last remark. My mind seemed to be going over so much as I looked at the scene of all the celebrations while remembering those wonderful times together as a family; and what it had meant to me then. As I continued to watch all that was taking place in the park then his words came back to me about being on a journey and sharing things while benefiting from the unique experiences that we were able to create. Then I recalled his explanation about the five windows, the physical senses and how I constructed my world from how I received things through my conditioned mental processes.

In viewing us as a family, all together and being happy, there was no other thought in my mind but that of appreciating the joy which came from being that way. I didn't question anything and so I allowed myself to take in all that there was to see in the fullest and most uplifting way possible. But later, things were different and then my view seemed to become contracted in how my mind wanted to convince me to interpret my circumstances. All of a sudden I was starting to get an appreciation for what had been explained to me. No sooner had this process begun to take its first illuminating step in through the gradually opening door of my consciousness than something quite large began to appear in front of me. It came so close that I had to take a few swift paces back so as to stop myself becoming completely absorbed by it.

As more of whatever was appearing came into my view then I stepped back even further as I saw what looked amazingly like the seven big widows of the apse beginning to form above the semi-circular balustrade of the balcony. They were just as impressive as when I'd seen them in the church but now I could see right through them as well as being able to see their imposing presence in full detail. It was the most fascinating experience. Before I had time to study this spectacle in any great depth I became aware of the eye in the centre panel which appeared to be a little brighter than its surroundings. It also seemed to be getting somewhat bigger while what looked like reddish brown feathers had begun forming around it.

This was rapidly followed by the area of the window around the eye appearing to bow out towards me. For a moment the significance of what I could see happening didn't register in my mind and before I could move away I could see more and more feathers as well as a golden beak starting to appear. Just as the window looked to be on the point of bursting out at me I found myself being rooted to the spot while not knowing what would happen next or what to do. This corresponded to the instant when I glimpsed the huge wings and body coming straight towards me at which point the window silently exploded as the giant bird erupted out of the glass with its massive eye coming directly at my face. At one point it appeared to be so close that for a fraction of a second I actually caught sight of myself in its perfectly reflective and highly colourful surface.

There was no opportunity to shield myself as all that I had time to do was to blink; but immediately I did then I found myself being instantly overwhelmed by a feeling of the most amazing lightness. It was utterly thrilling to experience as it completely took over the whole of my body and something that I found myself wanting to understand much more about through knowing what had happened to me. I opened my eyes to see yet another view of the valley but this time I appeared to be soaring above it.

It took me a moment or two to appreciate that I was actually flying but, once I got over the initial shock, I began to relish the experience as being incredibly exhilarating. I had no idea that it could be like this where all I initially wanted to do was to see how fast I could go. Travelling great distances in the space of a few seconds was the most awe inspiring of sensations which went way beyond words and nothing like I had ever experienced before. I looked down with breathtaking fascination upon huge expanses of the Valley of my Mind while sweeping across so many different landscapes that captured my attention one after the other.

It was all far too much to take in as there seemed to be no end to what I could see. The panoramic views were vast where just looking at the scale of them gave me an appreciation for what an incredible gift one lifetime really is. Through being able to survey so many of my experiences it made me realise just how much had happened and how incredibly rich my life had been; albeit I rarely, if ever, stopped to consider it in this way. There was almost too much to absorb but when I did see something of particular interest then I realised that I only had to think of it, and before I knew what was happening I found myself swooping effortlessly down so as to pass very close overhead.

When I made my swift descent into it then I could see everything so clearly where memories came flooding back along with all the emotions of that time. It was an absolutely magical experience but while in the midst of one rather intense encounter I heard the faint tones of my companion's wise words encouraging me to look at things anew in the way that he had suggested. I tried very hard to comply but I just couldn't get over how wonderful it felt to literally be as free as a bird. It was just beyond words and by far the best in-flight 3D movie I'd ever seen – by awesomely far!

For a moment, while being airborne again, I stopped looking down so that I could glance sideways and was immediately greeted by the sight of the most extraordinarily beautiful wing. I studied it closely in absolute fascination while appreciating that nothing whatsoever in my earthly experience could ever compare with it. The sheer size of it was incredible and very impressive but the deep rich colours of the feathers and the crystal finger-like tips way out at the end were positively breathtaking. I watched enthralled as many different vibrant colours trailed away from it while sparkling in such incredible radiance that they seemed positively happy to be contributing to their surroundings. Everything about what I found myself experiencing felt as though a sense of heartfelt joy existed where absolutely nothing could ever serve to undermine this state, whatever the circumstances may have been.

The delight of flying in such an awe-inspiring way, while soaring above my life in living detail, was to experience everything anew and in a way that I could never have imagined possible. No sooner had this feeling settled within me than it seemed as though I was soaring up to the gold and blue sky while doing a kind of celebratory loop. Going over the top, while finding myself momentarily upside down, I could once again see a great deal of all that was going on in the valley before plummeting towards it at what seemed like an impossible speed. With the valley floor getting swiftly bigger by the microsecond I was completely mesmerised by the sensation.

With what seemed like inches to spare I began skimming at treetop height right across the floor of the valley before swooping up once more. It proved to be the most breathtaking experience and one never to be forgotten. Anywhere that I wanted to go was met by the instant fulfilment of my unspoken wish. Anything I wanted to see more closely I could and there was so much that I wanted to see and be a part of once again. It seemed like countless hours had passed while I spent time after time looking at various episodes from my life and then re-living them at great speed. There was always a huge amount to look at as well as to reconsider when combining my sense of elation with that of the emotions from the time of whatever I had wanted to study.

It was impossible not to view things differently in how I was experiencing them in this unique way. Consequently there were many instances where I found that I could actually apply my companion's guidance in the way of coming to a true state of understanding how forgiveness could bring healing to so many situations. I could see that it was certainly how he had described it as being in that the past was most definitely the past but that how I chose to view it was really of the utmost importance. Once again I seemed to be reaching for the sky but in one big sweeping motion, while circling the valley, I found myself suddenly heading for the church. In doing so I could begin to make out the widows in the apse and all too quickly they grew larger and larger until they virtually filled my entire vision. Just before I blinked in a kind of defensive reaction, I managed to catch sight of the illuminated eye in the centre panel which I could have sworn actually winked at me almost at the same instant that I collided with it.

This was quickly followed by a feeling of my being expelled from something in a similar manner to that of a champagne cork flying out of a bottle. Then there was the sensation of something quite heavy pushing against my back as well as under my legs while I completely lost the sensation of lightness. I opened my eyes to see that I was now sitting in exactly the same place in the empty pew as I had been when I first found myself in the church. This time, however, when I began looking around I started to appreciate quite a difference in the interior of the building and its structure.

No longer were the pillars so misshapen and neither was the ceiling so jumbled. The centre aisle was much straighter now and everything looked more orderly as well as ... *"More balanced and in harmony would you say?"*

Once more the words just seemed to flow out all around me where there appeared to be no one speaking them. Although, I found that I really did have to agree with their sentiment in that things did appear to be much less haphazard and more pleasing in many different ways.

"And pray tell me oh most ardent seeker of great wisdom, where does this 'knowing' in you come from? Where does this appreciation for 'rightness of purpose', your sensing of the correct 'nature' of form, this 'attraction' to an idea of beauty or a sense of harmonious existence spring from? Is this arising from a place of having been taught or simply from a place of a trusted knowledge which has never needed to be learned?"

Again I looked to see who had posed the question and for a second or two I became distracted through examining the pulpit where I felt sure that I could see someone. However, I found myself being more caught up in what was being asked of me than trying to identify the questioner. It really did make me think about things especially in view of many vivid images still swirling around in my consciousness as well as all the emotions which I could feel as a result of my flight over the valley. In this respect it proved to be a highly pertinent as well as very insightful question which seemed to have been constructed so as to probe my new awareness of how I now viewed my life.

It also appeared to be one that it would not have occurred to me to ask before this time and I would probably not have given much thought to it, if any, had I done so. Again I was reminded of my shortcomings and what my wise companion had said about the limitations of my conditioned thinking. So, now that I had actually been asked this question then I needed to consider my answer in the light of all that I was now feeling about my recollections. Where exactly did my knowing come from? I had never really thought about this before. When I did then I wanted to understand how I knew that things looked better in the way that they were now appearing to me and why it should be that I felt more comfortable with them being this way. After all, I certainly wasn't any kind of expert on ancient church architectural design but there was no denying that what I saw around me did speak to me in a way that made me feel quite pleased to be in the midst of it. But what could it possibly be that affected me in this way and what part of me was able to determine what I considered to be acceptable and what wasn't?

Before I had time to formulate any kind of answer to this question, the half hidden figure in the pulpit leaned forward while resting his arms on the sloping section of the lectern. As he did so then one of the big blanked out panel windows in the apse started to let in light while gradually becoming as bright as all the others. In doing so, the ray which it allowed into the church shone directly onto the pulpit which consequently lit up like a beacon. It was then that I easily recognised the familiar features of my trusted companion who was smiling broadly at me. I looked at the sixth window while wondering what had happened to enable it to suddenly let in all the light as well as trying to make out what the very attractive symbol in the middle of it could be.

"That my dear friend is the symbol of your sixth sense. The aspect of you which many call intuition; that indefinable and immeasurable quality of a knowing which is immediately trusted when fully recognised for what it is. Intuition knows perfection while being essentially perfect in and of itself. It is immediately understood by all who hear its subtle calling as being infallible although there is no comprehension within the intellect as to why this should be. Intuition will not allow itself to be rationalised as it transcends the lowly and limited realms of logic and reason. Intuition is a force of apparently mysterious origin to the mind but one which guides the individual unerringly on towards the ultimate level of his or her happiness.

Intuition knows only harmony, joy and inner peace as its eternal companions while always following where they lead. But, my dear friend, what is it that you consider links you so closely to this wonderfully wise, compassionate and caring aspect of yourself. What is it that attracts you to its wisdom in the first place and why should you trust it so unquestioningly as you do? What do you consider allows this precious facet of your true self to communicate with you so subtly, often when you're not even aware of its presence in your decision making process. There must surely be some sort of mutual recognition between your conscious awareness and this wonderful sense which you have been gifted with.

What language could exist that so often speaks to that part of you which completely bypasses your mind and yet is still able to comprehend? Is this not a thoroughly fascinating concept my dear friend and does it not challenge your awareness of just exactly what makes you who you are? When carefully considering this matter of great consequence then please be sure to include within the equation the aspect of your twin flame energy which is constantly striving to be re-united with its other half. This magnetic attraction exists within the essence of a desire to return to a state of harmony which is already known. It is an eternal 'knowing' of rightness that is forever with you while constantly wishing to influence your choices whenever you give it the opportunity to do so.

Could this be a fundamental component of what you call intuition or is it the mediator for a more powerful Divine energy which calls to you constantly? A message from your true home which is forever asking to be remembered while you journey through the adventure which you call life. Could this be a way of understanding the concept of twin flames and the mysterious nature of your intuition that would be acceptable to you my friend?"

I watched as my companion began to step down from the pulpit and then make his way towards me. I was lost deep in thought about what he had just explained to me but then I couldn't help thinking about what it must be like to have his level of understanding and what life would have been like for me had it been so. Then I remembered my incredible flight through the valley and being able to re-visit so many instances from my past while looking at them through the eyes of absolute joy. I began to appreciate that none of what I had experienced would ever have happened if I had known beforehand much more about how things actually worked and why.

If this knowledge had been available to me then I would never have made the choices that I did and so I wouldn't have ended up having three wonderful children and sharing so much with my first wife as I did. For having been blessed with this opportunity I suddenly felt so very grateful to each and every circumstance of my life which had helped create it. From this new perspective it was impossible not to feel very happy about the way that everything had worked out for me. The more that I contemplated the whole subject, while exploring my new feelings, I suddenly found myself hoping that they too could one day get to feel the same way about me. It made me happy to think that their lives were just as rich for what I had helped them to see and appreciate even though they may not be aware of it in the same way that I been guided to a true realisation of.

Then, for some reason, I began to recall the view while looking out over the balcony where I could see the church on top of the huge stone tree-like mountain. I remembered looking at all the roots that had joined each of the experiences and encounters in my life and how they were eventually reflected in the structure of the church. I thought about when I had first seen it and how it had affected me. Then I considered what I had learned about the concept of true forgiveness and then how I felt when I returned from my flight. As a result of this it seemed as though so much had become clearer now, more settled and much less stressful. Far less fraught which left me feeling much more at peace with myself along with everything else in my world which was just what the whole building seemed to be reflecting back at me.

I had begun to see the wisdom in recognising how my journey had so obviously been lived through the conditioned impressions of my five physical senses which had in turn affected my four elemental bodies to one degree or another. The church interior had shown me how much out of balance I had become as a result of all that I had experienced, but now there seemed to be a much lighter feeling in me; even though the past remained just as it had been. What had changed was that I felt differently about it and that's what mattered where I only need look around me for proof of my new feelings. Apparently I still needed to give more thought to the subject of my intuition but so much was already starting to make sense that I felt very encouraged. Even so, I could appreciate that I probably still had a long way to go until I would be able to see things as clearly as my very wise and infinitely patient companion wished me to.

Sitting down gently beside me he placed his hand on my shoulder and then said,

"You certainly have come a long way my friend but I would ask that you take another brief trip with me, just one more short excursion to a destination which I'm sure you will be very pleased to arrive at. One last place to visit and then you will be ready to leave this valley behind us as we travel onward to pastures new. What say you my good friend, are you ready?"

For what seemed like quite a time I stayed looking around the interior of the church while going over a huge amount in my mind. I recalled so many visions and so much that I had experienced in this quite amazing place but I also appreciated how grateful I was in having been able to see so much from a different perspective. I had gained an intriguing insight into not only life's unseen gifts but also the quite mysterious forces of twin soul energies; as well as how they had influenced not just my life but those of others who I'd met along the way of my travels.

In the midst of my recollections I started to wonder just how much in control of my life I really had been. Or could it be that I had simply become a hapless marionette who dangled unconsciously on the end of some master manipulators strings. I felt a chill run through me as this came to mind but I soon discounted it when thinking about how I had eventually found my way to my twin soul and what a precious gift that had truly been. I was on the point of feeling that there was much more for me to just sit and contemplate but something told me that leaving to find out what else was in store for me might be a good idea, so I got up to make my way to the aisle.

My wise companion followed me but as I turned to head for the front door he began to make his way back towards the apse. I quickly did an about turn and then headed in his direction while wondering where we could be going. As I followed him, I couldn't help but look at the big panel windows once more while appreciating what they represented but then I noticed the seventh window which was still covered up. I had forgotten about this until that moment and wondered what it was supposed to represent. I felt sure that I understood the concept of a sixth window but what was behind the seventh?

My companion turned towards the doorway to the vestry and said quietly in reply,

"That's for later my good friend. Later, when you have come to a much clearer and deeper understanding of all that you have been shown here in this place with me. What illumination will fall upon you from that particular window will change the way you come to view a great many things, not the least of which will be your true self. First you must move to a place of even greater awareness and, to that end, you are progressing well on your journey. It

is the most fascinating of all journeys but the destination, I guarantee, will pleasantly surprise you."

He opened the vestry door and stepped into the surprisingly brightly lit room while saying,

"Now, with your permission, we will make another type of journey. However, this is destined to be one that will also surprise you in the most fascinating of ways while bringing about an enlightenment which, at present, is quite beyond the scope of your imagination!"

- **Chapter 19** -

Trusting Footsteps over the Bridge to Intuition

Reluctantly I prepared myself to step out from within the interior of what I had come to appreciate was effectively a highly accurate characterisation of my evolving personality. I was about to leave this place so as to follow my companion into the vestry but I couldn't help wondering if I would ever see any of it again. It almost felt as though I was abandoning a part of myself while consigning it to the annals of obscurity. Although, somehow I had a sense that it would always be with me. I guessed that there must have been a part of me that wasn't entirely convinced as I found myself taking one last long look around. There also seemed to be an urgent need in me to commit to memory every last detail of all that I had seen and learned from being so thoroughly immersed in its truly awe inspiring atmosphere.

My somewhat overwrought mind kept insisting that there must be a good deal more which needed to be studied and that I hadn't really had enough time to investigate countless other secrets; which I felt sure I must have missed. With this thought drifting around in my head I began to get a sense of my actually leaving somewhere that had come to mean a great deal to me. It had almost begun to feel very familiar and comfortable even with its quirky uniqueness and impressive size; which had initially overwhelmed me and even intimidated me. The sheer scale of its magnificently inspiring presence had quickly grown on me to the degree that it now even pleased me in a way that I could never before have believed possible. Albeit that it was the biggest structure that I could ever imagine existing which I had been encouraged to consider as actually being a part of me. And yet, that's just exactly how it felt even though I wondered if I could ever get used to thinking of it in this way. I did have to admit though, if I was being totally honest with myself, that my ego was most certainly flattered by it.

Reluctantly I managed to drag myself away while saying a silent goodbye as I patted the wall in a kind of affectionate and grateful way. Even as I stepped through the doorway, I continued to take in as much as my mind would allow me to absorb in the hope that all the images, emotions, feelings, sensations and experiences would stay with me for as long as I was able to retain them. Then, with a small sigh of resignation, I walked the few paces across the beautifully polished wooden floor of the small side room and out through a quite substantially built pair of large wooden doors.

These actually looked more like gates than doors but I paid them only slight attention as I stepped out of the open portal which they created. This, I quickly realised, led onto a wide expanse of a paved patio area which was surrounded by what looked like a large and beautifully landscaped garden. To add to my surprise at finding myself in such pleasant surroundings I was also greeted by the most delightfully gentle embrace of a bright sunny day, which was not at all what I had expected. More than that, there appeared to be a great many people standing around like there was some sort of well attended garden party going on. Several views of my new surroundings were obscured by groups of people all happily engaged in conversation with each other. As I glanced quickly around at many of the faces that I could clearly see, then it slowly dawned on me that they were virtually all of the same people who had been in the church. At first I couldn't seem to get my bearings in that I didn't understand what it could be that I had so obviously become involved in, and why all the people from the congregation should be gathered around in someone's garden.

In an attempt at gaining a little more clarity I began looking at the landscape. This was when I started to appreciate that I could see the familiar outlines of the mountains which ran alongside the lake. They did however seem to be a little different from how I remembered them being when I had seen them from the boat. Feeling the need to get my bearings I started to scan the horizon to the side of me so as to look for anything that I could recognise more clearly; any kind of unique feature that I could place on the map in my mind's eye. No sooner had I begun doing this than I quickly realised that, instead of the huge church being behind me, there was now a large stone wall which looked to have a lot of trees on the other side of it.

It took me quite by surprise while I worked hard at accepting that the big building was actually gone and for a minute or two I couldn't help but feel very sad indeed. This was a most unexpected reaction which made me wish that I could just be alone so as to deal with my emotions and not having to cope with facing a whole crowd of people who seemed to require that I be at my sparkling best. It was such an odd sensation that seemed almost as though it was beyond my capability to navigate my way through but somehow I found myself being able to draw strength from my encounters in the big church. This certainly was a great comfort to me as well as being very encouraging. Maybe I hadn't left it completely behind after all. With this thought in mind I managed to recover a little and then turned completely around to see that what I had stepped through was actually a large open gateway. Through it I could see a long road which stretched away through a beautiful avenue of trees. On one side of it there appeared to be many trees which looked to be part of a large orchard. Beyond where the road appeared to curve off to the left I could make out the golden tipped waters of the lake and for a moment I thought that I could even see the outline of our wonderful steam driven boat moored up a little way off in the distance. For some reason I found myself feeling pleased to see it as this was at least one familiar sight in yet another place that I had been led to, although there did seem to be something recognisable about the avenue of trees as well.

"Come my friend, let's you and I make our way through the crowd while I take you to a very special place where you have been feeling the need to go. I'm sure that these charming people have much to discuss but we really must start out on our little expedition. We have a rendezvous with someone who I know that you will be overjoyed to meet and, being the gentlemen that we are, we wouldn't want to keep her waiting now would we?"

I looked at my companion closely to see if there were any signs that he was pulling my leg but, as usual, he seemed to be his disarmingly genuine self. I was intrigued as well as feeling more than a little excited. I was also grateful to have heard this in that it served to further bolster my mood which was most certainly in need of a lift at that moment. No doubt he was well aware of this fact.

With a smile and a gentle tug, he led me off through the first group of people, mostly men, who surprisingly I didn't recognise at all. A few of them appeared to be highly engrossed in some light hearted conversation but this stopped as soon as I got close to them. Quite unexpectedly they all instantly smiled and then nodded as though they knew me. *"God speed good sir."* said one to which the others promptly joined in with a chorus of *"Aye!"* I nodded and smiled back while feeling completely perplexed but more than this I was curious about the manner of their speech. Then another group of similarly unrecognised people did exactly the same thing as we passed by them but before I had time to respond I caught sight of quite a few people who I knew very well. My attention flipped from one point of bewildered focus to another as familiar faces seemed to swim in and out of my field of view where all of them looked to have been in the congregation at the church.

Everyone waved and smiled at me, which started to make me feel a little self conscious in that I considered it polite to stop and then take some time just to talk to them, or at the very least saying hello. Even as this thought crossed my mind there were ever more people appearing who I recognised as being from many different eras of my past. There were even children that I remembered from when I was very young. Then again, there were groups of others who I didn't recognise at all but curiously they all seemed to express a certain distinct familiarity with me. I just didn't know what to make of anything that was happening so I just kept following my guide and smiling back at everyone while hoping not to look too mystified in the process.

All heads were turned towards me and for one fleeting moment I got the idea that they were actually waiting for me to say something to them; possibly by way of a speech. My trusty companion didn't appear to be inclined towards stopping on our path to wherever we were heading, so I guessed that addressing the gathering wasn't something that was required of me. I was mightily glad of this because I couldn't really think of anything appropriate to say.

The thing which I found most delightfully surprising about all that I could see taking place going on around me was that I had no trouble in appreciating the genuineness of everyone's greetings and good wishes. It felt just like a constant wall of joy flowing out towards me and I had to admit to finding it quite addictive. For a moment I began to glimpse what it must have been like to be some sort of celebrity who had been on stage while receiving the heartfelt applause from a very grateful audience. It proved to be an extremely satisfying experience indeed and one that further lifted my mood, which was already back in pretty good shape after recalling my encounters with the band in the church. That really was a very special memory for me.

All in all, this seemed to be turning out to be a really wonderful day but to have said that it had been a highly memorable one would have been the understatement of the century. Whichever one that might be! I still had absolutely no idea of time, but for some reason it just didn't seem to bother me at all. I was more than happy to go with the flow where I found that not having to be concerned over what the future, immediate or otherwise, may hold for me was very freeing indeed. No watches, no clocks, no calendars, no countdown ticking away in my mind proved to be a thoroughly joyful way to be. I did however get the hint of a feeling that somewhere within me there was a need to catch just a tiny glimpse of what the future may hold for me. Somehow my existence seemed to be threatened by the absence of time pacing anxiously up and down the corridors of my destiny, somewhere in the recesses of my psyche. I decided to ignore its irrational demands as it was far too nice a day to contemplate something so banal and uninteresting.

It was very tempting just to stop and chat with every individual that I recognised but it seemed that my companion had other ideas. I waved a kind of 'gotta rush might see you later' type gesture to each of them in the hope of not appearing to be too impolite. After what felt like negotiating my way out of a sports arena, as soon as the match had finished, we finally moved on towards a part of the large garden area which is when I noticed it. Just a short way off in amongst another area of trees was the entrance to a bridge that looked very familiar. I could see it rising up just above the trees but from my present position I couldn't get a clear idea of where it appeared to be leading to. While I was trying to remember where I had seen it before, I suddenly became aware of the church bells and then I felt sure that it must be the bridge which I'd seen from the boat. I also knew that it would probably lead me to the little church on the plateau but something else reminded me that it appeared to be incomplete; even though this didn't seem possible. I just had to find out for sure where the bridge went as my enthusiasm for getting to the church seemed to have been renewed and suddenly I was in a hurry again.

Without any encouragement I set off more purposefully across the grassy area while heading towards the entrance to the bridge. My companion followed while looking somewhat thoughtful but my mind was too focused on getting up to the church to pay attention to what it might mean. I didn't want to give over any more time to thinking up any more questions or debating things. I mean, what could be simpler than crossing a bridge and getting to the other side. My wise friend chose that precise moment to clear his throat and when I looked at him I could have sworn I saw that ominous wry smile of his putting in an appearance once again. I decided to ignore it.

Finally we reached the foot of the bridge but, while travelling towards it, I had already managed to appreciate that it was actually quite highly arched and would need a determined effort to get to the top. I could see that its surface looked to be made of some sort of broad wooden slats but the thick railed sides were of a design and wood-like material that I wasn't familiar with at all. I couldn't see what supported it or what was on the other side as it rose straight out of the tall trees where it seemed to go right over the tops of them and on to wherever it led to on the other side. The other side of what I wasn't exactly sure. Even why the bridge was there in the first place wasn't clear to me either but stepping onto the first wooden board of the 'pathway into the sky', I reckoned that I would find out soon enough. I was kind of right, but only a little bit.

At first I was tempted to walk in the middle of the bridge but the slope seemed quite sharply angled. The wood also appeared to be a little moist so it made sense to stay close to the side in case something solid to hang onto was called for. It was then that I noticed all the symbols which had been carved into the supporting material where some of them looked remarkably similar to those that I'd seen on the big panels in the apse windows. I couldn't help but wonder how odd it was to see them set into something so apparently un-inspirational as a bridge. It was tempting to take some time to study them a little closer while looking for other clues about whether they were just decorative or if they had some sort of hidden meaning. Fortunately I had learned by now that nothing I had ever come across, in any situation I found myself to be in, could be listed under the heading of being simply decorative.

While I was debating what to do, I gradually became aware that once again I could hear the attractive melody from the church bells. This time however they sounded encouragingly louder which made them seem tantalisingly near; I could almost visualise them merrily swinging in a white painted open bell tower. This had the immediate effect of making me want to keep climbing onwards and upwards towards my destination so as to find out for sure. The little church in the woods was summoning me in its charmingly insistent way and I was more than happy to respond. I drew a sharp breath in the manner of fortifying my determination, as well as my body, and then set off up the steeply sloping arched pathway in front of me. I began the ascent while listening to the crystal clear chimes coming from a place which seemed to hold such a strangely compelling fascination for me.

Not long into the steadily increasing slope, my legs were certainly feeling the climb but I managed to get my second wind about half way up. Surprisingly, my companion seemed to be quite unaffected by our efforts to cross the bridge while looking as though he was just out for a casual stroll by the water's edge. I pressed on while deciding to ignore him but couldn't help feeling that the more I climbed then the farther the crest of the bridge appeared to be moving away from me. I did however notice that it appeared as though we were getting quite high above the ground as I could see a fair way along the lake where it twisted and turned its lazy course towards a far off horizon. It certainly was a breathtaking sight; in more ways than one.

Although I had got to the point where I felt like stopping to rest for a while, I could see that the crown of the bridge was now just a short distance away. In one last push I encouraged my legs to carry me up to the top and, once there, I would get to see what waited for me on the other side. I put my head down and simply steeled myself for the final effort and with great determination I thankfully felt the angle of the pathway subside. As it did this I knew that we had reached the top, so I allowed myself to look up at what awaited me. In keeping with just about every other experience I'd had this day, I was quite unprepared for what started to come into view; or to be more exact, what didn't come into view.

I could clearly see the range of mountains on the right hand side of the lake along with the wooded areas. Then I noticed the little church on the plateau. It was apparent that I had finally found myself looking down on the place which I had been so intent on getting to but, at the same time, I became all too well aware that I had absolutely no way of reaching it. My feelings of frustration came bursting out as I slapped the handrail hard with the palm of my hand and then felt the pain of doing so. I just couldn't believe it and I also felt cheated. After going through all that I had and then finally coming so close to achieving my objective, I could see that my plan had been completely thwarted right at the very last moment.

The bridge, which had once appeared to hold so much promise, had come to an abrupt end. It just stopped half way, in mid span, for no apparent reason as though the builders had simply abandoned it and gone off to do something more interesting. There was absolutely nothing but fresh air where there should have been a wide wooden causeway leading over into the woods somewhere not far from the church. To say I felt totally perplexed, as well as very frustrated, would have been to describe my situation quite accurately, but added to that I also found myself having to deal with an overwhelming sense of disappointment. I just couldn't see how everything that I had been through could have ended in such a senseless way.

It had been a long climb where I had felt that my efforts would result in my achieving my objective but all that I'd done was to get to the top of a very steep, half-finished bridge. What could possibly be the point of that?

"*Patience my dear friend. You should have learned by now that everything which has ever happened to you has been for a good reason. Once discovered, it has then been fully appreciated for the value of its generous gift to you. This occasion is no exception but it certainly is one that requires you to apply much of what you have learned with me in order to move towards a very different awareness.*"

I could easily understand some of what he had said but my mind couldn't seem to stretch to the part about any possible value coming from standing on a half finished bridge. Especially one that seemed to be nearly as high as a mountain but which didn't get me to where I wanted to go. I was just about to verbalise my frustration when I noticed the white shimmering pathway which ran alongside the lake and then zigzagged up to the church. For some reason this got my attention where my curiosity overtook my other feelings as I began surveying this feature of the landscape. On the ascending part of the pathway, just a little way up, something caught my eye. There seemed to be a movement by a patch of trees and slowly I began to make out a figure. My heart skipped a little as something told me that I could possibly be looking at the image of the lovely lady who had waved to me while I was on the boat. Suddenly my mood changed as I remembered how I had felt on that occasion.

It just had to be her but I couldn't see anyone else with her although there was so much in the way of branches, bushes and trees still obscuring my view that I couldn't be absolutely sure about this. I wanted to get closer so as to find out. Then I looked at the precipitous edge of the bridge's incomplete boarded pathway and once again felt frustrated at my predicament in not being able to get to where I wanted to go. Not for a moment did I stop to question why I seemed to feel so compelled towards getting to the church; or to discover who the mysterious lady was. I did however consider the possibility of going back to look for another route but my view out over the lake from my vantage point on the bridge showed me that somehow I would have to cross over a not insubstantial stretch of water. While surveying this prospect I suddenly remembered the moored up steamboat that I'd seen through the gates of the orchard and then thought about using it to get to the shore. Then I realised that doing so would undoubtedly mean a long trek back and I didn't know if I wanted to do this as it would take much too long. The best way forward seemed to be in following a straight line to the church but to do that I would need a fully fledged bridge and not half a one the like of which I found myself so frustratingly stood on. What to do, what on earth to do? My mind churned over and over while searching for some kind of answer.

While stood in quiet contemplation of my predicament I began to absentmindedly study the landscape again for want of something better to do. I found myself really hoping for some sort of sign or inspiration to magically appear which would help me figure out what my best course of action could be. Going back didn't seem like much fun at all but if I had to endure it so as to get to my destination then that's what I would have to do. It wasn't in my nature to turn back from anything that I could see my way clearly towards but there were times when apparently insurmountable problems determined that I put plan 'B' into action. This began to look like one of those times and it did nothing to cheer me up at all. There just had to be an answer to my seemingly impossible situation.

While being very much caught up in the emotions of my dilemma and gazing out over the end of the unfinished bridge, I noticed for the first time another glittering white pathway through the woods. It got my attention because I didn't understand why I hadn't spotted it before the moment that I had debated turning back. On studying it more closely I could see that it appeared to be approaching the church from the opposite direction but that this particular pathway was anything but straight. Evidently it had been made of the same white shimmering material but it wound its way precariously through all manner of different routes that looked like some drunken surveyor had designed it. At one stage it seemed to climb up high into the mountains while crossing several long and perilous looking bridges in the process. Bridges which I appreciated looked remarkably like the one I was stood on, but with the notable exception that these particular examples were actually finished and whole while serving their intended purpose. I found myself feeling slightly envious of this fact.

For some inexplicable reason I suddenly found this all very intriguing so I began to study the route which this strangely meandering pathway took. In doing so I had to wonder at what on earth could possess anyone to have built such a bizarre track when they could just as easily have constructed one along the lower part of the lakeside; in a similar manner to the one on the other side of the church. I wasn't prepared for what I heard next.

"It's a good question my friend ... why indeed was it that you chose such a difficult route?"

The subsequent words which immediately followed my companion's unexpected question had actually burst out of my mouth before they had even registered in my consciousness.

"Me?! What does it have to do with me?"

There was a moment of anticipation-laden silence before he answered.

"Everything my delightfully mystified friend, absolutely everything."

I was about to demand an explanation when I spotted someone walking down what seemed to be the final section of the route; the part that would take whoever was following its erratic course to the church. This certainly got my attention where all other questions were instantly rendered irrelevant. My mind whirled as it tried to figure out who could have been travelling along that crazy path and what on earth they could be going to do now? The question of what connection it could possibly have with me also stood next in line for an answer. What on earth was all that about? I'd never seen this place before and couldn't for the life of me ever imagine carving out a pathway like the one I found myself looking at even if I had.

This all seemed totally nuts and something I couldn't make any sense of at all. A half finished bridge in the middle of the sky, a church stuck on the side of a mountain which kept chiming away at me and a woman who I thought I knew, with a whole bunch of children, who were all heading towards it. And now there was another person making their haphazard way to the same destination but from another direction where this one looked like a man, who I was quite sure I didn't know. And what were all those people doing in the garden and what on earth had happened to the big church in the valley which had been so interesting?

For a fraction of a second I felt sure that I was going to wake up back in the meadow by the pond at any moment and then realise that I had been dreaming. I had to admit, however, that what I was experiencing surely did feel very real and not like any kind of dream I'd ever had, however vivid it might have been. My tired legs told me that dreams didn't make you feel weary. In a gesture of frustrated anguish, I thrust my hands out towards a thoroughly disinterested landscape and then shouted "*Whaaaaaaat?!*" at it; as though that did any good!

"*Feel better now?!*" my companion said wryly and then stepped up beside me while looking to be closer to the edge than was good for him. He then turned to face me while having his back to the end of the bridge where, to my abject horror, he took a step backward so that the heels of his shoes were almost at the very edge. He started to say something but I was deaf to his words as all I wanted to do was to reach out and grab him by his lapels so as to pull him back from the edge. For some inexplicable reason my arms just wouldn't seem to respond to my panic-filled mental command and so I stood motionless while staring at his feet and willing them not to move.

What happened next made my eyes open wider than they ever had before just as my throat went completely dry. While still in the midst of some lengthy explanation, he proceeded to take another step back while making some sort of gesture with his outstretched arms. I didn't hear a word as my heart stopped at seeing him do this. I was almost tempted to close my eyes as I dared not watch what would happen next. Inexplicably, nothing did. All I could seem to hear was my frantic heart pounding away in my ears. He just carried on smiling and talking 'at' me but I still couldn't hear a word that he was saying or, if I did, then they didn't register at all in my totally frozen brain.

I mouthed something indecipherable to him while lamely pointing to his feet which were firmly planted on thin air. There was no bridge and nothing underneath him except for a very long drop into the golden blue waters of the lake below. Although, he seemed quite unperturbed while chatting away like we were back at the garden party. The look on my face must have registered with him while he was in mid flow because he stopped and then stepped back onto the bridge while grabbing me firmly by both shoulders. He did it as though I was in desperate need of his support. He was right! I grabbed him equally as firmly in return.

"My dear fellow, you look white as a sheet! What's come over you all of a sudden?" I stared in disbelief.

"As if you didn't know!" I managed to mutter while trying to remember to breathe.

"Oh that! Yes, well I did say that it would be an interesting walk didn't I?"

I frowned in a kind of petulantly frustrated manner but all that I got in return was the warmest of smiles; one which seemed for a moment as though it was going to precede a hug. That actually would have been very welcomed at that precise point in time. Albeit that it may have appeared a little overly dramatic to anyone looking at us high up on the bridge while wondering what on earth was going on.

"Take heart my dear friend. Have faith and learn to follow that which guides you so unerringly. Put aside your fears and misconceptions while focusing on what it is that you want. Now, make haste my brother as all of your guests are eagerly awaiting your arrival, so we really must press on."

My guests? What guests? Waiting where and for what? Good God, whatever next?! More importantly, press on where? I looked around quickly for any signs of a big bird creeping up on me but there was nothing to be seen except for empty sky. It seemed to match what my companion was suggesting we walk over so I wondered if he had any diving equipment or a helicopter tucked away in his jacket pocket. I dared not even ask!

Putting all the Pieces Together on the Way Home

Before I had time to completely take in the implications of all that he'd just said, my somewhat tricky friend turned on his heels and began pointing to the man on the wandering pathway to the church. I glanced briefly in his direction but then I caught sight of the lady on the other side and realised that she was getting very close to the entrance to the grounds as well. This time I definitely could see that a group of six children of varying ages accompanied her, where one or two of them looked quite familiar. Then I noticed that there was something about the way she carried herself, which also seemed to be very familiar to me.

Once again that feeling came to me in that in the midst of a distressing and quite taxing situation her presence seemed to settle me; but I just didn't understand why. This time I couldn't ignore it though as I really was experiencing a most difficult time, but having become aware of the tangible attraction which I felt towards her then things changed almost immediately. In so doing my resolve was revitalised, my burden seemed markedly less heavy and my motivation to succeed returned in a renewed sense of purposefulness; although my mind wasn't able to rationalise this in any meaningful way. Although, I was reminded of what my wise companion had been encouraging me to become aware of; it felt like I was starting to get the picture. Well, part of it anyway. I returned my attention to this fascinating lady and her surroundings.

While studying things in greater detail I began to get the impression that there was some kind of glow or a sort of special light around her, the sight of which caused something to stir inside me. I suddenly felt the need to mention this to my companion but he forestalled me when he said in a somewhat puzzled voice,

"Wherever can he be going now?"

I took my attention away from the lady and her children so as to look in the direction that he was pointing. As I did so then I saw the man on the other pathway starting to run back up a fairly steep incline while heading towards a particularly heavily wooded area. He appeared to be making his way to a house, which I hadn't noticed before as it had been partially concealed in the forest.

"What do you imagine he can be up to my ever inquisitive friend and why do you think he's changed his mind about continuing to head for the church?"

I watched in fascination as the man made his way back up the winding pathway and then got ever closer to the house. For some reason I found myself feeling really perplexed. On the one hand there was me wishing so much to be able to get to the church and here I was watching someone almost running away from it. I couldn't come to terms with that at all. I couldn't even begin to imagine what had suddenly caused him to have such a change of heart, but something seemed to inspire an idea in me. Whatever it was that I'd observed about what I considered to have motivated his sudden 'about turn', then it certainly did strike a very large chord in me.

As it chimed away in my head, almost in time with the bells, then certain uncomfortable memories started gradually drifting into my mind but with them also came the powerful emotion of acute anxiety. All of a sudden my conscious world seemed to be overwhelmed with thoughts about changing direction while giving up on heading for a specific destination. It was the strangest of sensations but at the same time most perplexing to the degree that I simply couldn't ignore it; even though I very much wanted to.

I continued to watch nervously as the man made a kind of dogged effort to reach the half-hidden house in the woods; but for some inexplicable reason something told me that this was definitely not at all a wise choice. In fact, I found myself willing him to turn around and then continue heading back towards the church even though I still had no idea who he was. I was totally unaware of how completely drawn into his situation I had become, to the degree that I was almost living it with him. I was that much affected by it. The closer he got to the house then the more I found my anxiety levels quickly rising until it got to the point where I almost felt as though I wanted to shout out a warning to him. I had no thoughts as to how crazy it would be to do such a thing. Neither did I stop to consider what useful purpose it could possibly serve. I was too far away to be heard, or so I thought. I stood anxiously holding on to the big wooden handrail while tensing myself up for the effort of calling out as loudly as I could; but would it be enough. Everything else in my world seemed to disappear as my only objective was to get his attention. His predicament had become the sole focus of mine.

Then I felt something urging me to appreciate that if I could just get a little bit closer then he might be able to hear me. So, without thinking, I took a few tentative steps forward while reaching for the next part of the very smooth and comforting handrail on the side of the bridge. Without being conscious of doing so, I took a deep breath while charging up my lungs so as to give as much force as I could to whatever I decided to call out to him. I took a few more steps and got even closer. Then it felt like I was getting within range and that he might actually hear me, but I still wasn't quite close enough and he was almost at the house. I exhaled all the pent up air and then breathed deeply once more in preparation for my next effort.

For some strange reason it actually seemed as though I had been moving backwards over the bridge, which only served to heighten my sense of frustration in still not being close enough to be heard. Undaunted by my apparent situation I redoubled my efforts in a determined attempt to make my way closer to the man as he neared the entrance to the house. I was beginning to panic more than a little although I had absolutely no idea why this should be. A few more steps to get nearer to the edge of the bridge and somehow it seemed easier to make progress towards him. For a moment I could have sworn that the slope under my feet had increased so that I was actually walking downhill. I took little notice as the man stopped momentarily at the gateway to the house. Seeing him do this sent my emotions completely into overdrive. I was now in full panic mode. I just knew that I had to stop him whatever the cost and so I took a few more steps while I began shouting as loudly as I possibly could. To attract even more attention to myself I started waving as well while also having to stop myself being carried away by the increasing incline of the bridge.

To my absolutely delighted surprise, the man stopped and then turned to look in my direction while holding one hand up to shield his eyes in an effort to see me. I waved even more frantically while taking more gravity propelled steps towards him and then felt a huge sense of relief as the man started back down the path. He began walking away from the house while staring in my direction and presumably trying to make out what I was doing. I stopped for a moment to catch my breath but no sooner had I done this than I caught sight of a movement out of the corner of my eye and so I turned to look up to identify it. What greeted me was the sight of a huge bird which appeared to be swooping down very fast while apparently heading in the direction of the man on the pathway. I became rigid at the sight of it while my mind attempted to make sense of what I was seeing.

Its wings were retracted like a bird of prey in a high speed dive as it homed in on its intended victim while its wide staring eyes were fixed on the target. It streaked through the air like a jet plane as it trailed streams of multicoloured sparkling plumes behind it which seemed to add a greater sense of speed to its movement. Within seconds it was almost on top of the house but before I had time to even think about warning the man on the path, there was a huge sheet of golden flame which erupted from the bird's sparkling beak. Like a shot from some giant cannon, the golden flame accelerated towards the man while I was convinced that my heart had stopped beating. I could hardly bear to look but I was totally mesmerised by what I could see happening in front of me. The flame sped towards the ground but instead of hitting the man it actually engulfed the whole of the house in the woods. Almost instantaneously the building burst into a mass of similarly bright golden flames. Very quickly it became an inferno of the most wonderfully golden white light which seemed to make everything around it sparkle in the most incredibly breathtaking way.

It produced the most stunning effect where the house appeared to grow and expand while every molecule of its construction became radiant as though it was filled with absolute joy. Even the trees all around it started to glow and flourish in a similar way while the man on the pathway just looked on in stunned surprise. He stayed motionless while taking in the sheer magic of what he was witnessing at such close quarters. I did likewise for a moment or two but then a feeling of the most amazing peacefulness began to overtake me where, for some reason which I couldn't fathom at all, I knew that everything was going to be alright. If anyone had asked me to explain my feelings at that moment then I would have been at a complete loss for words.

"I'm sure that given a suitable interlude in which to digest your current situation then you would indeed be able to express what it is that you are feeling at this juncture."

I turned to look at my companion which corresponded with the precise moment when things became a little hazy as my world went decidedly pear-shaped for a few confusing seconds. My legs became weak at the same instant. I grabbed on tightly to the handrail of the bridge while I remained looking up at the figure of my companion who was stood on the crest where the end of the wooden pathway had once been. I instantly looked down to see what was supporting me and felt a great sense of relief through appreciating that there were similar wooden boards attached to equally substantial looking sections of the bridge. My mind was not able to cope with this at all.

Inexplicably there appeared to be much more of the bridge than had been present when we had first come onto it and, what's more, I was now standing on what had once been fresh air! For a moment my mind seemed to completely freeze in response to a couple of very important questions which required urgent answers. How could this be and why hadn't I noticed it before that moment? My wise friend started making his way slowly down towards me while I turned to see the man on the winding road continuing his journey. He appeared to be heading back towards the church once again but I noticed that he was waving to me in what seemed to be a kind of grateful way. I found this to be also very confusing. What's more, I realised that I was still very close to the edge of the bridge but there could be no denying that it wasn't the same edge that I had been close to just a short while back.

Even more perplexing than this was the fact that there were no armies of construction workers to be seen anywhere in the vicinity and neither were there any signs of tall cranes or any other kind of supports. It really was most odd; not to mention quite scary. I looked up to see the big bird once more returning to its place in the sky after having skimmed low over the side of the mountain and then shooting up like a rocket, almost directly above the summit. For an instant I remembered what it had been like to do just that and then felt a little tinge of envy creeping into the equally mountainous landscape of my emotions. My companion arrived by my side. He was sporting his customary warm-hearted smile while a legion of questions began racing into my head. They all seemed determined to demand urgent answers at the very same instant but before any of them could utter a single curiosity-filled syllable, my companion stepped in to placate them.

"*Where shall we start?*" he said in his most patient of tones.

"*Ah yes, I think that it's probably a good idea to clarify that which supports you and then all else that follows will hopefully continue on in the same vein. Is that not a good idea my delightfully bewildered friend? Yes, I'm sure you agree. Now then, let's firstly take a look at what exactly is set into the designs of this magnificent bridge which affords us passage across to that charming little church. Well, almost to the church that is.*"

He pointed to one particular carving which I seemed to recognise as having seen quite recently.

"*Where exactly did you see it and what special significance did it have for you at that time? Think carefully now about what you've come to have a new appreciation for and then apply it to what has just occurred.*"

Even though there were subtle differences I had no real trouble recognising the symbol from the sixth big window in the apse. The one that had lit up not long before we left the building and which my companion explained was representative of intuition.

"Intuition, yes, very good my dear friend; that's exactly what it means and also what underpins the tangible nature and construction of this truly charming aerial footpath. Now then, please take a moment to consider how you managed to create more of this substantial structure so as to accommodate your wishes. What exactly was it that you did? What happened when you saw the man heading back to the house and why did you ignore all that your physical senses were telling you so as to warn him? To alert him to something that you didn't even understand the reason for.

Just before fully considering this, I would like you to pay particular attention to some of the other carvings. Look here, and also this one here. Then tell me what you see."

I did as he asked and then noticed that there were also symbols for the five physical senses as had been illustrated on the other big panel windows. These carvings, however, were set back into the thick wooden supports whereas the symbols for intuition were raised out of the wood in a kind of prominent way.

"Good, now consider what happened to you and then carefully consider your motivation and how well your senses served you. Where was the focus of your attention at the time? It most certainly wasn't on the aspect of your personal safety as you regarded something else as being far more important. The intentions and actions of a relative stranger overrode everything else as you created what you most needed – more progress in the direction of that which you felt so powerfully drawn to move towards. Would it be true to say this my good friend?"

This was undeniably the case but for some reason I just couldn't put into words why I had acted as I did as there appeared to be no logical reason for it. Nothing made any sense when it came to putting together a suitable explanation but I couldn't deny the way I had felt at the time and how confident I had been in what I had chosen to do. Something had urged me to warn the man not to go back to the house, but to explain what had motivated me to do it seemed to be beyond my ability to rationalise; and yet I had actually done it.

"Could it be that you recognised a similar situation from your past and how that circumstance had turned out? Would you not have instinctively wanted to warn this good fellow against doing the same thing? Please consider this possibility for a moment or two if you will."

For some reason I found myself feeling quite uncomfortable at the thought of what my companion had just suggested; which in itself showed me that there was something important in his words that needed careful consideration. I thought about the house and then the wavering path to the church but I couldn't quite see the connection, although the emotion in me was abundantly clear. There could be no doubt as to how I had felt about the man going back to the house; but why should this be?

"Think about your turning back on your own path towards your second marriage and your efforts to save the first. Was it not the case that you ignored your intuitive feelings while accommodating the overruling urges of your thinking, your troubled conscience? Having chosen such a haphazard pathway to your intended destination, can you not see that this arose as a consequence of your conditioned mind which constantly battled with your intuition? This most subtly compelling force which only ever wished to guide you to the happiness that was in your heart to experience. There was nothing to be gained by going back as everything that needed to be achieved by your journeying thus far with your soul mate had actually been accomplished.

Both of you needed to go your separate ways but your flawed intellect kept intervening. Our illustrious aviating friend kindly demonstrated how things would have turned out by showing you the light of love which had already been generated in that place of togetherness. It was and is something to be treasured by all who were touched by it and is also a gift of your creating that will never be lost. It is eternal but it also abides joyfully within the very fabric of your compassionate heart, if you so allow it, while journeying anew.

Yours is the choice to truly expand your unencumbered perception of what 'was' and how things really were in the mysterious process of life's unfolding. There is never anything of value to be gained through indulging yourself in any degree of guilt. This unhelpful state only ever arises from judgement and, as we have seen, this only leads to an inability to apply forgiveness in the true understanding of how each life evolves and progresses.

Your journey to the church turned out to be a long and arduous one but made eminently more so by your astute mind because you lacked the necessary wisdom to temper that level of intellect. As such, it only served to distort your perspective while obscuring your true objective. You only have to think back to the physical representation of this in all that you saw when in the church.

Visualise once more how you first encountered the interior of the whole structure and then look upon the nature of the pathway which you see through the woods on the side of the mountain. Is it any wonder that it's shaped in such a way, whereas the corresponding pathway of the lady is much straighter? What does this tell you my good friend? Who is paying more attention to the quiet guidance of their intuitive urgings and who has the less demanding route to walk as a result? Each will arrive at the same destination but at what cost for the journey my dear friend, at what cost?

Again, please be sure not to apply judgement to your deliberations but instead, learn to accept what you come to recognise as being simply how things are, or were. Also take into consideration that there is always value in every situation while knowing that no journey is ever wasted as there is much that can be gained from even the smallest distance travelled. Be constantly vigilant as to what your mind wishes you to be aware of in the respect of what your vision relays to it. Always be conscious of the fact that your thought processes have been continuously shaped by everything that has ever influenced you since the day you were born.

During its development it has absorbed so many opinions, rules, concepts, judgements and standards. Along with innumerable ideas, criticisms, ideologies and many other things from just about every corner of the society and environment which you have been conscious of. The construct of your entire mental outlook, which has evolved over the whole of your life, is largely a product of what others wish you to think. Now is the time for you to move past all that while broadening your horizons so as to look far beyond those limitations and, in so doing, you replace judgement with discernment.

Discernment enables unencumbered perception. To 'see' more clearly means that you make no allowance for any biased interpretation of what 'is' to upset the balance of your four bodies. The maintenance of harmony is essential. Always strive to rein in your emotions while feeling peacefulness within the physical and thereby allowing the intellect to acknowledge the intuitive guidance of unerring wisdom. Be aware my dear friend that you have already left behind and then risen above the Valley of your Mind while you presently journey through the Landscape of your Heart. This is where you must now focus your attention. Be certain to maintain the greatest possible peace and harmony within all aspects of your true being while intending to create that which your heart most sincerely desires.

Now then my good friend, with your permission and your firm intent we shall complete our journey across this delightfully illustrative and instructive aerial pathway. In so doing we will resume our progress to your rendezvous at the church. We mustn't keep our guests waiting as those behind us are already approaching the entrance to the bridge."

I didn't really pay much attention to the part about the others as all I really wanted to do was to find a nice seat and then sit comfortably while thinking about everything that he had just said to me. I could so easily remember my time of hesitating on my journey to marry Janet but I had never even thought to consider it in the terms of what I had now become aware of. I just wanted to go over so much in my mind but then the visions of the big church came back and how the interior first looked to me and that's when I got the idea that 'thinking' probably wasn't the smartest idea right at this stage of my journey.

"I know how difficult it may seem to be able to do this right now my dear friend but it will get easier once you appreciate that everything serves a purpose and that there was no fault on anyone's part. You did your best in the circumstances which prevailed at that period of your life given your level of awareness. With the knowledge and wisdom that you had at the time then the

consequences of your choices were those which taught you most what you needed to learn. If you hadn't done what you did then you wouldn't be here with me now. It all worked out perfectly but you must allow yourself to truly acknowledge this within that special place which awaits your quiet contemplation of its true value to you. It is most important for you to do so."

I gave him a quizzical little glance in not understanding what 'special place' he was referring to. Putting his hand gently against the centre of my chest he said,

"In the very depths of your compassionate heart my dear friend. In that wonderful place which holds the truth of all things, where everything is known if you but listen to it. To accept any circumstance as being free of all judgement at this level is to embrace true healing and, as a direct consequence, you evolve and expand the precious being which is you. And so it is."

In the midst of my trying to take in every word of his wisdom I became aware that the gentle pealing of the church bells had changed to that of just two bells which seemed to be chiming out in perfect harmony. At the same time I glanced up into the woods to see the man, who I had warned about going back to the house, now making his way much closer to the church. Not only this but I could swear that many of the trees were moving and so I had to study them a little more before I realised that it was actually people moving in amongst them. At first I only noticed a few but the more I looked then the more of them I could see until it seemed as though the forest was quite literally alive with oddly dressed people. For a moment I could have believed that an entire army was in the process of making its way through the trees while also heading in the direction of the church. I had absolutely no idea what to make of it.

"Come my fortunate friend, now is your opportunity to consolidate all that you have experienced here in these precious times. We need to get ourselves across to the pathway and then up to the church. I tell you in all sincerity that it's entirely in your hands to make this possible. All that is needed at this precise moment on your journey is for you to have absolute faith in what you are now aware of and to live that conviction without allowing any interference from your mind.

Hold fast to your intuitive urges while setting your intent to create whatever they lead you to desire. All throughout our journey you have wished with all your heart to see inside the church on the plateau so as to find out more about the mysterious lady and her children. Is this still your dearest wish my good friend and if so, will you create the means by which you can achieve this?"

Whatever else I found myself not understanding I didn't have any problems in knowing that I wanted very much to get to the church. That was a desire that had been with me from early on and, now that I was so close, I could feel it even more.

"Excellent! So shall we proceed on our way then?"

I looked down at my feet and then at the distance before the bridge ended and then at the gap to the path. I looked at my companion with a blank expression which kind of summed up quite a few emotions that I felt at that moment.

"Faith my dear friend! You have already seen what you can do by following your heart. Now trust that you can do the same again and then let your intuition guide your footsteps."

Easier said than done was the phrase which immediately popped into my head but the calling of the bells seemed to be more emphatic as it did. I drew a breath and stepped up to the edge while being determined not to look down. There was still a good amount of water to be crossed and I didn't want to imagine how deep it was. I looked at the boarding of the bridge and then at the symbols carved into the side while seeing once again the ones which depicted the physical senses set back into the wood. I raised my foot and prepared to step out into what was the empty space at the edge of the bridge. I was tempted to close my eyes as I set it down again but something told me to keep them open while the bells got even louder.

I focused exclusively on my determination to get to where I wanted to go and in doing so I felt my foot land on something solid. I looked down to see a kind of shimmering form made up of the most attractive light and without thinking I stepped completely onto it. As I put all my weight, and trust, onto the light then thankfully it became yet another wooden component on the pathway. Before I allowed myself time to think about what had occurred I determinedly stepped out again. The same thing happened exactly as before where the light rippled all around my foot before creating another board.

Once again I advanced and then again and again, until I gave no more thought to pausing so as to reinforce my courage. Now I walked in full expectation of the fact that when I needed the wooden board to be there then it actually would be; because it was my sincere desire for it to support my journey to the destination of my heart.

Each step of desire created more of the bridge until we were almost back down to ground level and on the other side of the water. I could see the white pathway much clearer now but I could also see a huge stream of men, women and children walking along it. I almost allowed myself to be distracted by this unexpected sight but I stayed true to my intentions and with one final step the completed bridge was anchored firmly into the ground. Even before I had time to congratulate myself, I heard what sounded like voices from somewhere behind me and so I turned to see exactly where they were coming from; and also from whom.

To my surprise I saw all of the people from the garden making their way across the bridge behind me while chatting as though they were just out for a Sunday afternoon stroll in the countryside. However, this was obviously no occasion of coincidence as I noticed that nearly all of them were carrying gifts of one kind or another, while quite a few carried musical instruments. It looked as though they were on their way to some kind of celebration but the only place nearby was the church on the hill. In my plans to get there I hadn't figured on having any company apart from that of my wise companion. Now it seemed as if I was in imminent danger of being left at the back of an increasingly long queue given the fact of the large numbers of people who were passing me by. I was just about to join in the 'parade' when my companion caught hold of me lightly by the arm.

"My friend, please come with me on a short diversion just to see something interesting before you head off to the church. I want you to have a full appreciation of one more important aspect to your endeavours before we make our final ascent up the pathway to your eventual destination."

Even though I was keen to make my way up the path along with everyone else, I'd heard him say the word 'important' and so I gladly followed him as we set off a little way along the bank of the lake. We hadn't gone very far before he stopped and then turned to look back at the bridge. I did so too and had to admit that it was worth the quick detour in that I found myself being presented with the most elegantly beautiful aerial structure I had ever seen. In studying its highly attractive form and design more carefully I got the impression that it could easily have been something which would support a rainbow. In fact, as my attention seemed to be drawn even deeper into it then I felt that I could almost see the many colours which went into making up such a memorable spectacle.

As much as I studied the whole length of the bridge quite carefully and knew that it was made mostly of wood, I just couldn't figure out what was keeping such a huge structure up. It looked so slender given its span but there appeared to be a kind of certainty to it that seemed as though it could have effortlessly traversed the whole lake if necessary. *"Trust."* was all that my companion said in the way of offering an explanation. I felt confused at hearing just this one word as, at first, I took it that he was asking me to do something. I quickly discounted this as I knew that he could understand what I had been thinking and so, I reasoned, he must be referring to the bridge and its design. However I figured it I just couldn't seem to apply this particular word to the subject of a bridge and its construction. Feeling that I was never going to arrive at a good understanding I suddenly wanted to say, trust what?

"Trust is the underlying energy of what keeps it together my dear friend. The highly motivating energy of absolute trust; it really is a powerful force as you have so recently proved. Consider this carefully for a moment. Your intuition gives it direction while your 'trust' in the guidance of that sixth sense is what keeps it together so as to support you. When you trust your intuition then you can create whatever you want as it will always lead you to a place of your

greatest happiness. Shall we see where this wonderful creation has led you to in this particular instance my good friend?"

Without waiting for my obvious answer he patted me on the shoulder. Then he began heading off towards the pathway which was by now completely empty of anyone while looking as though it was actually waiting for us to step onto it.

"Bear in mind ..." my wise friend started to say, *"... your intuition is the sense which communicates its desires to you but what is it do you think which provides that magnetic attraction to guide it? What subtle force is constantly influencing its compass needle that always points to your highest joy and which calls you so faithfully to it? Think on this my wonderful friend as you embark upon the last part of your journey here."*

I was just about to ask him what he meant as we rounded a sharp bend in the pathway but all thoughts of posing any more questions quickly evaporated from my mind as I tried to take in the view ahead of me. For a moment I wondered if there was someone else that I should expect to see coming along behind me but I knew that there could be no one but my companion and myself. I glanced to the side of me and then had to immediately revise that statement. To my complete surprise I realised that my wise friend had mysteriously disappeared and that I was standing completely alone. Then I looked up the inclined pathway which led to the church and that's when I became fully aware that absolutely everyone appeared to be looking directly at me. My heart seemed to stop at that precise moment.

- Chapter 20 -

The Congregation of Different Eras

What greeted me when I looked up the long sloping pathway to the church was not the quiet tree-lined route to the plateau which I had expected. Instead, it was now bordered by literally hundreds of people on either side of it. As far as I could see they were three and four deep in some places while smiling as though all of them were waiting for me to continue on my journey. I was completely speechless and more than a little embarrassed but there seemed to be nothing else for me to do, under the circumstances, other than to carry on walking up towards my destination. Getting to the church was still very much at the forefront of my mind but I had never imagined that my journey would involve my having to pass through a large crowd of people in the process. Never before this moment could I remember feeling so uncomfortably self conscious in my whole life. All eyes were on me, which had the most bizarre effect of making me feel acutely alone, and yet not, all at the same instant. This certainly did nothing to alleviate my confusion. As far as I was able to make out, it appeared as though my presence represented a 'parade of one', but what on earth the celebration was supposed to be in aid of I couldn't begin to imagine.

I took a deep breath as I attempted to steady my nerves while still trying to figure out what everyone could be doing gathered in such a way, but then I noticed something intriguing about how each person was looking at me. I had no idea why this should attract my attention but it seemed to make me equally as curious as I was nervous. I just had to find out what was going on so I commanded my firmly-rooted feet to carry me forward as confidently and supportively as they could possibly manage. I also tried to convince my legs to stop shaking but that didn't seem to have much effect at all. My first steps felt as though I was just learning to walk again, but once started I held my nerve and then kept the momentum going. Finally I was on my way and my ultimate destination was in sight. My racing heart made it seem as though I had to cross another universe at least so as to get to the church but I kept silently telling it that if this was to be the case, then so be it. There was no turning back now and nothing was going to stop me, not even a huge crowd of people who had apparently come to watch me.

No sooner had I begun to walk in between the tightly packed lines of people than I was greatly relieved to find that my emotional state began to change quite noticeably. The reason for this was that I quickly found myself feeling overwhelmed by the way in which everyone seemed to greet me, insomuch as they all had the warmest of sincere smiles; almost as though they knew me really well. This is what I had observed when I first saw them all looking at me but at the moment of my noticing it then it just didn't seem possible. Now I could see the truth of it. The sensation was similar to that of walking into a tropical breeze which instantly wrapped me up in its exhilarating energy. I could almost feel the calling of the ocean which wanted me to come and sit quietly beside it. It proved to be an almost irresistible request but I pressed on resolutely through the avenue of infectiously cheerful people and on towards the church.

What I found to be the most odd thing of all was that the first part of the route appeared to be lined with mostly men who were all dressed in a kind of old style uniform; which actually looked quite familiar to me. To further compound my mood of surprise, there also appeared to be very many faces that seemed somewhat recognisable as well. This certainly was intriguing where my sense of increasing fascination was quickly replacing my anxiety. But what made the greatest impression on me of all was how it seemed to affect me when studying these men. The powerful connection which I felt almost bowled me over through encountering the sheer strength of mutual feeling which I sensed coming from them. It was nearly as heady an experience as I had got from flying around the valley. Although this was slightly different in that, this time I found myself receiving the feelings of the deepest affection as well as joy. It was such an amazing combination of emotional energy which made my footsteps seem as though I was actually walking on air. This was an entirely different form of flying but without doubt equally as spectacular.

I made a point to acknowledge everyone that I possibly could and was delighted to see that they seemed so heartily pleased that I did. The sheer warmth of their obvious affection served to melt away virtually all of my anxieties to the degree that I was almost starting to relish all the attention. But, I have to say in all honesty that not once did I give any thought to my situation in any kind of egotistical way as it really was the farthest thing from my mind. I was much too caught up in the thoroughly uplifting spirit of the occasion and also why it seemed that so many men appeared as though they wanted to shake my hand or just come across to hug me. The truly confusing thing about this was that I actually found myself feeling the same about them. It just felt so incredibly good to see them all again although I couldn't say exactly why. So I kept nodding, smiling and giving little waves while not allowing my mind to get in the way of something which I found myself enjoying so much.

This was not an occasion on which to 'think'; as my companion, wherever he was, had taught me so well. Even in the midst of being so caught up in such an emotionally overwhelming situation I was able to feel grateful that he'd shown me how to approach circumstances such as this. I could almost hear his encouraging voice coaching me to abandon my conditioned responses and my need to 'mentalise' everything while trusting that my intuition would always provide me with whatever explanations or timely answers may be appropriate. This was somewhat unnerving at first and needed a determined effort to hold fast to on my part but I felt sure that it would get easier with practice. However, it did take a great deal of resolve to rein in my innate curiosity. So, even though I had no understanding of what was going on, I just allowed myself to go with the flow while being mindful of my mentor's guidance. I accepted that it was okay not to know. I kept telling myself that not knowing was perfectly fine while allowing things to be just as they were but being especially careful not to apply judgement in any way. It felt reassuringly good to utilise this wisdom and again I was pleased to have learned so much in a relatively short space of time. This realisation caused me to glow even more inside.

Slowly I made my way up to near the top of the incline which led towards the entrance into the church grounds. In doing so it seemed to me as though I was being swept along by a sea of smiling faces where, on this part of the route, there were many women and children as well. It truly was a delight to see them all but I had to admit that I found myself starting to feel quite overwhelmed by all that I could sense happening within me as a consequence of this amazing experience. Just at the stage where I felt that I was on the verge of needing a rest, I caught sight of a highly recognisable face in the crowd. I could never have mistaken that unforgettable smile. As soon as I saw him he stepped forward and once more my wonderful companion greeted me, but now he was dressed in the same uniform style of clothing as so many of the other men. His appearance caught me completely off guard for a moment as there was something very familiar about his new look which seemed to take me way back in time. In so doing I experienced a feeling as though I should be remembering something important but I just couldn't think what it could be, so I had to ask.

"What are you doing dressed like that and why are you with all these men?"

I was so intrigued by the highly evocative nature of his clothing that I found myself trying very hard to understand what it meant to me.

"I thought you might recognise me more easily like this."

All I could manage to say in response was a quite lame,

"Yes, me too!" but then managed to add,

"Tell me oh wise one, why would I recognise you like this? Have I seen you somewhere else, in some other time maybe?"

I'm not sure what made me say this last part but there was no hesitation in his reply,

"Indeed you have my wonderful friend, indeed you most certainly have for we have been good friends for a very long time. Would it help you to know what you used to call me?"

I nodded while wringing out every last ounce of storage space in my memory banks in the hopes that I might remember before he told me. It felt like I had the answer right on the tip of my tongue but somehow I just couldn't seem to get the words out.

"You used to call me the Battlefield Bard but now I would be most honoured if you would call me brother."

I looked long and hard at his wonderful face as a whole waterfall of memories came cascading into my head. At the very same instant a kaleidoscope of images erupted in front of me. Once again I saw the camp fires of many glorious nights where we had shared our hearts and our songs while forging our communal bridge to freedom. It was the most moving of experiences on a journey that had been so intense where a great many trials had been overcome through the healing bonds of friendship and trust. How could I have ever forgotten the master of melody and mirth who had lightened the hearts of so many in such a selfless manner. I began to feel a little tightness in my throat but just as I did, then once again I heard his gently comforting tones.

"Welcome home my dearest friend. I also bid you welcome from all of your other brothers and sisters who are so overjoyed to see you once more. I trust that you are able to feel the immense love and affection which comes to you from each and every one of us and which will always be with you no matter where your journey takes you. We are as one heart with you my brother and ever thus it shall be so."

I had no difficulty at all in appreciating the power and sincerity of his words while I could also 'feel' everyone looking at me. No sooner had I sensed this aspect of my situation however, than something quite unexpected happened. For what felt almost like a greatly expanded fragment of eternity, I imagined myself to be stood at the focus of some huge jury who, having been presented with all the evidence and passing their findings to the clerk of the court, were all eagerly waiting to see what occurred next. All was quite still in anticipation of a final pronouncement from the principal adjudicator.

Then, to my abject consternation, I caught sight of the judge sitting high up in his lop-sided chair; it was me. I was wearing a uniform as well as being blindfolded but what covered my eyes seemed to be the opaque bindings of unenlightenment. When being handed the piece of gold lined parchment, so as to be aware of the jury's conclusions, then I had absolutely no idea of what had been decided. Neither could I see the smile on the clerk's face where, if I had, then I would have recognised it as belonging to my wonderful companion. I anxiously watched as my judgemental self held the parchment in my hands while feeling sure that it must require me to think up an appropriate punishment. No one spoke as I deliberated.

Once again I heard my companion's stirring words echoing inspiringly in the recesses of my troubled heart and slowly I began to appreciate that my visual bindings were starting to dissipate. They easily melted under the irrepressible light of awareness which came streaming into my consciousness. Sitting less precariously in my chair, I squinted to make out the words on the parchment where, as the last of the bindings fell away, I could clearly see the beautifully scripted statement –

> *'In Love and Light we ask that the accused be released into a true understanding of what 'was'. We further request that the shackles of self doubt and unnecessary recriminations be dissolved within the spirit of Divine forgiveness. We the jury find the defendant to be in possession of a wonderfully compassionate heart. In so finding, it is our sincerest wish that he now be committed to sharing it freely with everyone in his sphere of influence; just as he has done with us.'*

The document was signed by everyone including the children. Reading it made me feel as though a huge weight had suddenly been lifted from within the uncharted depths of my heart; a burden which I had apparently been carrying with me for a very long time. With its disappearance came the vision of a long forgotten occasion where I remembered having been sat by a garden while listening to a group of people explaining things to me. I also seemed to recall being vaguely aware of many similarly uniformed men who were all coming out of a distant valley and then meeting up with loved ones after passing by where I was sitting in the middle of a big symbol. The more I remembered this occasion then the more vivid the images appeared to me but what came with them were also the feelings which I experienced at that time. I particularly recalled that my mind seemed to have been caught up in reliving something very unpleasant where I blamed myself for some awful tragedy. I wasn't aware that I actually felt this way but right at this moment in time then I could see that this was how I had chosen to see things.

With this memorable episode so clearly elaborated in my mind, reality once more returned where I found myself looking from man to man as though trying to disentangle the threads of a disjointed and incomplete presumption. Then I seemed to make the connection with the uniforms and suddenly I became much more aware of all the men and what they really did mean to me. Momentarily I was confused but, almost like someone stepping through the thick haze of my predicament, an ethereal messenger reached compassionately out so as to plant a profound understanding into the space where my burden had once lain. The healing was almost instantaneous which caused a gentle catharsis of tears to spring forth in the garden of my blooming awareness. In doing so, the cool emollient moisture served to quell the harsh flames of a highly judgemental fire which had been burning so detrimentally away in me for far too long.

Suddenly I was able to see clearly the true weight of the guilt which I had laden myself down with but it proved to be just as much of a relief to finally see it as it was to actually give it up. No sooner had this feeling settled deep within me than I heard a voice call out a brief command. This was promptly followed by a kind of heavy and prolonged rustling sound which almost gave me the idea that the forest all around me had suddenly come to life. After everything else which had happened to me on this journey then I wouldn't have been at all surprised, but I just had to check.

Looking behind me I watched in wordless awe as every uniformed man fell into line in a column of three. I turned to face them while briefly not understanding what they were doing but when I watched them all come to attention and then salute, I absolutely understood. My heart was instantly filled with a huge sense of pride as I did indeed remember my brothers and all their wonderful faces as well as all the love in their incredibly brave hearts. What an indescribably moving sight it was to be sure but the sheer depth of effect which it had on me was almost impossible to contemplate. My only regret at that moment was the fact that my arms weren't long enough to give all of them one gigantic hug. I felt the urge to just stay looking at the whole spellbinding assembly while committing to memory every single one of their happy faces. What an absolute thrill it was to be intimately reunited with them once again and to know how enthusiastically cheerful they all were. How could anyone standing in the midst of such overwhelming love not be the happiest and most contented soul in the universe? I certainly was at that moment.

I felt as though I didn't ever want to move from the spot I was viewing them all from but somehow I did manage to appreciate that I was expected to continue on up the pathway. Together my companion and I turned to face forward as we led the march off up towards the church and into the beautiful grounds through even more lines of smiling faces. This time I could see many more women and children as well and even they joined in the ever increasing numbers in the column. It made me smile to think of what fun the children were having after having become part of the parade. In contemplating this prospect it put me in mind of my own children and how much pleasure it had given me to share in their adventures as they discovered the many delights of the world around them. I marched on up the gradually lessening incline as the wide open gates to the church came quickly into view. They were white painted and somewhat uninspiring but in my mind's eye they were the prettiest guardians of any entrance that I'd ever seen. To me they marked the end of a journey which had taken me on the wildest ride of my imaginings, but one which had come to mean so much to me. Getting to the church almost felt like my homecoming and with a heavenly lightness to my heart, the like of which I had never dreamed possible, my companion and I turned to step through the wide opening. It really was a breathtakingly wonderful feeling.

Once inside the church grounds we were greeted by everyone who had come across from the garden on the other side of the water. It was so overwhelming to me that my already joy-filled heart pounded with such a force that I was sure that it would burst at the very next beat. For a moment I stood still by way of acknowledging each person present while the seemingly never ending column of men, women, and quite a few obviously excited children, poured into the area in front the church. Even though the grounds around this part of the church appeared to be somewhat modest in their proportions, they didn't seem to have any trouble accommodating anyone who wished to be present. The atmosphere which this whole quite intimate situation created as a result must have been felt equally by everyone as no one spoke; which suddenly made me a little nervous again as though they were all waiting for me to do or say something.

I turned to look at the front of the church where I saw that the doors were already open, although there appeared to be no one inside. Even though it seemed to be much smaller than the big church that I had so recently been in, this one looked equally as beautiful in its own charmingly unique way. I glanced up to see the white painted bell tower where just two gleaming golden bells were very softly chiming away in a wonderfully melodic harmony and I gave thanks for their inspiring presence. I couldn't help thinking about what an amazing gift they had been on my journey. Returning my attention to the interior of the church I could see many of the pews either side of the central aisle and the attractively decorated altar at the far end. What impressed me most of all though was the sight of a beautifully designed large, round stained glass window behind the altar. The light streamed through it in a blaze of the most vibrant colours which served to create the most stunning effect.

Everyone around me was completely silent as though experiencing a similar appreciation for this most delightful of settings and the truly wonderful atmosphere which the peaceful grounds were creating. It was difficult for me to see how anyone could fail to be affected by such a truly inspirational setting as this. Then I tried to imagine who could have dreamed up such a magical little haven tucked away in the mountains. To me it seemed so inspired. It was tempting to take in much more of the atmosphere but suddenly I got the impression that the large congregation behind me were probably all waiting for me to enter the church. So I turned to my beloved friend for a little reassurance and then heard him say almost in a whisper.

"Go to where your heart has led you but, when you do then be joyfully aware of what it is that you bring to each and every individual who has journeyed here to be with you at this delightful place. They have all come to bear witness to the light that you are while you allow your twin flame to burn so brightly. In so doing you have been, and are, an inspiration to everyone

gathered here in your presence. Know for absolute certain, in the very depths of your being, that you are the enduring expression of the manifest possibility which exists in equal measure for all who yearn to realise their fullest potential. You remind all those who see your brilliant light of what they have forgotten about themselves but so dearly wish to remember.

In witnessing what you have achieved then they too aspire to do likewise while listening to the guidance of their own hearts and making choices accordingly. They celebrate the glorious omnipresence of this inspirational light which has unerringly led you to a place of your highest joy. Each man, woman and child is eternally grateful that it is here for all to experience in the fullness of its innate attraction which serves to stimulate a heartfelt remembering. Nothing that they have seen and felt, or may yet experience, in this very special place will ever be forgotten as they too journey forth to become that same light on their own pathway that you have been on yours.

Go now my enlightened brother so as you may see for yourself what it is that lifts your spirit to greater heights by far than when you soared so freely over the valley. I will be waiting for you to recommence your journey but please stay as long as you wish while feeling all the most wonderful love which surrounds you. Forever travel your chosen pathway in peace my honoured friend while always walking in the loving light that you are."

I seemed to be transfixed by the words that I had just heard while holding my wise companions hand in both of mine and gently shaking it. Emotions were pouring through me like the water that I had imagined coursing over the edge of the big cataract under the mist. Eventually I stopped shaking his hand and once more turned to look at the sea of faces around me, but was immediately overwhelmed by all that I sensed radiating back to me. I was exhilarated but at the same time I found it quite hard to breathe as one particularly powerful emotion gripped me. For the very first time I truly understood what forgiveness really was and within this appreciation my eyes became more than a little misty in the process. Whatever else I felt the need to do right at that moment, I just had to take a minute or two so as to allow myself the opportunity to fully take in all the obvious affection which flowed out to me. It was like being comforted at the level of my greatest need where a long overdue healing was now well underway. I had no words to express my gratitude but somehow I felt that none were necessary. Time passed slowly while I seemed to be able to sense every heartbeat around me. It was the most amazing experience.

Reluctantly I returned my attention to the church and then stepped forward so as to enter through the quite stunningly carved wooden doors which led directly into the nave. It was difficult to walk away from what I had been so deeply immersed in but, as much as I wished to stay contemplating my new awareness, I still needed to get to my ultimate destination. Just a few more steps and that objective would become a reality and so I made my way through the flower-lined porch while the atmosphere of the interior almost raced forward to welcome me in. I felt the whole of my spine tingle in anticipation. The inside of the church was absolutely beautiful where the most imposing feature was the big round stained glass window which I had caught a partial glimpse of from outside. Now that I could see the whole of the thoroughly charismatic setting and design then it was impossible not to be drawn completely in by its captivating influence as it seemed to dominate the entire atmosphere of the seating area.

The most striking aspect about it was the central figure of a man dressed in long flowing colourful robes who looked very peaceful while kneeling in the manner of either praying or giving grateful thanks. I found myself feeling very much the same way as I moved along the aisle so as to sit in the front-most right hand pew while almost getting thoroughly lost in the simple but very powerful message of the image. To me it seemed to be such an unusually humble pose but it was certainly one which expressed a good deal of how I was feeling at that very moment. The more I studied the whole scene, with the people sitting close by him in the background, then the more I seemed to be drawn into becoming involved in its highly magnetic appeal. Never before had an image spoken so potently and profoundly to me as this one was doing right at that precise moment.

There was something irresistibly engaging about the larger-than-life central figure whose apparent entreaties to the heavens made me want to better understand the reason behind what he was doing. In light of what had been happening to me, I felt the need to appreciate what possible circumstances could have led him to act in this way. But, even while thinking this, I got the notion that I already knew the answer. It was the most peculiar feeling but one which caused something else to arise in me where, at quite a deep level, I experienced a strong sensation that a long and turbulent storm had finally come to an end. Until that moment I had been completely unaware of my continual efforts to battle my way through it. However, with the advent of its passing then I was able to truly acknowledge just how much of a disruptive presence it had been in my life. The most disturbing of all notions was that it may well not have been confined to just one life.

I steadied myself while feeling the currents of the galaxy come sweeping into the dusty corridors of my past while cleansing the detritus of accumulated misconceptions. In its wake I found myself to be standing in its gently swirling aftermath as the atmosphere all around me gradually began to settle back into a state of peaceful calm and soothing quietude. I stood very still while allowing myself to fully take in the refreshing newness of a circumstance which seemed to have been long forgotten to me. At last it was over and, in spite of all the challenges, I had prevailed; it felt exceptionally good to have done so. I had come through it all and once more I remembered the peacefulness of spirit which is achieved through existing in a state of stillness and harmony. This wonderful reacquainting with an 'old friend' brought with it a certain serenity which reached into the very depths of my sense of 'self'. As it did so then I could seem to recall in much greater clarity the person who I knew myself to be. This I wholeheartedly welcomed along with an overwhelming feeling of gratitude for my new awareness as well as the incredibly precious gift of life that I had been granted.

As I studied every aspect of the scene depicted in the magnificent window then I began to appreciate that the silent message portrayed by the beautifully painted kneeling figure expressed so perfectly what was already in my heart to say. Suddenly I was at One with his peacefulness. It was such a powerful feeling which allowed me to sense a degree of the most intimate connection where, for what seemed like a unified instant in an eternity of time, I could have almost been him. This truly wonderful sensation was immediately accompanied by a lightness of heart and spirit within me that was absolutely impossible to describe. All at once everything felt right in a world where so much that had once seemed so confusing, suddenly made complete sense to me.

In experiencing this level of such a profound affinity, I also became aware that it wasn't just within me but also outside of me as well. The whole ambiance of the church was equally as peaceful while being filled with what felt like wonderful memories. They seemed to be wrapping me completely up in their warm embrace just like greeting an old ally while encouraging me to feel a strong sense of belonging. Whilst being thoroughly immersed in this new level of peacefulness, I suddenly realised that the bells had ceased their melodic chimes. In so doing they allowed an atmosphere of the most moving silence to prevail which certainly did speak to me. It was a highly emotional quietness where the most gently stirring memories crept enthusiastically in to greet me in their awakening. They were like very much missed comrades who had come back to be reunited with me and once more we shared our times together while giving thanks for the precious healing opportunities that they had so lovingly brought with them. So many friends and so much to be grateful for where even the most challenging of memories seemed to be equally as welcomed for the gift of their presence.

Everything that I had been through and what I had come to appreciate as a result, combined with all that I was sensing at this moment, had the effect of giving me a completely new perspective on so much of life. It was almost like waking up into an expanded consciousness and so it was that I had begun to see my long journey in a very different light. The appearance of this new found awareness corresponded with the exact moment that I began to really pay attention to the candles all around the church. I hadn't noticed them before that time but now I could see that they were all glowing very brightly while sparkling just like millions of diamonds. It was the most amazing spectacle and thoroughly captivating as it made the whole of the interior of the church shimmer as though it was infused with a vibrant light all of its own.

No sooner had I begun to take in the truly captivating splendour of this effect than I was aware that many people were starting to come in through the front entrance. Slowly they were making their way along the aisle and then moving into the empty rows of pews while quickly filling them up. I could see that some of them were carrying gifts which I had noticed that the people coming across the bridge were bringing with them. Many of the children were placing small baskets of the most colourful flowers on shelves at the end of the pews. Then I saw that some of the women were carefully pouring essential oils into delicately shaped crystal glass dishes situated above the larger candles.

The effect was quite remarkable as everything they did seemed to begin spreading the most attractive aromas throughout the whole interior of the church. Each individual fragrance could be identified but somehow they all combined to produce the most amazingly soothing atmosphere of peace and calm. The highly scented air seemed to come alive and was simply wonderful to the degree that each of the fragrances could almost be seen to have its own colour. To breathe them in was to experience the sense of smell in a way that I had never known to be possible before that time.

Then I noticed two very able-looking men carrying what appeared to be large earthenware jars as they made their way towards the area behind the altar. They took opposite routes around the altar and then positioned themselves in front of two big, floor-standing glass containers. In a kind of reverential manner they began filling each of them with a clear sparkling liquid which almost seemed to burst out of their jars as they poured. As soon as this was done, two of the children placed small saucer-like candles on top of the liquid where they floated gently as they were being lit. No sooner had their flames grown to full strength than they sank slowly through the sparkling fluid but the effect which they produced through doing so was quite remarkable.

The clear liquid substance and the glass containers seemed to merge together into one spectacular ball of light which began to illuminate the whole of the wall until it literally glowed. There was no sensation of heat at all, even though the intensity of light seemed to indicate that there should be. The children looked on in fascination while obviously being very pleased at having been allowed to initiate such a wonderful spectacle. After a little while of revelling in their handiwork they returned to the seating area along with the two men.

As I watched in wordless fascination all that was happening, I could also see that many people were placing gifts of food on the altar; although what they were offering looked to be anything but ordinary everyday food. These gifts were stunningly presented with combinations of not just the individual fruits or vegetables but the vines, leaves and plants which they grew with as well. Many of the presentations were woven like intricate tapestries of living nourishment which looked so delicious that it seemed possible to almost

307

taste every single aspect of the display. The fruits literally glowed in such an attractively radiant way that they appeared to be simply bursting with life.

While my taste buds seemed to be relishing everything on display, I noticed that after each person had placed their gift then they would look up at the figure of the kneeling man. Immediately they would smile and then bow in a way which seemed to respectfully and accurately reflect his own humble expression of gratitude. Everyone's smile was so genuine and appreciative where even the children seemed to understand the inspirational message from the colourful scene depicted in the big glass window. One lady and her daughter, at least I presumed it was her daughter, stopped to look up at the window for a few moments after placing their gifts but then turned to come across to where I was sitting. They were both dressed in a style which seemed very dated but I assumed that it may have been something to do with the ceremony. The young girl sat down close beside me and the lady sat next to her but no sooner had she settled herself comfortably than the young girl reached out and took hold of my hand. She looked up at me and with the most attractive smile she said quietly,

"Hello, I'm Louisa ... but my really special friends call me Loucie ..." then, almost immediately she looked a little embarrassed as she added *"... but, of course, you already know that don't you."*

As soon as these words were out of her mouth she squeezed my hand quite firmly while looking at me as though she had known me all of her life. I returned her smile in being genuinely pleased that she had chosen to sit with me but I was puzzled by her remarks of apparent familiarity. My flustered mind did a few somersaults while rummaging frantically around for any kind of information which would make sense of what I had just heard. I drew small comfort from the fact that somewhere in the dark recesses of it there was a glimmer of light which seemed to get steadily brighter as I continued to look at her beautiful, and strangely familiar, little face. Before I had a chance to come to any kind of meaningful conclusion, or even reply to her greeting, she said in a most disarming way.

"Don't you think that the big window up there has the most beautiful picture of Jesus on it that you've ever seen? I do. He looks so kind and so loving that it just makes me want to smile at him every time I see it. I just can't help myself. Sometimes I imagine that I can almost hear what he's saying."

She squeezed my hand again and then shrugged her shoulders in the most delightful manner which seemed to indicate her level of excitement with all that she could see happening around her while sharing it with me. I have no idea why but it had the most profound effect on me and, after pausing for a few moments to kind of catch my emotional breath, I felt as though I wanted to respond by putting my arm around her. It seemed to be the most natural thing to do but for some reason I was reluctant to act on my impulse. To my surprise she squeezed my hand yet again while moving a little closer to me and then catching hold of the ladies hand as well. This was something that I had not expected at all but after the initial shock I found myself quickly becoming accustomed to her presence as well as the familiarity of her touch, which was altogether very welcomed.

Without my realising it I had started to feel more than just her closeness as well as her infectious excitement. It was as if I had somehow caught a glimpse of the world around me through her eyes while appreciating how new and thrilling everything looked to her. In how she saw things there existed no judgement but simply a kind of fascination for the magic of everything that life had to offer and what fun could be had as a result. Her thoroughly refreshing way of looking at things took the complexity out of the unnecessary confusion which adults bring to almost every situation. To Loucie, there was no need to see anything other than how it really is while simply enjoying herself in the process. I just couldn't get over how freeing it felt to be like this and then suddenly found it difficult to imagine why any of us would want to grow out of this delightful way of seeing the world in which we exist.

In returning my thoughts to my own current predicament I found this new view of life to be surprisingly reminiscent of something which stirred a distant memory in me. I began thinking about being young but not just the youthful time of my recent journey. Somehow I suddenly seemed to be able to feel what it was like to see life in a way that was free of grown-up attitudes and prejudices. What an amazing revelation that proved to be! Thankfully it was one which brought with it a sense of the most deep-seated completeness. To me it was like finding the missing piece of an emotional jigsaw puzzle; a very important piece which I hadn't even realised that I had lost until that moment. Even describing it in this manner seemed to be quite inadequate as what I could sense so acutely went way beyond that which my mind could interpret.

At that very instant of awareness I began to appreciate the true depth of the void between how I experienced my feelings and what my mind was capable of understanding about them. Much of what my companion had been telling me, all throughout our quite memorable journey together, suddenly came back to me during that moment of revelation. The energetically sparkling light all around me seemed to inspire a similar light within me which suddenly illuminated much of what I hadn't previously seemed able to make any sense of. Now, thankfully, a much greater depth of clarity had arisen within my awareness but in some other more subtle aspect of my intuitive being there was a distinct impression that it wasn't emanating from my mind.

What I could sense coming to me was a kind of 'knowing', just like my wise guide had been encouraging me to see. It certainly felt as though it was a very special moment for me as so many things fell neatly into place but it also proved to be one which brought with it a sense of such intense joy as well. This was something that I hadn't expected at all and so I squeezed Loucie's hand gently while smiling in gratitude for the very precious gift that her presence had bestowed on me. I could truly appreciate the value of what I had been blessed with as the contentment and happiness which came from it was so wonderfully freeing.

While being caught up in these delightful sensations I found myself becoming conscious of the fact that many more people were still coming into the church. Before too long I could see that the whole place was getting quite full while the atmosphere seemed to be charged with a certain degree of anticipation. Just when I started to wonder if the beautiful building could take any more, the final group of uniformed men came in so as to line the aisle and the sides of the church. I had no idea how many of them there now were but it seemed as though there was no space left to be filled anywhere in the whole place.

What I also noticed was that the sparkling light all around had intensified to the degree that everything seemed to be glowing, but the area where all the gifts had been placed appeared to have a very special glow of its own. The voluminous glass jars of light were getting brighter when suddenly the candle flames grew very much bigger until they literally burst out over the tops of their containers. Each flame then quickly expanded upwards in the most unusual manner in that they seemed to literally become one with the wall while illuminating it even more. I found the light from the flames to be quite fascinating but while studying them I had the strangest of feelings that I'd actually seen them somewhere before. As they burned brightly with an almost mesmerising energy I could see that the entire wall was giving off some sort of sparkling shimmer which quickly grew in intensity as I continued to look at it.

Then, to my surprise, many people standing in the aisles produced instruments and immediately started to play. It was so unexpected that it took me a while to appreciate exactly what was happening while adjusting my ears to the new sounds; although I could sense that Loucie was simply thrilled to be hearing it. At first there were just a few instruments playing a simple melody but these were soon joined by others which then flooded the inside of the church with their enchanting choruses. The music was absolutely wonderful while seeming to want to lift the spirits of the entire congregation. The captivating melodies and accompaniment were so very gentle as well as being soul-penetratingly moving which made the whole atmosphere in the church quite the most magical that I had ever experienced.

What with all the heady aromas from the heated oils and the flowers, the delicious displays of food which looked so good that they could almost be tasted and with the feel of the young girl holding my hand while sitting so close to me, it crossed my mind that I may decide never to leave this place. It was such a temptation to just get completely lost in the whole sensational experience while being thoroughly fascinated by the spectacle of light in front of me. It seemed to me that I couldn't possibly be more contented than how I considered myself to be at this precise moment. How incredibly happy I felt with so much love coming from within and around me.

Looking at the illuminated wall in front of me I noticed that the twin flames were now shimmering so completely in unison that they were becoming almost indistinguishable from one another. As a result, the stonework had gradually taken on a very different aspect to its nature in that it had become more like a wall of pure light than of any other substance; albeit that it still surrounded and supported the big circular window. This gave the stained glass mural even more of an imposing effect as there now seemed to be much more light actually around it than coming through it.

The orchestra played on as I found myself being drawn into the wonderful imagery of the big window while admiring the beautiful blue sky depicted within it. I wondered what it must have been like to be the big bird that was flying so freely in its midst as I followed its path around the small group of stars. I became aware of another gentle squeeze of my hand as I did and then felt myself respond by doing the same thing as I guessed that Loucie had been caught up in watching what I was. I noticed that there were five twinkling lights which seemed to weave in and around the four heavenly bodies. They appeared to be illuminated by a light quite unlike that of anything else which was present in either the interior of the church or on the other side of the window. All except, that was, the two large flames which had now merged into the blazing stonework so as to become part of the wall. In doing so they had produced the most amazingly subtle effect but also a very powerful one in its own way.

For a while my attention was captured by it, until I began to notice that the sparkling flame-filled wall around the window had changed. Now it had taken on a sort of mirror-like quality to it where I could almost make out the complete reflection of the interior of the church; or so I thought at first. It took me a little while to get used to what I was seeing as the intensity of the sparkle decreased until the whole wall became just one big reflective surface. As it did so then I could finally study things more clearly but this corresponded to the point when I first began to appreciate the differences. What had become the focus of my attention, and no doubt everyone else's, didn't seem to be a true reflection of anything that was behind me. From what I could make out, the people who were sat in the pews of the reflection looked somehow different and there were also a lot less of them. In the mirrored image it was apparent that no one was standing in the aisles as I could see right out through the outer open doors and into the open area at the front of the church.

While I examined the many dissimilar aspects of the image in the wall-of-light then I became aware of the fact that the illumination on my side of the mirror was gradually becoming less intense. However, I could also appreciate that the light from the reflected scene in front of me remained the same. This contrasting effect continued to the point where I realised that what I could see in the wall was not a mirror at all but more like a huge panel of transparent light. A thick glassy substance which seemed to have a quality that made it appear as though it was almost alive but within it I could still see the strikingly powerful essence of the two large flames. I found it to be the most incredibly awe inspiring experience especially in being seated so close to it as I was.

I felt a small movement in my hand as Loucie repositioned herself so as to get even closer to me. Her actions allowed me to appreciate that she too was becoming thoroughly caught up in the whole mind-stretching experience. Without thinking about it, I released her hand so that I could reach across to put my arm around her and to my delight she responded by snuggling up very close to me indeed. It was the most comforting of sensations and one that I never ever wanted to forget. For a moment I could almost have believed that we were in the movie theatre together where something breathtakingly exciting was about to happen and we were both in need of each others reassuring touch in anticipation.

The flames within the wall-of-light seemed to react to my feelings by burning in a particularly intense way which I found irresistibly attractive; although I had no idea why. They were energetically ablaze with a brightness that seemed to speak of the very essence that life expresses in so many facets of its eternal existence. My attention was drawn to the one that I found myself sitting closest to. Almost at the point of my getting completely lost in its mesmerising effect I began to make out what looked like some kind of pattern. The more I looked then the more I thought that I could recognise something familiar about its unique design although nothing readily came to mind. As the image became clearer then my mind worked overtime to identify a kind of decorative shape which seemed to be very memorable but which I just couldn't place.

Slowly I went over many different things including all of the symbols which I'd seen in the big panel windows and on the carvings of the bridge but none of them matched what I could see in the heart of the flame. For an instant my mind went completely blank but then the lines of the pattern seemed to sparkle in a way that was highly reminiscent of something I'd seen quite recently. My thoughts raced as I tried to recall what it could possibly be and where I could have seen it. Then I began to feel that I was so close where the answer was on the tip of my tongue. I have no idea why but I seemed to be drawn to think about what had happened to me on the bridge, at which point something clicked as an image popped into my mind.

Suddenly it dawned on me where I had seen this twisting shape before and then I knew without doubt that I was actually looking at the meandering track through the woods. The pathway that I'd so recently watched the man walking the last winding part of so as to reach the church where I was now sitting. I couldn't for the life of me imagine why I should be seeing this image superimposed on a sheet of living glass within the heart of a powerful flame but what I saw next really did get my full attention.

- Chapter 21 -

Through the Labyrinth of Illusion and Towards the Light

The image which I found myself to be studying so intently seemed as though it was gradually becoming much more clearly defined as it got progressively larger. The quite impressive detail which I was able to see allowed me to make out the figure of the man who I had previously observed making his way towards the church. It proved to be a bit of a challenge in seeing things this way but it surely was breathtakingly fascinating in that I felt as though I was literally peering into another world while looking down on it from the top of a mountain. I had no trouble at all in understanding that I could see the church in its lovely grounds as well as all the trees and the pathways through them. The setting was perfection itself where I could appreciate that an intelligence way beyond our current level of attainment had aspired to create something so magical. There was even a small part of the lake visible as well which made the whole cameo look like a little piece of heaven.

Everything about this totally amazing view in front of me expressed nothing other than the most captivating peace and beauty where once again I was reminded of these timeless expressions of the Divine which Mother Nature so freely gifts us with. Although, I have to say that to be seeing such spectacular artistry set in the midst of a very large and energetically burning flame was to experience it at a completely different level of admiration. In so doing I was able to catch a glimpse of just how incredible 'life' actually is but then I also seemed to be reminded of how little time we take to be aware of its mysterious presence; or even what it really means to us.

This realisation caused me to take a brief pause so as to ponder my own question. I hadn't really thought about it in this way before but in all that had happened to me over the whole of this quite remarkable journey, not once had I stopped to even consider what life in actual fact is; or even what the word itself really implies. Like most everyone else I just accepted it as it is. But, through seeing as much as I had, and now with this truly extraordinary display in front of me, I really had to ask myself just what it was that I could be missing out on by not being aware of as much as I needed to.

I mean, what else could there be that 'life' could offer me if only a fraction more of its incomprehensible mysteries were revealed to me. This was definitely a question that I would like an answer to. Then I began to wonder if it was even possible to know this. And yet, looking at the stunning view of the church and its surroundings in the heart of a living flame, I could see only too well 'life' in all its amazing glory being displayed. I knew it to be so, but I hadn't a clue as to why. I could even sense the 'life' within the flame itself although I had no words at all to explain how this knowledge was present in me; it just was.

Could it be the life-force in me acknowledging another similar life-force or was it simply responding to a separate expression of itself? I stared at the truly spectacular scene of the woods and the church while seeing nothing else but 'life' being expressed in everything; even the stone of the church and the timber of the trees. Life was everywhere while nestled in the heart of an energetic flame which seemed to stimulate my awareness of its priceless gift to me. I just sat in silent awe at the realisation of my mind really having no way to grasp the enormity of something so incredibly complex and yet so deceptively simple. Life was a complete mystery but one which I suddenly wanted to understand much more about. So I continued to gaze into the sheer wonder of the display in front of me in the hope that something, anything, would be revealed to me.

I found myself to be totally captivated by the very existence of some ethereal alchemy which I knew myself to be a part of; or was it a part of me? Yet I still had no understanding of how I knew this or even came to have any idea of it in the first place. It seemed as though I was trying to step back into a dream having just woken up from it while not knowing where to find it or even in what state it existed. In attempting to stretch my mind into realms beyond its capability, it appeared as though the flame grew brighter, if that could be possible, as though it was encouraging me to try just a little harder. I could almost feel its desire to share with me an enthusiasm for a supranatural expression of eternal creation which it already understood. How I longed for it to tell me what I felt the urgent need to know. A twinge of frustration flashed through me at not being able to reach beyond the confines of my present level of understanding. I sighed slightly as a little wave of impatience arose as a consequence. In the hope of achieving some kind of minor breakthrough, I stayed quietly contemplating this whole subject for a few minutes as the gentle music from the orchestra played all around me.

As there appeared to be nothing in the way of any specific answers or awareness expanding revelations forthcoming anytime soon, I made an effort to focus my attention back on the man who I'd seen on the winding pathway. As soon as I did then I realised that he was now in fact not all that far away from the front entrance. I could see quite clearly that he had already entered the church grounds while making his way across to the congregating area in front of the wide, semi-circular steps. It also seemed evident from the way he walked that he had a certain air of eagerness about him now. From this I could appreciate that he was making no allowances for any degree of hesitancy with regards to what he intended to do. I'm not sure why, but I found myself feeling quite relieved to see this level of determination in him, although there did seem to be a lasting image of his returning to the house in the woods lurking somewhere in the back of my mind; this could well have been something to do with it. No sooner had this notion arisen in me than I experienced little pangs of anxiety about my own journey and how it had actually turned out for me. This poignant recollection was made all the more disconcerting by what my wise companion had pointed out about how I too had gone through times of changing my mind on the subject of my direction.

This was a very unsettling recollection but I drew comfort from also remembering the eventual appearance of my own determination when I had finally made up my mind to head off on the last part of my journey to the church so as to marry Janet. Then I realised that here I was again, back in another church after making a long and highly memorable journey to it. This I had done in anticipation of something very special happening when I arrived. I hadn't actually considered it in such a way until this point in time but there really was no other way of looking at it. This thought unquestionably did make me feel strange. It was as if I'd lived my experience twice over, but on this occasion I was all too aware that the objective of my present trip had turned out to be far more complex than I could ever have imagined; although it felt as though someone had supervised my choices this time. Is this really what had happened though? So much had occurred on this 'voyage of discovery' that it seemed almost impossible to rationalise anything any more. I was suddenly overwhelmed with the need to turn to my insightful friend for his advice on this aspect of my recent journey but then I remembered that he was still outside the church; so I hung on to Loucie instead. I surely was glad of her company at that moment where the familiarity of her presence proved to be wonderfully reassuring.

Realising that there was a great deal going on in me, I felt the need to close my eyes just for a minute or two so that I could create a little breathing space for myself; just so that I could deal with all the emotions which I felt welling up inside me. I relaxed and took a few deep breaths while concentrating on letting the tension in my shoulders just slip away as though I was taking off a tight fitting coat; I let it drop to the floor. In doing so I seemed to become more aware of just what a long journey it had been to get to my wedding and how much determined effort it had taken to find my ultimate happiness. All the twists and turns along the route to the church made it seem very much like the pathway I'd been studying which the man had been taking through the woods. This realisation triggered something in my mind.

Quite unexpectedly I felt an urgent need to look at this again. I opened my eyes to more closely inspect the view of the winding path in the 'living' image which was portrayed so graphically within the heart of the big flame. Even though I was getting a little more acclimatised to seeing what was in front of me, I still needed to catch my breath each time I found myself being confronted with the existence of such an incredible spectacle; one that sometimes felt as though it was just inches away from my face. Something that I hadn't been prepared for was the fact that it seemed to have already come to mean so much to me in such a short space of time but I just couldn't allow myself to start thinking about how it had got there in the first place or even why. Too much else was going on in me to do this.

Bringing my attention back to my emotional and thought provoking quest, I traced the shimmering white pathway through the woods but then quickly found myself getting quite dizzy from following such an erratic journey. As much as it grieved me to do so, I had to admit that if I'd been asked to chart the course of my own route to my second marriage then it may well have looked something very much similar to that which I could see being portrayed so clearly in the big flame. It took me a little while to get my mind around this realisation but the more I looked then there really did appear to be many similarities; far too many for my liking. I kept staring at the long and winding path through the trees, especially the parts where it seemed to head wildly up into the mountains or crossing over scary looking bridges, while remembering so much about what had happened during that period of my life.

The more I studied it then the deeper I felt myself being drawn right into the fascinating image, almost as though I knew what it was like to have walked that pathway. But while contemplating this, I remembered my wise companion's statement to me about my choosing to make it that way. I also recalled my reaction at being so surprised to hear him say this but the more I pondered the meandering route in front of me then the more his words seemed to ring true. I shifted a little awkwardly in my seat while feeling the need to pace up and down the room but I resisted the temptation in that, with all the people present then pacing wasn't really a practical option. I had to settle for running my fingers through my hair and letting out a long sigh instead.

In recalling so much of what I'd seen in the Valley of my Mind, as well as peering down into all the powerful images under the boat, I could appreciate how I had altered directions so many times. In being able to relive so much of what had happened in that eventful era of my life, it became easier to see just what influences there were going on around me and how much I'd been swayed by circumstances which were not of my making. Sometimes I found myself wondering how I ever managed to find my way forward at all, where so many things could have undermined my resolve if I'd let them.

As crazy as it may have sounded I also found myself having to agree with him about my carving out such a haphazard course to my ultimate destination; but that was the problem wasn't it? How was it that I was able to 'see' my destination when I really needed to? What came to me when I thought about all this was my wanting to understand just what it was that had driven me on to make the choices which I did and also what gave me the courage to follow my convictions once having recognised them. It was quite a sobering moment for me but no sooner had I posed this question for myself than another image began to appear in the wall. I sat back in my seat and once again experienced a certain degree of tension at not knowing what to expect. Something prompted me to take notice of the gentle music which is just what I did, and thankfully it really helped change my mood.

Intriguingly superimposed in the transparent divide between the two congregation areas in the church, I realised that we were being presented with the breathtaking scene of the two big birds flying towards one another above the cataract. This came as something of a nice surprise in that I hadn't expected to ever see it again. Without realising that I was doing it, I patted the back of Loucie's hand in the manner of letting her know that something exciting was about to happen. I was kind of conscious that I also wanted to reassure her as well. The really stirring thing for me about this unexpected appearance came from appreciating that I would get to watch the whole incredible spectacle happen all over again. Once more the feelings which I'd experienced on the first occasion came racing back to greet me like old friends.

From the many expressions of whispered surprise that I could hear coming from those around me, I guessed that quite a few others in the congregation were no doubt encountering similar feelings. This thought made me smile through knowing all too well what was in store for them but I also felt a sense of excitement at remembering what would be happening very shortly. The thrill of this anticipation while seeing these two magnificent creatures quickly drew me into their mesmerising magic. This time however, I noticed how the birds appeared to be drawn along a path which, at first glance, looked potentially disastrous. Well, that's how I'd seen it back on the island of trees anyway; but now something was different. At the time of my experiencing this unforgettably dramatic event I really hadn't understood what I was witnessing so closely. But now, sat in this beautiful little church while seeing it so vividly portrayed once more, as well as viewing my journey in a very different light, then things were a lot clearer in my mind.

Once more I watched the magnificent birds on a collision course but now I found myself being completely caught up in the fascination for what I could recognise as being their determination to head towards one another. With no obstacles in their way, they could clearly see where they wanted to go and were doing so in a thoroughly single-minded way. Oh that life could be this uncomplicated. Even though I knew what was about to happen, it was just as electrifying to see their meeting unfold so gracefully once again. I was very thankful this time not to be distracted by panic so that I could really enjoy the whole spectacle in the true beauty of its meaning. It was every bit as thrilling as the first time; as was born out by the sounds coming from all around me. This left me in no doubt as to the fact that everyone watching had been truly astonished by what had occurred; especially the children, as I could feel from Loucie's reaction.

In a stunning blaze of light, the two birds heart-stoppingly but joyously merged into one another where, for a moment, I felt the sheer power of the most exhilarating blissfulness sweep right through every molecule of my whole body. It proved to be an incredibly energising sensation which I dearly hoped that everyone else in the room was able to experience just as I had. I detected a small squeeze from Loucie's hand which I took to be confirmation that there was at least one other person who had benefited from this completely amazing aerial transformation; although I felt sure that no one could have been left unaffected by it. Even the music had momentarily stopped which I took as confirmation of my suspicions. In the quiet of the interlude I appeared to be aware of my heartbeat and then realised how I had reacted. In that very same instant I was convinced that I could feel every other heart in the room beating just as quickly. It was a wonderful sensation in feeling myself to be so connected to all who were sharing this experience with me and, as a consequence, I suddenly didn't feel so alone any more. That really was a very pleasant shift in my overall emotional outlook.

What came to mind next was my having studied the big dark cloud and then seeing the lone bird appear from behind it way up in the sky. So I found myself tensing slightly in anticipation of witnessing something of this nature happening again. It was almost like waiting for a new life to be born; the prospect of which caused a surprisingly primal stirring somewhere deep inside me. I really, really liked this feeling. With this memorable vision of the even more spectacularly colourful bird emerging not long after the huge flash of energetic light had occurred, I started to hear the words of my wise guide when he had first introduced me to the concept of twin souls at that same time. I could pretty near feel myself standing with him while remembering how confused I was. It almost seemed like a lifetime ago when he'd tried to explain how things worked but at that stage of my awareness I had struggled hard to understand much of what he told me. My goodness, how things had changed since that point on my journey. What a long way I'd come in being able to appreciate so much more and what a gift he'd given me. Now I was beginning to get a much better grasp of so much of what he had been trying to get me to see. It still wasn't totally clear as yet but I was definitely getting the idea about the existence of some kind of attractively guiding force; albeit a very subtle one.

Just like my emerging awareness, I watched the big colourful bird appear as expected but this time it soared right up into the stained glass window where it began to play in the sky above the kneeling figure. I felt as though I was urging it to reach up as high as possible in the way that I was encouraging my understanding of so many things to attain even greater heights of perception. For a few intense and intimate seconds my aviating companion and I were almost as One with each other where I somehow sensed very strongly that we had been together for all time. It proved to be a really special feeling and one which I was very happy to have experienced. All the tension seemed to drain out of my body at this moment as I allowed myself the privilege of thoroughly enjoying a kind of connection which I'd never imagined possible before this had happened. This surely was another 'first' for me on one very memorable trip.

I could also feel the sense of achievement which this magnificent bird inspired in me as it seemed to be celebrating its arrival at a destination which was very precious to it. While sitting in such a pleasantly enthralled state in the front pew of this extraordinarily influential building, my mind was able to fully take on board the fact that I too had succeeded in getting to somewhere very special. I was also aware that without doubt, something had drawn me to it. I still couldn't put into words just exactly what it was but while trying to better understand it the image of the mutually attracted birds kept playing out in my mind. Their airborne gravitation towards one another gave me the impression of being irresistibly magnetic where all they wanted to do was to be reunited with one another. I knew that feeling so well and didn't have any difficulty at all in appreciating this part of twin soul attractions after what I'd just seen. But I guessed that what gave me the greatest problem of all was in figuring out why this mysterious force is so apparently invisible in everyday life.

I mean, what could be the harm in having sight of your compass. After all, you needed one to cross oceans and continents didn't you, so why not one for helping you find your way on your life's journey? But then I was reminded of the fact that many people don't see life as a journey and that's when I began to think about some of my wise companion's words on the subject. I remembered him telling me that through making choices then we get to experience the consequences. Whatever outcomes arise from our actions, good or not so good, then they help us learn what we need to in order that we can evolve in the most beneficial way possible. As many times as he'd told me this, I still found it difficult to accept that even the bad times were valuable in helping to learn something which made all the suffering and struggles worthwhile.

I guessed that by doing what I did, without being fully aware of what kept guiding me forward, then I got to encounter the type of life which helped me get to where I am at this present point in time. To me now, it was all a journey but looking back at earlier times, as I had been able to do so amazingly with the help of my wise guide, then I could easily see that for much of it then I didn't regard it in this way at all. It was difficult to imagine how life looked for me at that time, given how I saw things now, but whichever way I cared to consider it then it was still such a complete mystery. Undoubtedly it is to a great many others as well, but it surely is one huge enigma which keeps me wanting to know much more about it. Whatever else, even if I didn't fully understand how twin soul energies or 'attractions' worked then I was mightily glad that on at least two occasions they'd led me to the place which my heart knew I really wanted to go.

After this thought had settled gently into my consciousness I found myself looking around at the inside of the church and everyone gathered there. With the beautiful light from all the candles and the wonderful scented air, the whole atmosphere felt very much as though I was surrounded by a little piece of heaven. I couldn't imagine how my life would have turned out if I had discovered this place earlier on but having found it then I really did feel very grateful. Without doubt what made it so special was the gathering of such wonderful people. Just being in their presence seemed to make me feel as though even the heaviest of my past burdens would have only appeared to be as light as a featherweight had I been able to be with them like this. There was something so wonderfully reassuring about the genuine companionship which they had expressed and, after being an only child, it suddenly felt like I had more brothers and sisters than I could have ended up with after a few hundred lifetimes. Once again I found myself feeling so happy to be in this place.

But on reflection, it wasn't so much a 'place' as it was a destination which I felt incredibly grateful to have arrived at. Not only that but it was also one that I could feel how very important it had been to me to get to. With this realisation came an awareness of the fact that this feeling came from actually having made the trip where the journey in itself had contributed an essential part to my understanding. In how I looked at things now then I was much more conscious of the reality of being successful which I couldn't have truly appreciated beforehand, where I had to rely solely on tangible factors such as my faith in myself and my determination. I had nothing else to go on where my thoughts so often got in the way but, just like the man on the path, I was now able to accept that something kept steering each of us in the right direction however far off course we happened to wander.

I could only assume that while viewing his haphazard journey, my feelings about his resolve to reach his destination were being projected onto him as a result of my own experiences. It was a huge subject that I felt the need to pay more attention to, but before I had time to even think about what his reasons for coming to the church might actually be, I could see that he had arrived at the entrance. Then, to my surprise, I realised that in looking through the wall of glass I could also see him standing outside the big wide open main entrance doors. It took me a few seconds of studying him to fully understand that it was in fact the same man. Then I noticed that he appeared to be looking across at the opposite direction to where he'd just come from. As he peered intently at something of obviously great interest to him, I realised that while doing this he seemed to display a moment or two of anxiousness. But then, no sooner had this expression cast its unwelcome shadow than it was replaced by one of joyful relief.

The reason for this quickly became apparent as a whole group of children came rushing up to gather around him in a quite excited manner before eventually making their way into the church. My interest level increased even more as I thought that I recognised nearly all of them, especially the younger ones. At that very same moment I suddenly became quite conscious of the fact that I still had my arm around Loucie as well as appreciating how good it felt to be holding her so close to me. After having been so wrapped up in trying to fathom the mysteriously motivating power of twin soul energies, I couldn't immediately identify why I seemed to have such a compelling need to act this way towards her. Initially it took me quite by surprise through becoming aware of it but then I realised that it felt very much as though I was simply reacting to a perfectly natural fatherly response. This was born out of an almost identical feeling to that which I'd experienced when looking at the other children who had made their way into the church. At first I found this all very confusing as there were a lot of other competing thoughts and emotions swirling around in me, but over and above all of them came the sensation of a wonderful completeness which made me very happy indeed.

This totally magical feeling seemed to arise from appreciating that something extremely precious had been illuminated in the very core of my heart. With it came a thoroughly captivating wave of nostalgia which erupted from out of somewhere very deep inside of me. In what felt like a flash of continuous images, which lasted for less than a handful of heartbeats, I found myself being presented with a great many wonderful times spent enjoying my own children growing up. So many precious moments of appreciating their gifts to me in being a part of my life while I was so proud to have been able to provide them with a childhood which had turned out to be very much different than my own. Sometimes I seemed to see a few images which were tinged with a little sadness but I got a sense that somehow they were from another time or another place. In the instant that I reacted in any negative way then I was somehow able to feel Loucie's presence more keenly. This allowed me to relax to the degree that things didn't seem to be quite so upsetting. It proved to be the most intense experience which was over so quickly but even in such a short space of time I got the really strong impression of having lived more than just one lifetime of very treasured memories.

Shortly after all of the images had finally disappeared, I was left feeling that I wanted to hang on to Loucie forever but I had no real idea as to why I should be experiencing this emotion. Suddenly, to me, she had become so very precious which kind of embarrassed me to feel this way as I didn't really know who she was; or so I thought. Evidently I still hadn't fully learned to completely trust my intuition without my mind getting in the way; but I was certainly getting a lot better at recognising when this aspect of myself was actually present. Instinctively I looked up at the kneeling figure of Jesus in the big mural and for what seemed to be the very first time I could almost feel a little of what had inspired him to act in adopting such a pose. I even got the idea that if I listened close enough then I would be able to hear him offering a quiet prayer of thanks and, while briefly closing my eyes one more time, I did the same thing.

No sooner had I said a few words of my own than I could have sworn that I felt something or someone touch me lightly on the shoulder. It was the softest of intimate gestures but it served to bring me a great sense of comfort in the way that I very much needed it. I just had to sit deeply wrapped up in my thoughts and emotions for a while before I could manage to open my eyes again. When I did so then I realised that they were a little damp around the edges and so I wiped away the moisture while inadvertently giving Loucie a hug at the same time. I saw her lovely smile again and while listening to the very gentle music which the musicians were still playing, it proved to be greatly helpful to me in dealing with all that was going on inside me at that moment.

So much appeared to be coming at me all at once that I didn't know if I could cope with any more but just as my emotional coffer seemed to be in danger of overflowing, I suddenly noticed that the scene in front of me was starting to change yet again. In the wall of living glass, the big flame which had been burning away on the opposite side of the altar also started displaying some kind of image. Even though it was a little way away from me I could still see that something similar was beginning to take shape as to that of the one directly in front of me. Briefly I assumed that it was just a recreation of the one I had been studying but quite quickly I realised that this wasn't the case at all. As the image became more well defined, I began to make out similar details and features to the one which had already been displayed in front of me. People who were sat on the opposite pew to me were pointing out certain things which they appeared to recognise while looking across to compare it to the image on my side of the altar. Even I could see that they looked quite similar but the one on the left was showing a slightly different view from above the church. I was tempted to get up so as go across to get a better look but no sooner had I thought about doing this than it grew much bigger and infinitely more detailed.

It didn't take me long to figure out that we were being presented with a view of the pathway along the lake which I had seen the lady taking while making her way towards the church. There was no mistaking the attractively shimmering whiteness of its surface as it gently meandered alongside the lake with only a handful of faltering twists and turns; quite unlike the one on my side. I wasted no time in scanning the zigzagging part up to the plateau but there was no sign of her. This made me feel a little anxious but then I caught sight of some movement very close to the building itself where I quickly realised that she too was inside the grounds and obviously getting near to the entrance; in fact, she was virtually there. Almost before I had time to change my focus so as to look out through the glass wall and into the other part of the church, my heart skipped a beat as I caught sight of her coming into full view in the entranceway. The beautifully framed scene through the decorative archway over the open front doors was one to remember forever. What I found to be so especially moving however, was the strong sense of exactly how the man felt as she stepped up close to him and then took his hand.

It was such a simple gesture but one which had a profound effect on me. The certainty with which they held each other was something that I found extremely moving as I understood it so well. I knew that feeling, where having made the journey and then arriving at the destination there was no more doubt about what would happen from that point on. Holding hands was a kind of statement but one which had so much loving energy to it where nothing or no one could ever undo what had been determined at that moment. The way that they looked at each other said it all. I watched in breathless excitement as the lady reached out so as to take the man's other hand and just at the point where their fingers met, a bolt of powerful electricity shot straight up through my spine and out through the top of my head. It made me tingle all over. The effect was so strong that it almost felt as though I was in danger of being lifted completely out of my seat by it. All I could seem to do was to look at the couple but in doing so, once again I seemed to know exactly how the man was feeling.

I was aware that my heart had begun beating very quickly in response but I also appeared to be experiencing a certain degree of anxiousness about what would happen next. This really didn't make any sense as it seemed pretty obvious why they were both meeting like this. Well to me it was anyway, but something in me didn't seem able to settle until their reason for coming to the church had been fulfilled. I began to feel myself experiencing a similar sensation to that which I'd often been gripped by while watching a suspense movie where the hero and heroine were just at the end of their adventure. The part where they were almost about to reach a place of safety. Their much longed for secure haven of enduring togetherness where they would end up living happily ever after. I had no idea what should be making me feel this way but I realised that I was almost holding my breath while willing them to start walking down the aisle towards the altar. I just wanted them to hurry up in case something bad happened although I couldn't for the life of me imagine what this might be.

Without realising that I was doing it I looked up at the kneeling figure in the mural while trying to come to terms with my anxiety. I just couldn't seem to get past this unpleasant sensation so as to allow myself the opportunity to enjoy the magic of this moment along with what I knew all too well was to come. What possible reason could there be for my denying the feeling of happiness which this occasion generated from replacing the tension that had suddenly erupted in me. I began to take more notice of the robed figure while studying his face but then I seemed to become more aware of his overall manner. When I had first entered the church then I had taken it for granted that he was offering a prayer of thanks. But now, in my current state of mind, I was seeing it differently. Could it be that he was also asking for clarity, some kind of explanation so that he too would be able to better understand something which confused or upset him, just as I was doing? I, like many others no doubt, assumed that he had all the answers but this probably wasn't the case was it. He had to live this life with all its pitfalls and trials where not everything was patently clear about the process. Maybe he was praying for guidance about something which was important to him while trying to get a better understanding of what life is all about.

This really did make me think but then I looked back at the view of the path through the woods in front of me and especially at the parts which went over rickety looking bridges or shooting up into the mountains. Then, in my mind's eye, I began to see faint images of the big church as well as hearing the wise words of my companion explaining to me about my distorted views of life being reflected in my choices. No sooner had I started to immerse myself in all this than I was once again flying through the Valley of my Mind while viewing countless episodes from my past. Through seeing how I was influenced by so many things, it almost felt as though I was doing battle on innumerable occasions where my decisions were made from the point of view of acting out of considering what was best for everyone else. I was often lucky to come third in the consideration sweepstakes when it came to these situations.

I didn't like seeing things in this way but in how I had become aware of many different aspects of my journey now, I had to acknowledge the truth of this. It was a sobering view of my past but looking at the various kinks and twists en route to the church I understood all too well why they were there. I empathised greatly with the figure in the mural who could be asking for guidance in that he may well have been able to appreciate how his own pathway was turning out. I stared at his face while feeling that I really wanted to ask him about his journey and then listen to his opinions. Right at that moment I would have given anything to simply be sat beside him in that garden and having a quiet chat just like two fellow travellers who were sharing their experiences while resting up before continuing on their way. No sooner had this wish been born in my mind than two quite extraordinary things happened at virtually the same instant.

The Perfect Rainbow to Heal
a Broken Promise

The first and most disturbing thing was that I found myself being able to see the reflection of so many people in the congregation behind me, who I knew from my past life, coming back at me from the wall of living flame. They were all looking at me in a manner which I seemed to regard as them asking me a question; which right at that moment I could neither answer nor even understand. The second was that looking at the figure in the big mural I could see that something had changed. Quite low on the horizon behind him I noticed part of a really beautiful rainbow which almost glowed while displaying its vibrant colours. At first I tried to remember whether it had been there since the beginning and maybe I'd missed it but somehow it felt to me as though it hadn't been there until now and that I needed to pay more attention to its presence.

What came to mind when I looked at it was the old wives' tale I'd often heard when I was younger about rainbows appearing after a heavy storm. They were said to represent a reminder of the promise from the supreme being that never again would a deluge of biblical proportions come to devastate mankind. Somehow I found this hard to believe but it did nothing to undermine my appreciation of such a wonderful spectacle and what its true purpose really is. I felt sure that there had to be more than just some boring scientific explanation to it. In light of nothing more romantic, it seemed more preferable to think of Divine promises or at least a pot of gold at the end of it. Once again I looked at the kneeling figure and then back at the rainbow. This time however, I started to realise that not only could I see its picturesquely incomplete arch but that it had also begun to look very much like the bridge which I'd come upon after having left the garden party with my companion. This really did spark my interest as I couldn't understand why I should be seeing such an unusual and evocative image depicted so amazingly in the mural; and also why it should appear to be so much like the unfinished bridge.

Turning my attention back to all the faces in the mirrored wall, I felt as though I wanted to ask them why they were looking at me in such a way. Then suddenly, without understanding exactly where this notion had come from, I sensed the need to review the image of the rainbow bridge again. As soon as I looked at it then I couldn't help thinking about the old proverb which spoke of a Divine promise. I had no idea why this seemed to come tumbling back into my mind but then I thought about what my companion had said about my creating this structure through my trust and my intuition. I could feel him saying it in the way that his words had affected me at the time but just why I should be remembering this I hadn't a clue. Neither could I seem to understand what was going on in the way that I was being presented with this image and what thoughts were coming to me as a result. From everything which had happened to me on my recent journey then I had learned by now that there was never anything which came to my awareness that didn't have either a message for me or was offering me a chance to see something anew. This, I was well aware, could be no exception so I just had to find out what was behind it.

I could still see the man and the woman outside the entrance to the church and again I was reminded of my anxiety that they should begin their journey to the altar. In my mind's eye they were already walking down the aisle, but through visualising this something clicked into place in the midst of my thoughts. Once more I looked at all the faces who were studying me, but this only seemed to make me even more conscious of my vision of the couple walking down the aisle. I was momentarily confused. Glancing back at the incomplete rainbow bridge I began to feel uncomfortable to the degree that I almost wanted to hide. I felt so exposed but in understanding this I could also start to see where my anxiety had come from and why. My attention returned to where the couple were standing outside the main entrance but when I looked in their direction then I had difficulty seeing them as the light coming in through the doorway was much brighter than before. Instantly it put me in mind of the rays coming through the big panel windows. As soon as I'd made this connection then I could see the door to the vestry opening within its illumination. This made me feel really odd indeed but before I had chance to process my emotion I was treated to the appearance of the bride and groom.

I seemed to be transfixed by the sight of them coming through the doorway but for a moment I found myself being transported back to that point on my journey. The ceremony was over and our promises had been made to each other in front of the congregation. I could almost recall speaking the words but then I looked at all the faces staring at me and then back at the bride and groom; then something quite mind numbing hit me. I had made my promise in front of witnesses but I hadn't kept it. Or had I? This really got me thinking. Suddenly it felt to me as being very important that I think carefully about this. Looking back at the half finished rainbow bridge I began to hear the words of my companion once again where he had explained to me about my making a choice to create an opportunity and that a great deal of good had come from it. I could almost see myself stood on that partially formed bridge and wanting so much to get to the church which I eventually did by trusting my intuition. I followed my heart and from doing so I also created something wonderful and evidently very enduring.

This thought stayed with me as I began to understand that even though I had chosen a different path later on in my life, I really had stayed true to the promise of my first marriage in the spirit of creating all the happiness which I possibly could. Looking at the figure of Jesus, I could almost hear his words of advice in reminding me that in forgiving others then it was always important to forgive myself while understanding that life simply 'was'. To accept that I had done my best and that pathways diverge, as is often the nature of everything, where each soul evolves at its own pace. No promise was broken and no devastating deluge was encountered where I was simply following my heart after having experienced a journey with my soul mate. The time had eventually come to continue on with my twin flame so any guilt which may be felt was best left outside the church for Mother Nature to sweep up in her loving arms and then carry off to the golden pot at the end of the rainbow. There it would be transformed from emotional guilt into glittering gilt which would be lovingly applied to the decorations on the bridge.

For quite a while I was unconscious of the fact that I had quickly become completely lost in the imagery of all that I had become aware of. In dealing with the emotional energy which I felt as a result, I got the distinct impression that I needed to sit for much longer. Evidently someone had other ideas as Loucie tugged my arm and then pointed to the rainbow bridge in the mural which seemed to be growing more complete as my thoughts became totally immersed in understanding how everything had worked out for me. I nodded my thanks to her for bringing my attention to it and then smiled in wanting to reassure her that everything was okay; to me it just seemed to be a completely natural thing to do. I felt happier and less anxious about what would happen for the couple waiting at the doorway as I relaxed at appreciating that I really had done my best and not betrayed any trust.

Even as this realisation was blossoming in me, I noticed that the rainbow bridge was in the process of becoming more fully formed but in doing so the part which was emerging got surprisingly larger. Loucie was obviously very much caught up in this, as no doubt was everyone else. I don't know why but just seeing it growing this way made me feel really good inside and with a kind of flourish at the very last stage of its formation it simply burst out of the mural while anchoring itself in the middle of the congregation. It was the most spectacular sight which caused an instant eruption of applause but when I turned to look at everyone then I was momentarily confused again. Instead of applauding the rainbow they were actually all looking at me. My face flushed immediately. But underneath my embarrassment I did get the message that everyone had recognised the spectacle as being an indication of my having reached an important understanding about promises and that they were genuinely happy for me.

I can't tell you how good this felt and how much of a difference it made to me especially while watching everyone bathed in the stunning colours produced by the rainbow bridge. Once again I had completed its indescribably wonderful structure but this time it had come about through following the guidance of my intuition which led me to trust that I had done my best and that this was all that had ever been required of me. I had done what I did with love and always with the very best of intentions; at no time could I take responsibility for anyone else's journey or the choices which they made on it and this I really did now understand. I sat more firmly back in my seat so as to go over in my mind what I had just told myself. It seemed almost as much of an exertion as it had been to climb the bridge in the first place but in having got me to a destination where I really needed to go then I was very grateful indeed. Yet another part of my journey had been fulfilled. I looked at Loucie and smiled as I appreciated what an incredible life this is and how precious so many things really are when we choose to take notice of them. She shrugged her shoulders in response and then turned to the lady sat next to her so as to share her enjoyment but to my delight I could see that the lady was already smiling at both of us. I felt a really warm glow inside me at realising this.

The clapping began to subside as did the rainbow colours as once again everything within my field of vision started to change quite dramatically. I glanced back at Loucie who gave me a quick flash of her eyes while putting her fingers to her lips as if to say that she was anticipating something quite special to take place very shortly. Even the mood of the music seemed to change as well. I had no idea what to expect but I felt the need to prepare myself for just about anything after everything which had happened thus far. I looked back at the wall while wondering just how many more surprises it could contain. I didn't have long to wait for the answer. What I could now see happening in front of me caused me to experience a quite different kind of anxiousness but this was very much more leaning towards the excitement category. This time, I really did hang on to Loucie. Quite evidently I wasn't alone in feeling as I did in that I could feel her doing very much the same with me.

As a result we hugged each other in an emotional expression of mutual support which made me feel very glad indeed that she was there; suddenly having become aware of this it had the most unexpected effect on me. While holding her so close I had the most fleeting of thoughts of what I would like to buy her for Christmas. I had absolutely no idea where this bizarre notion could have come from but there was too much happening for me to stop to even give this idea any space in my overcrowded consciousness. Somewhere however, it must have registered in the back of my mind and in some special place within me it felt really very precious indeed. In response I managed a little half smile in spite of my apparent state of tense anticipation.

The images in the twin flames within the living wall of light gradually began to merge while showing us all much more of the land on the side of the lake. They did so in the most amazingly three dimensional way but the clarity and realism which formed as a result made it much easier for me to see both pathways through the forest. I couldn't get over how much detail I could see and how incredibly life-like everything appeared to be. Gradually the scene began to open out so that more of it covered the wall but in doing so then the view of the congregation on the other side quickly disappeared. There was little time for me to react to the fact that I could no longer see the man and the lady before I realised that what had begun to spread across the wall was a stunning aerial view of the lake. It was almost as though we were seeing things through the eyes of the big bird flying high up in the mural as more of the mountains and water came into view.

From the sounds of quite a few oohs and aaahhs coming from around me I guessed that no one present was unmoved by what we could all so clearly see. The sight of the little church in its wonderful setting, while it nestled on the slopes of the forest covered mountains, allowed us all to appreciate so much more acutely the atmosphere which we were enjoying whilst inside it. The view was one which I could have happily studied for a long time as the whole feel which seemed to be coming from it had the effect of making me relax while being wrapped up in the magic of it all. The sheer scale of what I could see was almost too much to get my mind around, and in a way, it actually was quite intimidating through being able to appreciate the incomprehensible vastness of nature and the world we live in. Out of the corner of my eye I caught sight of Loucie tugging the arm of the lady she was sat next to in the manner of wanting to share her excitement with her. The smile on the lady's face said it all. Loucie was absolutely thrilled.

The view from above continued to expand so that the church was now quite small but the pathways to it from either side were still clearly visible. I was about to take in more of what surrounded them when I happened to look across to the opposite side of the lake and to my surprise I noticed that there were similar pathways or small roads. This realisation threw my concentration for a moment as I really hadn't expected to see anything of the kind in this part of the landscape; so it took me a good few seconds to get my mind around it. Curiosity quickly overtook my surprise and so I focused on what I had now become aware of. Studying where these narrow roads led, I was able to make out what looked like some kind of encampment which had been spread over a wide area where the layout appeared to be somewhat familiar. From the mutterings of a few uniformed men who were stood quite close to me I guessed that they had seen the same thing and were discussing it. I was very tempted to join in their discussion as I wanted to hear what they had to say about it but something else got my attention before I had the opportunity.

Looking farther out along the valley I could see that on both sides there were areas of trees which seemed to have been cleared in preparation for more paths or roadways to be laid. There were even what looked like places where bridges could be constructed in the mountains but as yet nothing had been put in place. This really was puzzling as I couldn't imagine what they could be for but in light of what I could see of the routes to the encampment then I felt that I might have a clue. Briefly I recalled my flight over the Valley of my Mind while looking at all the scenes from my past and then found myself trying to make a connection with what I'd experienced and what I could see in the woods. I felt that there was some kind of definite link but before my thoughts had any opportunity to join up the dots, I noticed that Loucie was pointing at something which she apparently wanted me to explain to her. At first I couldn't think what it could be as there were so many things of interest, including the other pathways and the clearing of the trees but then she said,

"What's that? Those pretty looking river things by the sides of the lake?"

It took my mind quite a while to even process her question as I was sure that I hadn't heard her correctly; but before I could ask her to explain what she'd meant I watched as she leaned forward in her seat so as to get a closer look. Then I noticed a few people close to me apparently examining the very same thing which left me even more perplexed as, at that time, I had absolutely no idea what they could be looking at; especially in view of what Loucie had said about rivers. Loucie sat back in her seat while looking at me for some sort of explanation. I was just about to shrug my shoulders when I began to notice something odd about an area of land by one side of the lake. I decided that this needed more careful analysis as something was obviously going on.

What became immediately noticeable was that if I focused too intently on it then the effect, whatever it was, seemed to be harder to see. If I relaxed my gaze then, oddly enough, it became clearer. This just didn't add up but the less intense my concentration then the easier it was to see the effect. Then, to my surprise, I became aware of it on the other side as well and for a moment I scratched my head while obviously looking somewhat puzzled. Both Loucie and I studied this strange phenomenon together while giving each other the occasional disbelieving glance. I got the idea from the cute look on her face that she was treating it very much like a fun game so I reckoned that this was a neat approach and happily joined in. The results were almost instantaneous.

What I thought I could see was something either just under the ground or just above it; I couldn't decide which. To describe it in the way that Loucie had, as being like a river, didn't seem all that strange in the light of what I could now see but it certainly wasn't any kind of water course that I'd ever come across before. Although there was undoubtedly a distinct kind of flow to it. It was so incredibly strange but also really fascinating at the same time. I leaned forward to study it more carefully in the hopes that whatever it was would reveal itself in the way that I could recognise it. Nothing came clearer at all so I relaxed again. Whatever they were then they could only really be seen from high up but the most noticeable thing about them was that they ran much straighter while following the shores of the lake. They were almost like some kind of mysterious highways which seemed to run underneath the smaller pathways but these apparently travelled a great distance. Then Loucie got all excited as she had suddenly noticed something important and was very pleased to have been the first to spot it,

"They're different!"

She pronounced this in the way of it being not only a question but a statement as well. I was about to ask what she meant but then found myself looking back and forth between the one on the far side of the lake and the one which ran under the church where we were all sitting. At first there appeared to be little or no difference but the more I casually studied each of them then I could indeed see what Loucie was saying. In the best way that I can describe it, the effect was like looking through a clear mountain stream at whatever was beneath the surface. In being able to see what was there it becomes apparent that there is a flow of clear liquid running over the top of it as the gentle rippling effect indicates. In the case of a small stream it's easy to appreciate that the water is above the bed but in viewing what was going on with these large fluid highways alongside the lake, then it was difficult to tell if the 'flow' was in the bed or on top of it. Something else was also apparent which made matters even more tricky to determine.

The rippling which was produced all around the trees and every other object within its influence seemed to have a kind of sparkling quality to it, almost as though whatever it was had imparted it with a sort of very light frosting. It was the most magical effect albeit a very, very subtle one. By now, many people in the congregation were all seemingly wrapped up in studying the mystery displayed so wonderfully in front of us. Even the children appeared to be captivated by this most unusual sight which quite evidently no one had any kind of suitable explanation for. Then Loucie said something else,

"I can't be sure but it seems to me as though the one on the far side of the lake is going slower than the one on our side. Also the sparkly bits have a really nice violet shade to them. I think they look so pretty don't you? The ones on this side are kind of bright blue but they're really nice too."

I nodded in agreement but in truth I found myself to be struggling hard at seeing the colours which she could obviously identify with apparent ease. I decided to let my attention dwell lightly on the closest 'flow' to me and then found an area along its course where I felt that there was the greatest opportunity to see the colours which Loucie had identified. I then realised that I was studying the part where earlier I had noticed that some trees had been cleared in preparation for what I assumed was a new pathway. The ground had been uncovered but as yet it hadn't taken on the shimmering white quality which I'd seen the paths to the church being made up from. As a result, many things were more readily apparent where the effect of whatever the flow was causing to occur could be more easily seen.

To me it looked as though there was some kind of powerful yet almost transparent magical force moving across or under the ground while making everything sparkle; but right at the edges of the new pathway I could definitely see some kind of colour to the glistening effect. The more I just let my gaze drift over it then I could see that it definitely did have a kind of electric blue tinge to it; but then I became aware that there were also many other more subtle colours present as well. I just let myself get more relaxed as I seemed to experience an urge to let the colours express themselves to me, but in doing so I hadn't appreciated that my eyelids were starting to feel a little heavy. It wasn't until Loucie tugged my arm very gently that I realised just how deeply involved in the total mystery of this effect I was getting. I looked at her to see what had caused her to attract my attention but then discovered that she was looking up at something else.

When I turned my attention to where hers had apparently been distracted to, I could see that there appeared to be some kind of movement high up in the big window. When I looked up to see what it was then I noticed that in the sky area of the stained glass design there were two sets of five stars where each group was weaving their way gracefully in and around a cluster of four heavenly bodies. The big bird flew effortlessly around and through each of them while trailing the most beautiful sunset colours behind it. I found that I had to readjust my thinking after being so distracted by the strange phenomena at the sides of the lake, and to be honest, I felt that I wanted to get back to examining them as I really didn't understand what was going on in the stained glass window. Almost on the point of my taking my attention away from this scene, I chanced to look more intently at one attractive group of stars. Then to my surprise I recognised that they were tinged with exactly the same colour blue as that of the 'flow' on my side of the lake.

I just stared at it for a moment or two but then quickly looked back to the place which I had been studying it in the wall. They were exactly the same but I had no idea what it could mean although I was surely aware that there had to be some kind of connection. I looked back at the mural and once again studied the pattern of five stars and four planets but after only a minute or so of doing this I began thinking of the five illuminated windows in the apse. Not only this but also the four aspects of the church which my companion had made me aware of. An idea was beginning to form in my mind but it just wouldn't come clear enough for me to make any meaningful sense of it. The immediate impression which I got from the spectacle was that of a supreme simplicity to its presentation but there was something else about it which just seemed to be so right; as well as everything being very much in harmony. It appeared as if there was a kind of energetic joyfulness in the way that all the different elements interacted. A kind of mutual understanding where each individual part served to compliment the whole so as to produce an inspirational vision of togetherness; a wonderful alliance of Divine purpose.

While I was beginning to really appreciate this very appealing and highly intriguing quality to the quite heavenly display, I noticed the bird had begun to get bigger as it flew around in front of the planets. Each circular swoop in the sky got progressively wider which brought it ever closer into the interior of the church at certain points on its flight path. I found myself regarding it as though I was staring at a hypnotist's pendulum where nothing else could attract my attention. Somewhere in the recesses of my highly occupied mind I felt certain that everyone in the congregation had been affected in a similar way. No sooner had this thought entered my head than the complexity and speed of its aerial manoeuvres began to increase. As they did so then I became aware that Loucie had tightened her grip on me, where for a moment, I got the idea that she was about to climb into my lap in anticipation of what would happen next.

- Chapter 22 -

Loucie's View of the Lake, the Pathways and the Stars

Before either of us could make a move to do anything, we watched mesmerised as the bird seemed to be coming at us from far away in the very depths of the sky. Alarmingly quickly it got bigger to the point where it almost filled the whole window and then, in one powerful flap of its wings, it flew completely out of the colourful mural and into the nave itself. Needless to say the effect was totally electrifying which caused an immediate communal intake of breath while every pair of eyes followed the huge bird. I did manage to notice however that not one of the musicians missed a single beat of their wonderful harmonious creation. In the best traditions of the performing arts, the band played on but I appreciated all too well that this was no small miracle in itself.

No one in the assembled congregation could fail to be impressed by the sight of this most magnificent creature bursting into our midst. Apart from its spectacular presence it seemed impossibly big in contrast to the quite modest size of the inner space of the little church. The speed with which it had appeared out of the window caused the air all around us to flutter and swirl which made virtually every candle flicker in response. This had the immediate effect of making the whole inside of the little church literally explode in the most attractive dance of highly excited light; much to the delight of all the children who were totally caught up in something so completely unexpected. Combined with this wonderful effect, the aromas from the heated oils also joined in so as to create the most thrilling experience which encouraged an atmosphere of heightened expectation in the most joyful of ways. I wasn't sure which captivated me more, the giant bird in the middle of us all or the children's reaction to it. I had a feeling that I was more biased towards the children.

Somehow the beautiful bird managed to perform the most spellbinding horizontal half loop without disappearing out of the front entrance. In a kind of effortless way, like it was something it did every day, the bird proceeded to head straight back towards the wall of living light. In doing so it flew even lower over a veritable sea of upturned faces as everyone found themselves being treated to a close quarter's view of the underside of this most majestic of avian creations. This time the entire host of candles flickered even more enthusiastically where every surface of the building quickly burst into glittering life while being showered with intensely sparkling light. It was a true joy to see the looks of awe on every child's face, as well as a great many of the adults too, where the whole congregation had been completely captivated by something so spectacularly close that anyone of them could have reached out and touched it. Loucie seemed to be grabbing onto me as though her life depended on it while her head almost twisted off her shoulders in her effort not to miss one tiny instant of all the breathtaking action.

Much to her delight, as the big bird headed for the wall, she caught sight of its huge reflective eye as it passed swiftly overhead. When it was almost parallel with where we were sitting, it actually winked at her in an almost playful kind of way while seeming to say – 'just watch this'! This seemed to raise her excitement factor to a completely new level and it certainly made me very happy to appreciate how she was feeling. This time it was my turn to experience a sudden thrill of delight as its familiar gesture certainly did stir up a lot of extremely pleasant memories for me in the process. I remembered all too well seeing that wonderful eye so close up when it had appeared through the big windows on the balcony. I had never seen anything quite so beautiful in a living creature and would never forget how much of an effect it had on me in marvelling at the true magic of creation; and here I was being reminded of it yet again. Now it was my turn to be thrilled and I can assure you that I really, really was.

After briefly savouring this wonderful feeling, I realised that everyone was now closely following the flight path of the big bird while becoming mesmerised by the prospect of its imminent destiny. This appeared to be that of impacting the wall of light with great force in just a few short seconds. But in appreciating this, I like everyone else, became aware that nothing was the same any more. I heard a little gasp from Loucie which served to express just exactly what both of us were feeling at that precise moment in time. Looking at what was in front of us now it seemed as though our bird's eye view had changed coincident with its descent from upon high. Now, we were being treated to the view out over the lake where we could see the mountain ranges stretching far out into the distance. This in itself was indescribably impressive but what really took my breath away, along with Loucie and every one else no doubt, was the fact that it looked to be so incredibly real. It was hard to credit that we were still sat in the church as it appeared as though we were literally flying over the lake in between the mountains. Not even the musicians could manage to keep playing at this point where it became quickly evident that what we were all now seeing was almost too much for anyone to take in.

Men, women and children alike watched in breathless amazement as the big bird began racing towards the open spaces of the lake which we all knew in our totally dazed minds to be the very solid substance of a supporting wall. I dared not image what would happen when it reached that point. I'm not sure whether it was the effect of all the adrenaline rushing around in me but time rapidly slowed to almost a standstill in anticipation of this eventuality where I just seemed to have no way of knowing how to react. The big bird flew on but much to our surprised relief, at the very last second, it appeared to decelerate very quickly. Now it looked as though it was approaching the living light barrier, with the twin flames still blazing brightly away, in a kind of hovering slow motion. As it did this then its huge wings began to tremble in a manner that caused the air to move rhythmically all around us. I'm not sure why but it produced a kind of magically calming effect, which I for one was very grateful to be on the receiving end of. I'm sure that many others felt the same. It was the most impressive experience which seemed to give us all an indication of the sheer power that emanated from this fabulously enthralling creature.

Whatever its intentions may have been, there was not one person who could have been in any doubt as to the certainty of purpose which the masterful nature of its presence required that we follow. All eyes were on the big bird as well as the ever expanding view in the wall. Even the music had started again but this time it felt as though it was encouraging a mood of heightened expectation. My attention was too caught up in what was happening for me to see how Loucie was doing so I gave her a little hug just to let her know that I was thinking of her. We both watched in rapt attention as the entire three dimensional vista in front of us seemed to reflect exactly how the big bird was seeing it from its low flight path over the water.

Not only that but the smell of the sea appeared to be surrounding us as well as many other familiar aromas of the area. There was even a fresh breeze which carried them all to us. No sooner had we begun to adjust our senses to this incredible expression of Mother Nature's creation than things began to alter dramatically in perspective which made me want to hang on to my seat. The big bird, even though it appeared to be stationary, flexed its powerful wings while starting to gain height above the water. As it did so then the whole of our view began transforming in all three dimensions just as though we were climbing up with it. To describe it as being totally awesome would have been to understate what was happening.

The temptation was to grab onto something which is just what must have been going through Loucie's mind as she pulled my arm across in front of her and then hung onto it. This time I did manage to take a quick glance at her only to see that her eyes were as wide as saucers while her face was a picture through her being completely caught up in the amazing sensation. It was easy for me to see that nothing else in her world existed at that moment as her attention was one hundred percent focused on the breathtaking scene in front of her. I could easily understand that it was impossible not to be thoroughly engrossed in what we were all seeing as it really did appear as though we were all in some kind of flying gallery where the pilot was a huge bird of prey; it was all just so incredibly real. Nothing that anyone present had ever encountered I'm sure could have compared with this stunning experience which made me even more grateful for my wonderful adventure when I got to fly so freely over the valley.

In front of us all was the most thrilling of panoramic sights which anyone could have possibly imagined where everyone could see so much from a height of what seemed like a hundred feet or so in the air. I felt sure that the whole congregation must have been holding their breath, just as I was, but I could also appreciate that the intrepid musicians were still playing their wonderfully gentle music. Either that or someone had an incredibly good CD player going; I doubted this very much though. I saw the lady beside Loucie pointing towards something and then realised that the whole wall had now turned into one huge panoramic aerial view out over the lake as the big bird gradually moved completely into the light. In doing so, the crystal tips of its powerful wings passed right through the twin flames which caused the light in each of them to alter where colours burst out the like of which I'd never seen before.

They were the most vibrant that I could ever have imagined existing where each one of them seemed to glow with a quality that defied description but which made me feel really wonderful through just looking at them. I was instantly reminded of something but I had absolutely no idea what it could be although it was a very positive feeling that I got from the memory. It felt almost like being home within a recollection of somewhere very special but again I had no idea where this could be or even why I should be thinking this. Slowly I was starting to become accustomed to the view from above the lake which allowed me to really concentrate my attention on just what it was that we were all being presented with. Looking closely at the living scene of the loch then I quickly began to appreciate just how far the big body of water stretched out into the distance and how little of it I'd been able to see before that time.

While studying the mountains either side of it, I could once again see the fascinating fluid highways which were running so subtly but so mystifyingly powerfully along each side of the lake where they seemed to be headed straight for the horizon. I found myself longing to understand much more about what they were and why they were there at all, as I had never seen anything like them. I was tempted to watch them longer but I soon realised that I had become thoroughly absorbed in the sheer scale of the aerial view as well as beginning to really enjoy the whole incredible experience. Loucie was also quite obviously still completely captivated by all that she could see. I gathered this from the way that she continued to hold on so tightly to my arm. It really did give me a wonderful feeling to know that she was enjoying it so much and I was very happy for her. As strange as it may seem I also found myself experiencing a strong connection to her happiness in a way that I felt to be quite refreshing. For some reason I wasn't even tempted to analyse why this should be as I was much too taken up with simply enjoying it.

My attention quickly returned to the bird as it began to move slowly forward into the stunning panorama while trailing its wonderful colours behind it. It was then that I noticed how the energetic colours from the bird's wings were flowing out and over the sides of the mountains in a gentle rain-like fashion. In doing so then each flame seemed to be inundated with what I can only describe as being like star-filled little galaxies. I was so lost in the whole spectacle that I hardly heard Loucie whisper to me in a quite excited way,

"Oh my! It's the magic of creation. My teacher told me about it but I've never ever seen it until now. Isn't it the most thrilling thing you've ever seen?"

Without thinking, I said in a kind of distracted way,

"It's what?" as I hadn't fully taken in just exactly what she'd been trying to say to me. Without hesitating, Loucie took the opportunity to share something very special with me which she considered that I was obviously not aware of.

"Oh yes! My teacher told me that it's the magic of creation and that it's what helps us have all our really exciting adventures. I never really knew what she meant before now but I can see how it makes everything happen just like she said it does. Isn't it exciting?"

All I could manage to say in return was,

"Oh! I see. Well I think I do, I mean, I'm sure I do, yes."

My confusion must have been patently clear to her as she turned to look up at me and then said in a quite disarming way.

"Don't you see what's happening with all those pretty colours?"

I had to admit that I didn't, although I certainly could see the fascination of it all. Loucie was obviously as thoroughly caught up in it as I was but somehow her young perspective had grasped something that I had evidently missed. She wasted no time in sharing her wonderful wisdom with me.

"Well, it's simple really but then all magic is isn't it? Would you like me to tell you about it?"

Without waiting for an answer, and with her infectious enthusiasm, she gently gave me my arm back. Then, while confidently pointing to the right hand side of the landscape, she said in the manner of addressing someone younger than herself,

"Well, you see that wiggly white road going through the woods? Well, that's where the man chose to go when he made his way to the church. He didn't have to go that way ... but he did."

I was intrigued, so I had to ask.

"Why would he choose to make it so wiggly then? Why not go in a straight line and get there quicker?"

Her answer came with an all-knowing smile.

"Because he couldn't see the church until he got really close and when he'd listened to his heart which was telling him that he wanted to be with the lady forever."

She pronounced this like a true veteran of explaining the mysteries of life to anyone who would listen. For a moment or two I felt the need to humour her while just allowing her to express what seemed like childish excitement but something about what she had said made me want to know more. I decided to put aside any prejudices while asking sincerely,

"What do you mean Loucie? I don't quite understand although it sounds really interesting."

To my amazement she gave a little sigh which made me feel as though she was about to say something so obvious that I ought to have known it. However, her thoroughly appealing smile was very reassuring.

"Well, I'll tell you ... but you have to promise me that you'll pay attention now won't you?"

Suddenly it was my turn to smile and so I nodded my happy agreement.

"That's good because it's important. Now, have you ever been lost in the woods? Yes, of course you have. I have too and it's not very nice is it?"

Again without waiting for a reply or even seeming to take a breath she continued,

"So you see it's really important to have something to guide you and that's what the stars do. They are like your teachers but you have to be really quiet and pay attention to them or you'll get more lost than ever. Then you go wandering all over the place and you'll never find your way out and worst of all you'll get really tired and hungry. See, I'll show you."

We looked down together from our place up in the sky as Loucie began pointing to one part of the path through the woods which started to go up into the mountains before returning to the lower level by the lake.

"See, there?"

She said as though being proud to have got an 'A star' for her homework.

"That's where he nearly went over the mountain and would have got really horribly lost and probably never come back. That was the time when he really, really wasn't listening to the stars while they were trying so hard to tell him that he had gone the wrong way. But you know men! He just wouldn't listen."

She rolled her eyes most endearingly as she said this but then continued without missing a beat.

"But one of the stars was really determined and so it stayed in front of him until he could see his path more clearly. Then, when he did, he changed his mind and went back down the mountain ... but he got to have lots of

adventures before he ended up back to where he should be. His choice not to listen or to see in the darkness took him up a steep hill and into a strange part of the woods where he had to fight all sorts of dragons and demons."

She gave me a kind of sheepish look at this point and then shrugged her shoulders a little before continuing.

"Well maybe not big monsters of the woods in how you might see them because your monsters are tricky as they come all dressed up in lots of different disguises. But I like to think of them as being strange looking scary creatures because I don't really understand grown up stuff yet. My teacher tells me I will when my time comes and that I'll see it all very differently then. Is that what you think will happen? Is that how it will be for me?"

I nodded and smiled while not really being sure of what to say. Suddenly I could see how it was to look through the inexperienced eyes of a child once again. In that instant I could almost feel myself being that age and wondering what life had in store for me and how things would turn out when I became old enough to understand life much better. It sometimes seemed very scary to be in a world of grown-ups where I was so dependent on others for my survival while they interpreted so many things that I didn't have a clue about. In thinking this way I got to appreciate how it is that we end up making a great many of our decisions through watching how others more powerful and influential do it and then copying them. How else can we do it? We have to learn somewhere.

This, in my new way of seeing things, didn't seem to be a very helpful way to get through life as it appeared as though you were destined to simply repeat the mistakes of your elders. So, the obvious question that needed answering is, how exactly do you get to make beneficial decisions of your own while finding the happiness that is most important so as to lead a fulfilling life? Suddenly my time on the bridge with my companion came back to me as his words about intuition echoed gently around in my mind. Then I figured that this was what Loucie must have been referring to when she talked about following the stars. She continued after giving me what she considered to be a suitable time to digest her wisdom.

"We have to follow the stars because they know us and they are always offering to guide us but we don't take any notice of them because we don't appreciate what they're trying to do. They just want to take us to our happy place where we can play all day and not have to worry about anything; but, we think we know better. That's how we get to have adventures when we get lost in the woods and find the dragons who know we're close to their caves. They can never hurt us but they make us afraid and that's when we really have to listen very carefully to the stars. They brighten up our way out of the darkness while leading us back into the light and away from the dragons; but we have to pay attention and watch carefully because the stars are always there. Always, they're even with us when we sleep."

I smiled in response to her words and then raised my hand to my chin so as to show her that I was deep in thought about her explanation. She nodded knowingly while turning her attention back to the scene in front of us. Looking into the woods and studying the pathway to the church for myself, it was suddenly easy to appreciate how many deviations and excursions had been taken on a route that could have been quite a lot more straightforward. I thought back to my time of needing to change my course while heading in another direction and all the problems that it had caused me when I did.

In fact, the more I looked at the path and how it was shaped then the more I could almost feel the choices and circumstances which had caused its individual twists and turns. It seemed to reflect extremely well just exactly what I had ended up doing while finding my way to the church and eventually marrying Janet. Disturbingly enough I found myself considering the distinct possibility that it actually was my path. How scary was that?

Then I thought about what Loucie had told me about how the stars had helped the man on that path. Even though I could appreciate her way of looking at things I was aware that something must have been leading me to make the more beneficial choices that I did. There was no denying the fact that, no matter how often or how far I'd strayed from the direction I really wanted to go in, there was always something guiding me on towards my ultimate happiness. Within this appreciation I found myself thinking about a lot of things that had happened to me after I had first met Janet. So much seemed to be coming at me in the way of having to make choices about what I wanted to do but there was very little in the way of guidance, or so I assumed, and so it could hardly be any surprise that some of my choices may not have been the most helpful ones to make.

Then I found myself wondering why it was that I had first got married and then started a family. Then I got into imagining what would have happened if I hadn't. This begged the question of whether I should have just waited to find Janet but then I considered that I needed to have done everything that I did in order to have found my way to her in the first place. Gradually I began to appreciate that if I'd made any other decisions or choices along the way, other than I did, then my pathway wouldn't have led me to where I most wanted to go. Or would it? If what Loucie had explained to me was correct then didn't it mean that I would have found my way to where I wanted to go eventually, or was I interpreting her words incorrectly?

As soon as I started to think like this then I remembered what my wise companion had told me about sharing part of my journey with my soul mate and having the experiences that we did while being this way with her; a brief togetherness on our individual journeys as he explained it. I thought about this for a little while as I tried to get my mind around what had come from doing so and what I would have missed out on had I not made the choices I did.

Quickly I began to get caught up in this emotion but no sooner had I done so than once more I seemed to be able to look through the panoramic wall and into the scene beyond it. At the very same instant I recognised my three children whereupon a wonderfully warm feeling came to settle in my heart. I gazed at them in absolute amazement as I felt a lump come into my throat. I swallowed as an emotion of heartfelt pride swept through me at being partly responsible for bringing them into the world while also being able to share so much with them on their own individual journeys.

There was no doubt in my mind about my choosing to do this and neither were there any regrets about the circumstances which had made it all possible. Everything had been perfect.

Suddenly those 'loops' in the pathway on the mountain looked to have been essential to achieving all that I had. What had come from making them was worth everything that I had gone through even though I had sometimes been headed straight up the steepest slopes of the inhospitably rocky terrain. To me it had all been ultimately necessary even though I could now clearly see how far from my true 'river' highway it had taken me.

Glancing down onto the golden blue surface of the lake, I found myself being drawn back into experiencing my flight over the Valley of my Mind when I had been allowed to revisit so much of what I had encountered at different stages of my life. Then I also recalled seeing the huge church high up in the landscape and thought about all that I had learned from that experience as well. I tried to put things together in my mind but it all seemed so incredibly complex in terms of trying to identify what came from within me in the way of making choices and why.

All that I could seem to come up with was that something must have always been guiding me as I had eventually got to where I most wanted to go; even though I hadn't been aware of that illusive destination for much of my life. Something, some guiding force, just had to have been constantly present so as to help me to make those all important 'right' choices as I could never in a million years believe that 'fate' had anything to do with how my life turned out. All that I was seeing, and had seen with my companion, demonstrated so clearly that my life had been all about my choices and the consequences of making them through what I experienced as a result.

I could see now that nothing had ever been left to chance and that there was definitely no such thing as a coincidence. Somehow I had known what was right. Or, to put it more accurately, there was 'something' that had a knowing which I had often been able to get a sense of whenever I took the time to listen to it or to see what it was showing me. But this left me with the question of what it could possibly be that had this 'knowing' about what was right for me and why I wasn't consciously aware of it in the way that I felt that I needed to be. Suddenly I experienced a certain degree of confusion once again but I had to admit that things were starting to make more sense in the way that I could see the view out over the lake and the pathway through the wooded landscape. Then I noticed something about one of the flames.

There appeared to be some uniquely special quality to the energy in the flame which encompassed that side of the valley which kept drawing my attention to it. What could it be that I was seeing and why was it so important for me to understand it? Loucie chimed in again before I started to get much more off-track and back into the thickest part of the woods once again.

"Look at the other side of the lake. At those big mountains over there. See?"

She was pointing to the other side of the wall of light where the corresponding flame had surrounded that part of the landscape.

"Can you see all the stars doing the same thing? Well, they're all coming from the same place aren't they? Look at the big bird and watch all the pretty stars coming out from the end of its wings and then falling to the ground on each side of the water. Isn't it just the most magical thing ever to watch how it does that?"

I had to admit that as much as it was fascinating it appeared equally mysterious as there seemed to be no end to the streams which were flowing from its crystal wingtips.

"That's what I mean when I'm telling you about the magic of creation. It really is magic because it's always there and it's always creating and it's for you to use or not depending on how you wish it in your heart. See how the big bird is making all the stars by flying through the light. It's just like a boat going through the water where the waves go one side and the other but they always want to get back together again afterwards. So that's what happens with the stars. They want to get back to become light and so they give you their magic to help them do it. Don't you think it's wonderful how they do that? I do!"

From looking at the spectacular scene in front of me, it certainly was easy to appreciate the 'magic' of it all; as Loucie had so aptly described it. Through her eyes it was easy to explain all that had been taking place but, even though I was beginning to get a glimpse of the incredible mystery of it all, there did appear to be a kind of profound simplicity to what I could see happening. As I rummaged through the memories of my past, and then thought about what it was that kept me 'on track', I started to get an idea of something quite powerful at work. Then, when thinking about my time on the bridge where my companion had tried to explain 'intuition' to me, I began to get an idea of the whole remarkable process.

Journeying through life, while experiencing all that I did, seemed to come about by virtue of my making choices through listening to the urgings of either my mind or my heart. If I listened to my heart then I could begin to appreciate that there was a kind of benevolent force which only ever had my best interests held foremost in its wisdom; one that surely wanted to guide me to a better way of being. This 'force', for want of a more suitable word, appeared to be coming from the 'stars' which Loucie had described as being my gift. One which had come about as a result of my being one part of a twin soul.

Somehow this force served to guide me unerringly on; but towards what and, more importantly, why? All of a sudden I seemed to have a lot of questions as once again I found myself in the position of needing to understand this particular subject much more clearly. I got the idea that this had come about from my beginning to piece together much of what I had begun to truly appreciate from all that I had learned up to that point on my journey with my companion.

Right at the moment when this quandary came to demand some kind of resolution, Loucie gave a little tug on my arm. I glanced at her quickly and then realised that she was staring intently at the 'screen' in front of us where I immediately appreciated that something quite dramatic was happening. Whereas previously the big bird seemed to have been hovering over the lake, it was now appearing to be moving over the surface while the scenery began to change as it did. At first it was relatively slow but gradually it picked up speed until we were travelling swiftly along the course of the water. In so doing it certainly got my full attention as it undoubtedly did that of everyone else present.

What captivated me most about this experience was that the whole wall of light took up so much of my field of vision that I found it easy to convince myself that I was actually in the air above the lake and flying again; exactly as I had done over the Valley of my Mind. This time however, the light seemed to be much different as was the scenery where everything looked so wonderful in how Mother Nature offers us her endless display of true magic in what she creates.

My mind tried to take in the sheer scale of what I could see in front of me as we followed the gently winding contours of the mountains which served to shape the flow of the lake. The speed of motion was impressive where we quickly left behind the view of the church as the big bird took us on a journey of discovery. After getting used to the sensation and the changing scenery, I started to notice the rivers or highways that Loucie and I had been investigating at the sides of the lake. I have no idea why but they were surprisingly easier to see as we gained speed. They were fascinating to watch and so I felt the need to bring them to Loucie's attention but as soon as I looked at her then I could tell that she was caught up in studying the same thing as me. We both instantly looked out at the magnificent views which were unbelievably captivating in themselves, but seeing the really beautiful 'rivers' on the lake shores was by far the most intriguing thing of all. Then something happened that gave Loucie and I a thrill which had us both pointing excitedly at the view ahead of us.

As the big bird speeded up then all the colours trailing out from its wingtips appeared to have one predominant colour on each side. On the left hand side it looked to be a kind of shimmering violet, while on the right it was a kind of vibrant electric blue. This in itself didn't give us a complete clue but when each of the big flames took on a similar shade, and then we could see the tiny sparkling stars of the same colour falling into the 'rivers', the penny finally dropped. Loucie started doing a little dance beside me while the lady who was with her rolled her eyes, although she had a big smile to go with her expression. I responded similarly which made us both laugh; Loucie was far too caught up in her emotions to even notice. I looked back at all the colours flowing from the big bird's wings and then at the tantalising 'rivers' by the lake shore and somehow I began to connect so much of what Loucie had said. It was starting to make sense in a way but I could appreciate that what I had been able to gain an insight into was just the beginning of a process which would probably take me a very long time to fully understand; but at least it was a start.

What I also noticed was that as we progressed farther along our journey then each path became straighter, as did the shoreline, while I also realised that the lake was narrowing. At the same time our speed of flight felt as though it was increasing as did the light from the horizon. It also appeared that the two ranges of mountains were getting closer and the lake was becoming consequently less wide. As a result I was able to see more of the landscape on either side of the mountains which looked quite different to what I had been used to seeing. It did however have a very attractive quality to it while also having a kind of peaceful appeal which felt somehow familiar. I was just about to study things a little clearer when I heard Loucie whisper something to me.

"We're coming to the end of the lake now. This is where the stars get back together in the place of the magic kingdom. It's where the big bird lives and when he gets there he can go to sleep for a while and rest because he doesn't have to make any stars until the next time. My teacher says that it's where we all go and that it's the most beautiful place that you can ever imagine. It's a land of magic where all our dreams come true and we get to find our completeness but I don't really know what that means even though it really does sound nice. You have to watch now because this is where it all happens."

She squeezed my arm tightly and hung on while we both watched enthralled as the scenery passed by even quicker. The big bird began a gentle descent so that we were almost level with the tops of the mountains which gave me the idea that we were about to land on the lake. Being so close to a gradually narrowing mountain range certainly did give us all the impression of speed, even as the peaks seemingly closed in around us while the lake narrowed even more. Consequently the rivers of shimmering violet and electric blue grew more pronounced and noticeably much more energetic while coming closer together. The light from the horizon was getting ever brighter in the process where it was becoming almost too difficult to look directly at it. As the landscape passed by even faster then things started to become a blur while the lake became a small river and then a stream as the rivers of light alongside them were almost getting to the point of meeting.

The tension in the whole room was palpable as could be appreciated by the fact that no music could be heard any longer where everyone present had been thoroughly transfixed by what they were not only witnessing but experiencing as well. The big bird led us all into an adventure the like of which no one could have imagined but having come this far we all wanted to know what was about to happen next. Not a sound could be heard in the whole church as the wall of light drew us inexorably into its incredible magic.

To our collective surprise the light from the horizon came rushing at us where the immediate temptation was to cover our eyes but no one, not even the children could bring themselves to do it. We all watched in stunned fascination as the mountains seemed to be literally sucked into the blaze of intense light which was now filling the view ahead. With one final burst of speed, everything instantly merged where the waters disappeared as did the mountains while the 'fluid highways' finally met. I could feel Loucie gripping onto me very tightly at this point.

Just at the moment when the rivers of light began to spectacularly interweave themselves into one, then the big bird sped forward through the light and promptly vanished. Its disappearance was immediately followed by the most blinding flash of golden white light which had the effect of transforming the entire interior of the church as well as the atmosphere. The power of the soundless blast was so great that it swept through everyone present while seeming to pull us all into a completely different world. There had been absolutely no time to be analytical about what had just happened as there appeared to be no sense of time at all; just an intense peacefulness which had an incredibly welcoming familiarity to it. What came to me at the very same instant was that I became acutely aware of absolutely everyone in the room with me. It was as if we were all just one person having the same experience. Their thoughts were my thoughts, my feelings were their feelings and together we looked in awe at what was in front of us.

Framed in the bright light we could see a garden some way off in the distance. It was a simple setting, some would say almost humble, but an extremely pretty one. We were all there as one big family while enjoying the most perfect day which felt as though it would never end. We were cheerfully chatting with one another while there was nothing that we could possibly want for where music played all around us as the rippling sounds of small streams could be heard nearby.

We were happy, very happy indeed but more importantly, we were together. The feeling was indescribable but so wonderfully natural. The robed figure in the background looked on as he smiled at appreciating our togetherness while we shared our love between us and with him. We knew that he was always there and would ever be so; it could never be any different and never had been. Any other way of looking at it was just an illusion. How we were, is how it ever was and would always be. All else was just a game that we sometimes played. We were home. Home in love and light; and so it is.

Suddenly all was quiet again but within the silence there existed a definite 'presence' the like of which we had never known. It wasn't so much around us as it was everywhere all at once. The vision of the garden gently faded but the light remained, although within its intensity there came from the very presence of it a calling which felt so incredibly good. It seemed to reach out from a vast distance but at the very same instant it was so close that it touched us lovingly on the cheek. It gave me the impression of being very playful in spirit but at the same time I somehow had a wonderful awareness that all 'knowing' was contained within it.

There appeared to be such an indescribable joy in its intent where a gentle encouragement could be felt which held a promise of discovering something extremely precious. There was a language, but one which communicated solely with our heart and as it spoke the first words then once again we could see the two blazing flames in the wall. One was tinged with violet and the other with electric blue but in the intensity of their display we knew their true meaning at last. We closed our eyes to allow our heart to speak for us. Our breath of the present was the breath of the universe as well as the eternal flow of spirit. Everything existed in that very moment and all was at peace.

Journey's End - A Welcomed Resolution

Even though the blazing light lasted for only a fraction of a second, what happened for us all within that tiny splinter of time felt as though it had been an experience of timelessness itself. The absolutely superb vision which it afforded us all had persisted just long enough to allow us an understanding at a very deep level within the inner self; although my mind had no opportunity at all to attempt any kind of analysis. Everyone in the room had been deeply affected by this most incredibly moving encounter which felt so much like a glorious and much longed for homecoming. A returning to a sacred haven where only enduring happiness and love existed while eternity was an unknown concept in a world of such sublime qualities which exceeded even the most glowing of descriptions. The magnetic influence of the language which could only be heard in the heart of each individual brought with it a remembering of something very precious but long forgotten. Nothing within the tranquillity of this ineffably enchanting garden would tolerate anything but the most loving intent where a level of happiness existed whose attraction was absolutely irresistible.

This most precious place felt as though a profound yearning to return to it had been ever present and that this clarion call from its own heart could be heard in the 'stars' which were sent to guide us home. Loucie had been absolutely right, it was indeed pure magic and if there were such things as spells then this was most definitely one that I wanted to be influenced by for as long as I lived. I looked across to see her smiling while obviously wrapped up in her own thoughts but I really had no trouble at all in appreciating what was going on in her mind. But what came to me in that instant of understanding was also a kind of connection to her presence in a way that I hadn't been aware of before. I studied her young form while knowing that she was in the process of growing up but there was some other part of me which seemed to know that this was only really a physical thing. There existed another aspect of her which only needed to evolve and knew nothing of age at all. Even as I looked at her I could feel this subtle presence although nothing at all was visible in the way of being an identifiable part of her. I realised that I had never experienced this with anyone else in my life before but that it really must exist in each of us. There was something very comforting which came with this new awareness.

While becoming increasingly lost in the quite overwhelming sensations which I found myself immersed in, the light in front of us suddenly increased to the point where it was no longer possible to look directly at it. The flames from the jars also grew in intensity which made the wall of light feel like it was actually some kind of incredible living force which could have been as deep as the universe itself. The sensation of space and time which came from it was extremely moving at a level which allowed me to glimpse a depth to myself which I had not been aware of before that moment in time. It was a wonderful feeling and one which made it seem as though I felt lighter in spirit; almost like waking up from a really heavy sleep. At the very same instant of my appreciating this, there was the brightest of flashes which made me feel as though every atom of my body had been energised. In doing so it seemed to give me the most amazingly heightened sense of awareness. It was the most fascinating feeling.

With my eyes tightly closed I realised that I could still see something in front of me although it was tempting to open them again so as to confirm what it was. Before I had a chance to do this I quickly began to appreciate that I could once again see into the other church beyond the wall of light. In being able to do so then I immediately caught sight of the man and the woman framed by the arch of the doorway. They were starting to make their way along the aisle towards the altar and as they did so then it suddenly became clear to me who I had actually been looking at. This realisation caused something inside me to stir in a way which felt so incredibly wonderful. What I could see was myself and Janet walking together on our way to be joined in marriage. But what proved to be so moving about this whole vision was seeing the two beautiful flames which surrounded us as we walked arm in arm along the aisle.

These flames of radiant light were exactly the same as those that I had seen emanating from the two big glass jars but the ones around us were now merging into the most beautiful light that I had ever seen. There were so many more colours than I had ever thought possible to exist. Their thoroughly captivating beauty filled me up to overflowing with the same level of happiness that I had glimpsed within the heart of the brightly flashing light from the horizon on the landscape. I watched all that was happening while remembering how I had felt at that very special time when we had finally got together. However, now I could actually 'see' our happiness and so I completely understood why I had experienced it as being so incredibly good.

At the moment of this appreciation I also began to notice that each of the guests in the church had similar lights around them. They were fascinating to look at but I could see that theirs were subtly different in a way that made them unique to each particular person. At first I couldn't fully comprehend the significance of what I was seeing after witnessing what the big bird had been doing over the lake. Then I thought about how Loucie had explained it all and slowly I began to appreciate that there could be other lakes and other birds. I soon realised that everyone must have their own special place just like mine and that's how they travelled their pathways while being influenced by their own guiding twin flame energies; or stars as Loucie so delightfully put it.

Once again I looked at Janet and myself as we slowly made our way to the altar and for an instant time stood still for me while I remembered the emotions of that occasion so well. I could easily recall how so much seemed to be going through my mind at that stage of my journey. From how I could see things now though, it gave me a completely new appreciation of what was truly happening and how 'magical' it really was. Before I had time to start thinking about how my life would have turned out had I known then what I did at this moment, I noticed two more figures appearing in the doorway. They were dressed quite differently but both of them looked equally happy as they too made their way along the aisle. The man looked to be dressed in an old style military uniform while the lady was wearing a beautiful wedding dress that was very grand and had a long flowing train. While studying the couple I began to appreciate that the aisle which they were slowly progressing along looked as though it was an extension of the one that I was sitting beside and not part of the church on the other side of the light-filled wall. This seemed very odd at first but there was just too much else going on for me to pay that much attention to it.

No sooner had this newly arrived couple made their way along the aisle than they were followed by a group of four children. At the very same moment this little group made their appearance in the church entrance I felt an excited tug on my arm which was quickly followed by Loucie burying her head in my chest. I kind of glowed inside at appreciating that she seemed to be excited beyond measure. Even though I was aware that I still had my eyes closed, I could see things so clearly as well as feeling so much of the emotions which were coming to me from all that I was observing in the light.

With one final enthusiastic hug Loucie released her grip on me and then stood up from her seat. She looked absolutely radiant in her happiness as she walked across to the aisle by the side of us and then along it towards the couple and their four children. Everyone greeted her with a huge amount of affection where it was obvious to see that she was overjoyed to be with them. As they all made a fuss of her I felt my heart becoming so light as to be in imminent danger of taking flight in a more energetic way than I had seen the big bird doing. It was such a touching scene of reunion and one which I would love to have been able to capture somehow. I got the idea that it would be forever ingrained in my heart but nevertheless the visual image of it was something which seemed so special to me.

While being so engrossed in their displays of such heartfelt affection it was then that I noticed a very similar light around the man and the woman. The more I studied each of these very attractive lights then I could see that they appeared to match almost exactly that of myself and Janet while we were stood at the altar. I found this just as fascinating as it was perplexing but the more I focused my attention on the two pairs of flames then the more I realised that they really were the same; even down to the slight difference in colours between the male and female. I just had to give myself up to a moment of peacefulness so as to fully take in what I was seeing.

No sooner had I started to do this than I began recalling the time which I had spent in the quiet meadow. A very memorable occasion when I had been with a group of wonderfully wise men and women who were going over things with me from what seemed like a very long time ago. Out of everything I remembered them saying at that time something kept drifting into my mind about my family and what had happened, but I couldn't think of exactly what it was. Then I could see someone handing me a small child and how happy I was to hold her in my arms, but again I wasn't sure about why this was.

So much seemed to come racing into my recollections but just as I was about to get lost in a whole host of thoughts and memories, the couple and their children began to get closer. I watched them approaching me and was absolutely thrilled to see the huge smile on Loucie's lovely face. She looked as though she couldn't have been happier. When they were not far from where I was sitting, I suddenly became aware of a lot of movement behind me. I could see that the men in the aisle were standing to attention as the bride and groom approached. No sooner had they begun to do so than the wonderful music changed to something which I seemed to recognise and which was very stirring in a reminiscent kind of way. The couple passed by the first few men but in doing so each person's individual flame grew brighter as did those of everyone seated in the adjacent pews. It was so incredibly impressive to watch as their steady progress along the aisle brought every single person's individual flame to a new peak of expression. The effect on the interior of the church was absolutely electric where even the children were smiling with a kind of fascinated delight.

As the couple got nearer to the door then all the men began to follow them and slowly a larger and larger procession gradually formed up behind them which gracefully flowed out of the church. It looked to all the world as though there was some kind of spectacular midnight candlelit pageant taking place except that it wasn't night time. I watched enthralled by not only the spectacle of their departure but also the way in which I could see so many wonderful individual flames burning so brightly, just as did the candles all around us. The difference being that each persons flame radiated the kind of energy which spoke of life at its most promise-charged potential. In so being, the whole procession looked almost like it represented a future whose brightness could never be diminished no matter what circumstances may arise to challenge it.

Through appreciating this I also became aware that everyone seemed to be moving as though they had a much greater sense of harmony and connection with their own twin flame energies. It truly was unbelievably inspirational to watch. The combined light which their individual flames were producing felt to me as if it knew no boundaries where even the apparently solid walls of the church were responding to the electrifying effect. It certainly was one that I could appreciate the Divine nature of in how something so utterly incredible as this could have been created by an intellect quite beyond our comprehension.

The last to join in the lines of the slowly exiting people were the musicians who seemed to be drawing with them a kind of light that danced to their music. The harmony of their melodies blended in so well with everything about the atmosphere which surrounded the entire congregation who were, by now, making their way along a pathway which looked to be headed in a direction that I couldn't determine. I just sat listening to the sweet strains of the music which faded more with every passing second until it was just a faint murmur in the background.

Then, like a new presence in the little church, silence fell and once again I realised that I was alone. But my aloneness didn't appear to be of the type which I had experienced before, as somehow I could still feel so much of what I'd just encountered. If I concentrated enough then I was even able to feel Loucie's gentle touch while she hugged me so excitedly during our adventure together. Looking back into the other congregation I could see the wonderful sight of Janet and I being married and then feeling how proud and happy I was.

I couldn't help thinking that so much had happened to me on the pathways which I'd followed but in the final summation I had to admit that everything seemed to have gone by so incredibly quickly. Time appeared to be such a difficult commodity to grasp where only memories gave any hint of its possible existence. Whatever, I gave thanks for all that I had been allowed to experience on my journeys and I felt extremely grateful for those who I'd been privileged to share parts of it with. What a wonderful gift that had turned out to be. As I watched Janet and myself walking back out of the church beyond the wall, and all the guests following them out into the grounds beyond the entrance, I gazed at the doorway while seeming to recall so many happy times; and again I regarded myself as being tremendously blessed.

Gradually I began to appreciate that the light coming in through the doorway was changing and for a moment I felt sure that I could see a figure standing in it. He seemed to have his arms out while looking upwards but then he brought his hands together as though in prayer. Then he smiled broadly as he gradually disappeared. The last I was able to see of him were the hems of his robe and his sandal covered feet but what I could sense so strongly coming from him surely didn't go away; and I never wanted it to either. All I could do was to sit wrapped up in the stillness and the silence. No words were necessary as I just got lost in myself.

I have no idea how long it was that I remained seated with my eyes closed. There seemed to be so much flooding through my mind and my emotions in the quietness of the church interior that I felt as though time really didn't matter any more. There was so much to think about that I imagined there could never be enough time in all the world for me to go over so much of what I'd become aware of. Almost on tiptoe, a very gentle and thoroughly familiar voice crept into my highly emotional state while saying,

"When you're ready then maybe we can go to a place where things will become even clearer for you."

On hearing these words I opened my eyes and to my surprise there was no wall of living light in front of me any longer. Where it had always been there was the stone wall behind the altar where the big stained glass window looked down on me while the commanding figure of Jesus continued to pray and give thanks. Suddenly I seemed to have much more than a passing connection with his gesture as, once again, I found myself feeling overcome with a compelling need to express my own heartfelt gratitude for what I had been given the opportunity to experience.

As a consequence of this I could feel myself welling up with an overwhelming desire to simply throw my arms around someone while demonstrating my appreciation for all the joy which my awareness had brought me. I found it to be such an irresistibly strong sensation that I could hardly contain it. My companion shifted his position on the seat beside me so that he could place his hand on my shoulder. At the very instant I felt his touch then I instinctively grabbed for his hand in the manner of a drowning man catching hold of a lifeline. I have no idea why but I just wanted to burst into tears even though it seemed to be a totally irrational thing to do, given the way that I was feeling.

"It's just a release of pent up energies my friend. Don't be in the least bit concerned about letting it all go. It will be beneficial for you to give vent to this emotion as it will help you to consolidate all that you have seen and felt here at this time. Let yourself go with the flow of whatever it is that you feel drawn to do. This is the natural way of being which always brings with it a sense of peace that facilitates the greatest healing. This is where we must journey to next my wonderful friend and when you are ready we will set out on the final part of your adventure."

It was quite a while before I could answer him as, even before I had consciously decided to do as he suggested, my body appeared to be taking command. Things were getting more than a little wet as a miniature tide came rushing up through me and then cascaded gently down my cheeks. It was all extremely emotional to say the least but the release which I felt through doing it was something that I had not imagined possible. So many things from my past appeared to be shifting in a way which brought with it a sense of some much needed healing. I got the distinct impression that a whole host of negative emotions had simply evaporated in their doing so.

As this process unfolded, I was reminded of what my companion had once told me about forgiveness and how looking at the past in a different way could facilitate the bringing about of true healing; the essential balancing and readjustment which comes from deciding to remove judgement from what were once considered to be painful situations or experiences. Finally I had truly begun to see what it was that he had been trying to get me to understand at a level that would be helpful to me. Again I was filled with a sense of gratitude.

"Come my dear friend, it's our time to be setting out for an important destination."

I looked somewhat quizzically at him in that I didn't have any idea what he was talking about. No questions were necessary as he continued,

"You have experienced a great deal here on this occasion and you have begun to appreciate much that is of benefit to you. There is, however, something else that you must address which is very important for you to understand as well as being essential to your healing process. It concerns the latter part of your life and beyond. This is where we must look in order to become aware of what it was that surrounded those times and why so much happened in the way that it did.

First of all, before we do this, you must take advantage of our time en route to consider carefully the lessons that you have been privileged to learn in all

that has been revealed to you. What valuable insights you have gained here will serve you well for what is to come but for now we must make our way towards the very special place which awaits you. And so my courageous brother, let us see what new wonders are in store for us as we journey forward."

Slowly I got up from my seat and then turned to make my way into the aisle while believing that we must be going to leave by the front entrance of the church. No sooner had I stepped on the path to the doorway than I had to wipe away some remaining moisture from my eyes. Without thinking I hung onto the side of the pew to get my balance but to my surprise it felt cold and metallic, but what proved to be even more disturbing was that it also appeared to be swaying.

I quickly wiped away the last little tear as my mind began demanding to know what was happening but when I opened my eyes it just went completely blank. We were back on the boat and I was hanging onto the handrail beside the cabin but instead of the lake, which had been bordered by the high mountains, we seemed to be far out to sea. The view ahead looked to be one where we were approaching some kind of city but it was too distant for me to make out for sure.

"There is time enough to prepare yourself my wonderful brother but for now you must rest and partake of refreshments so that you can feel renewed and relaxed when we arrive. Take a seat while you reflect on all that you have learned thus far and then just enjoy the view as we make our steady progress to somewhere which I'm sure that you will find fascinating as much as it will be enlightening."

I needed no encouragement to sit down and I was certainly feeling more than a little hungry although I couldn't help but wonder where it was that we were headed and where in the world we were. I decided that it could be of little use to keep wondering about the unknown and, besides, there was so much to think about after what had happened to me. I trusted that all would become clear in time but, for the moment, a good rest and lots of nice food seemed to be a really good idea. In the meantime I would be happy to let our valiant little ocean-going steam-powered liner transport me across the flat calm surface of what looked to be a quite substantial expanse of golden sparkling water.

I glanced behind me to get some idea of where the horizon was but I had a difficult time trying to make it out as there appeared to be some kind of storm coming. I just hoped that we could make landfall before it caught up with us but, whatever happened, it looked as though I was in for another very eventful time. I closed my eyes and decided not to worry as there was far too much to think about.

Something nice to drink seemed to come rushing to the forefront of my mind when suddenly I had the overwhelming urge to saturate my taste buds with the delicious concoction that my companion had once given me in the big church. I remembered how wonderfully refreshing it had been at that time and how much I was in need of it again right at this very moment. All this emotional stuff had made me really, really thirsty but I can't tell you how grateful I was to be feeling this way. Let's just say that you absolutely have to find out for yourself! Trust me; you will!

THE
TIMELESS LOVE
OF
TWIN SOULS

— There is a Plan —

Trust Children to Always Tell the Truth

Teacher to 9 year old pupil:

"Winnie, name one important thing we have today that we didn't have ten years ago?"

Winnie's immediate answer:

"Me!"

- Chapter 23 -

What Does it Mean for Me? Suggestions and Plans

After having read all that you have about twin souls, and how we are so beneficially affected by this mysteriously compelling energy which is ever present within us, you may be wondering how you would go about finding your other half; your twin flame. Many people ask this question but it's one which has no straightforward answer in that all life is a complex dynamic, a unique process which unfolds in a way which is specific to each individual. Circumstances are different for everyone. However, there are things that you can do so as to gain a much better and deeper understanding of a way forward which will enable you to move closer towards your twin soul; or even recognise their existence in your life. If Ron's and my story has struck a chord within you which has left you feeling intrigued by the very idea of your own twin soul energy, and you really feel inspired to find out more about this fascinating aspect of yourself, then I have included this chapter to give you certain helpful tips and personal 'strategies' to practice. Hopefully you will find these very useful.

In your busy everyday life it's often difficult to find the time or even the inclination to do something other than to cope with all the pressures of modern day living. Your twin soul energy, as you will have no doubt gathered by now, is very powerful; but it's also illusively subtle unless you allow yourself the mental and emotional space in which to be aware of what it shows you. Being ever vigilant while listening out for the quiet messages which are always present, as well as cultivating an attitude of peaceful anticipation within yourself, is essential. Many spiritual teachers or gurus will encourage periods of quiet meditation so as to connect with your inner self in order to achieve this, but it's not always practical to do so. It certainly is a very beneficial thing in many respects to include in your life if you have the time and the space to practice this, but there are also other ways to help yourself. For me, meditation has been a way of life since as far back as I can remember and I would certainly encourage you to think about doing it in the near future; if you don't do it at present. So, to help you in the interim I have put together a simple but powerful twelve step plan which you can easily work into the daily routine of your busy life. If you follow my advice and put this into practice then you will be able to find your way into a greater awareness of what will guide you on towards your ultimate happiness.

Each step of my plan will only take up as much time as you are willing to allow them to but please remember that, as with all things in life, the more you practice then the greater will be the rewards. There are some steps which you may find that you can easily include in many different circumstances that you find yourself in; those where you are able to just focus your attention on your inner self for a few minutes or more. Even when you are doing something so mundane as standing in line at the supermarket checkout, you can still use that time to reflect on your own stuff instead of worrying about what will happen next. Many such opportunities exist for you to devote time to yourself. It's just a matter of appreciating that your needs are important and that it's more beneficial to practice a step of my plan instead of worrying about something which is out of your control. The only thing which you have control of in your life is your thoughts, words and deeds. To believe anything else is possible is simply buying into an illusion. If you want to change your world then first you must change yourself.

By just making a statement to yourself that you intend to change how your life is at present then you will have set yourself on the path towards finding out more about your twin flame and the true you in the process. The plan which I am offering you is one which you can choose as much or as little from and then apply it to your life as you feel it to be appropriate. In doing so then always be conscious of the fact that anything you do in this respect will be very valuable to you as just one small positive intention will start moving you in a much more beneficial direction. Also be aware that while reading these deceptively powerful steps then anything that you experience a noticeably negative reaction towards is an indication of something which you really do need to work on. Always trust your intuitive feelings while making sure to appreciate the difference between this aspect of yourself and your emotions; they are not the same!

Janet's '12 Step Plan' for Discovering Your Pathway to Greater Happiness

(Inspired by Ron)

#1 – Change who you think you are

The first thing I think of when I say how to change who you think you are is to also say, "and who others think you are". We are programmed from the beginning from ancestral beliefs to family members labelling who they believe you are. We all buy into this where it limits us in knowing who we really are. It produces the feeling of lack and fear. Look into your mirror and say – 'I am more than I see, or what others think they see or know about me'.

As you will have read, while Ron was being guided by his wise companion, this life we lead is one where the opinions and influences of others greatly impact our everyday lives. We make so many choices based on what others think of us or what they have conditioned us to believe about ourselves. In so doing we often fail to appreciate why we make the decisions to act in the way that we do or to say what we do. Whenever we make choices, while under the influence of others, then we are simply acting out other people's lives and the way they view the world; while denying our true selves in the process.

The realisation of exactly why we do something is the first step towards changing who we think we are, or more specifically, changing who we have been taught to believe that we are. No one knows you in the way that you do. However, since the time you were born you have been bombarded by the opinions of a great many influential people who think they know you better; as well as what's best for you. In order to find yourself again it's crucial that you begin to appreciate and accept your true nature. Finding yourself first will open up other doors which will eventually lead you on towards an even better and deeper understanding of many important aspects of the 'real' you.

Don't be afraid of finding this person who you consider in your times of greatest uncertainty that you might be. If I were to say to you "If I show you who I really am and you reject me then I have nothing else to offer" then how would you react? Would this be a statement that you could apply to yourself? Do you fear the prospect of revealing your true self to others in case you are considered unacceptable? If you do feel this way then it's a good indication of how much you allow the opinions of others to rule your life. This, I'm sure you will agree, needs to change. It takes courage to stand up while being your true self, but at the end of the day your feelings about yourself are much more important than those of others who are only ever crossing the course of your present journey. Walk your path with your head held high and be proud to be you! What's to be gained by doing otherwise?

#2 – Get lost in your thoughts

You may say I don't know how, or I don't even have the time to sit around while allowing myself to daydream, or taking time out in meditation. I say - No problem. Simply take advantage of your time when your mind is at ease and you are at 'one' with the task you are doing. You could be folding clothes, doing dishes, walking in the park, washing the car, gardening, decorating or anything that doesn't require your full attention like driving your car. In those special moments let your dream mind talk to you.

People often complain about being bored while doing something which is either repetitive or uninteresting. Try turning these times into an opportunity for yourself through benefiting from controlling your thoughts. Practice detachment by letting your mind focus lightly on what you are doing while also allowing the cares of the day to subside. When you find yourself fretting about what will happen next, or something that may possibly happen sometime in the future, then bring yourself fully into the moment while appreciating your 'presence' in the world. To be able to find your twin soul you must first have a lasting awareness of yourself. If you are unable to do this then it will be almost impossible for you to be conscious of, or alert to the presence of your other half.

Even the most boring task or the emptiest of times can be turned into an opportunity which will allow you to get in touch with yourself while cultivating the awareness of what makes you who you are. Don't just drift through life while letting the tide of events carry you on. Take control by first appreciating your circumstances and then asking if they reflect who you truly consider yourself to be. This is the first step to cultivating a sense of 'presence' as well as an important shift in the direction of your path towards finding your twin soul. This will naturally lead you into the next step.

#3 – Feel what's really right for you

When sitting in your favourite chair then settle in. What comes to mind when you do so, then let it go into your heart and sense how it feels. If it feels right then it's real. It's not about the physical; it's about your spirit and your heartfelt responses which are eternal and real. Open your heart to Love. God is in every act that comes from love; when the heart is peaceful about a decision then this means that it has ultimately come from love.

Be kind to yourself first and foremost. At first this can appear to be a deceptively simple statement and one which is very much misunderstood in the context of how important it is to show yourself the depth of love which you deserve. If you can't be loving of yourself then you will have difficulty in expressing love to others. Love is the natural language of the twin soul and, like learning any language, you just have to appreciate how to speak it while understanding what's said to you in return. Fortunately, unlike foreign languages, you already know the language of love but you have simply not practiced speaking it often enough as more important things demanded your attention as you grew up. You came into this world knowing full well how to communicate in this way, so all that you have to do now is to allow yourself to remember. The first step towards this is to feel what's right for you, which is actually your way of expressing love to yourself. Rehearse the phrases, practice them every day. Here's how to do it.

Whatever doesn't feel right to you then move away from it as quickly as you can. Not necessarily physically but in the way that you view things. Stop looking at anything which you don't like while focusing more firmly on the things that you do. Give up saying things which don't make you feel good and start saying things that do, while ignoring what others tell you about yourself in the process. This is allowing love to express itself and in so doing you will get to see the truly wonderful gift which is in your heart to share with not only yourself but everyone else around you.

#4 – Ask for guidance and take notes

As you are resting before drifting off to sleep for the night, ask to be shown in your dreams clues to who you really are. Keep a journal of your dreams. Over time they may well tell a story. It's beneficial to journal your negative and positive thoughts as well as all of your day to day activities. By doing this you will be aware of what underlies your thoughts and actions which in turn will lead you towards creating a freer and happier life.

Don't be afraid to ask for what you feel yourself to be most in need of. Life is a huge mystery the true nature of which is completely beyond the capability of any human mind to even remotely comprehend. There are very many things which are not understood but we have been given the ability to find our way through the 'maze' by asking for guidance. Use this gift wisely and as often as you can so that you will get more familiar with hearing the answers which will then move you ever closer to your ultimate happiness. The way in which the answers come to us are many and various while being of a nature that modern science has no concept of at all. We cannot know where anything comes from but we surely do know that it does come. You only have to be aware of your thoughts to confirm this. After all, where do thoughts come from in the first place? Do you think them or do they think you? It surely is an enigmatic conundrum which has given many a philosopher sleepless nights throughout each and every century that mankind has existed.

Our thoughts are important as they tell us so much about who we are, but just as with the language of love, we have to learn to listen while becoming aware of the hidden messages. I would encourage you to pay much more attention to what and how you think while using your journal to confide your innermost feelings and visions to. Keep this very private as to let others offer their opinions and interpretations is to dilute and distort the information which you discover. Your messages are created specifically for you; whether you believe this to be true or not. No one else will understand them in the same meaningful way as you do. Just remember that even if your mind can't often make sense of them, there is a part of you which always can. Trust this aspect of yourself while getting to know it better while you journal.

#5 – Make every effort to be at peace with yourself

When your heart is open then you will be able to more easily attract your twin soul's loving energy to you. If you are already together in some way then this circumstance will bring you a much better understanding that your love of each other is a part of the Father/Mother God creative energy.

Who is the best at beating you up; you or everyone else in your world? Who is the most critical of what you do or how you act or what you say, or anything else which is particular to you and how you express yourself. Remember the timeless wisdom which states - *What you Give out is What you Get Back*. If you are criticised then it's because you are critical of those around you and that's what you get back. This is like fighting a never ending battle where the constant attrition will eventually wear you down. Give it up! It's useless and a total waste of time.

So what if people or things around you are not how you'd wish them to be. Who cares! You are far more important, but specifically your attitude of mind is more important. While you are being critical of your surroundings (or judgemental – because that's what criticism is) or being critical of others in your life then you can't find the necessary state of being at peace with yourself. This is essential to you if you are to walk the path towards your ultimate happiness. Criticism is an energy which is directly opposed to that of love. You cannot be critical or negative in any way and express love at the same time. Only one energy can exist within your emotional state so it's up to you, your choice, as to which you express.

In every battle there has to be someone who eventually decides to quit. Looking back over the course of history then tell me what good has ever come of war? Was it all worth it? The same goes for you. Why fight? Even if it's just being negative about something (which is only your way of wanting to be right), give it up and be at peace with yourself. Give the world a chance to reflect its true beauty to you by allowing the peace of love to un-cloud your vision. Make the choice to look at life in a positive way while allowing it to reflect back to you what it wants you to see. Take a flower to the soldier while asking him to put down his gun. Let peace come to make a home in your heart and then shine the light which comes out of it onto everyone else. Some may not see it but that doesn't matter to you. Finally you will have heard the message which you are now sending out.

#6 – Set an Intention and then Stick to It

When looking for love you don't give up. You keep calling for it until you find it.

Living day to day is an effort in itself but what we set our intentions on while navigating our way in this world is very important. If you were to set out on a river journey then you'd be nuts to just drift aimlessly along with the current without at least having some sort of idea as to what you wanted to do along the way. Sometimes it's very beneficial just to go with the flow, but you didn't come into this world simply to float along with the tides until they carry you off across the eternal horizon into the land of happily-ever-after.

Your will is important and that's your gift from the Creator. We all have free will but how we use it is what determines whether we experience the placid lake or the rapids; or anywhere in between. Choosing to find love is a statement of intent which you make, but one which is not like a letter to Santa at Christmas. You don't get given love through being a good person; you are already showered with more love than you can ever hope to appreciate. By setting the intention to find it then you hold firmly to an agreement that you wish to recognise it not only in someone else but in yourself as well. Make a commitment to do this and then stick to it each and every day. Write a note to yourself to this effect. You'll never fail to get a reply and it's the best Christmas present you will ever have.

#7 – Value yourself (you're worth it)

Don't ever settle for less love than you deserve. This you do through experiencing the pain which your soul is constantly bringing from your past so that it's always present in your life. This state of being totally confuses your creative energy. Ask yourself "would I want to spend eternity with this person or in this situation?" If you have any doubts at all then set your intention to change things as quickly as possible and then move on.

We learn through pain just as we do through experiencing joy and happiness. Pain is the feeling we get by removing ourselves so far away from the state of being joyful (filled with joy to the exclusion of every other emotion) that we erect our last line of defence. Pain is our reminder that we have lost our way while wandering into the forest and getting drawn ever deeper into the darkness. Pain stops us falling into the ravine and being consumed by oblivion. We take notice of pain but very rarely do we listen to the important message which it brings us. While reading about Ron's journey to the restaurant, where he first met me, you may have got the impression that I just happened to have been there for some time while waiting patiently for him to suddenly appear in my life. In actual fact my journey to this restaurant was just as inspired as his, but when I eventually made the move to take the job it was literally a few heartbeats before he showed up. At that time in my life I was deeply caught up in figuring out a way to patch up my ailing marriage; which certainly was causing me a good deal of emotional pain.

This very difficult situation motivated me to do something positive. Although, I had no real idea about why I chose to leave a job and environment that I enjoyed so much just to go somewhere completely different where I initially felt so out of place. My reasoning and thoughts, at that precarious stage of my life, were that my new job would allow me the opportunity to spend a lot more time with my husband and my children. This, I prayed in my darkest of moments, would hopefully help me turn things around in a home life which I felt thoroughly dissatisfied with. I also had a strong sense that I deserved far better and I very much wanted the same for my children.

My nurturing instincts seemed to be providing me with an extra level of determination which made me want to create a more loving environment for them to grow up in. Needless to say I had reached a very unhappy and fraught point on my journey, but I really thought that my dilemma was all to do with my marital situation and nothing else. Little did I know that something subtly powerful was gradually moving me in a direction which I needed to go. Thankfully I had the presence of mind to pay attention to those urgings which then helped me make a very reluctant decision to leave a company of wonderful people who were all like family to me. At that time I remember that there was a part of me which kept telling me that it seemed like a totally crazy thing to do, but I was desperate to make a positive change in my situation.

So, one fateful day, I threw caution to the wind and began working at a restaurant which I had no idea sat right in the middle of the crossroads to a happiness that I'd so longed for. I never dreamed for one second that there was someone walking along his pathway to meet me and that something would happen, very soon after I started, which would change my life forever. But some part of me must have known this or been aware of what I needed to do otherwise I would never have left somewhere that I at least got to enjoy a certain degree of happiness while working there. After all, that was what I felt I wanted, so why would I have decided to move away from the one place which provided me with it when there seemed to be so little else going for me at that time? There had to be something which was strong enough to prize me away from that little oasis in an otherwise barren landscape of joy.

When I look back on the circumstances which surrounded my change of employment I can see now how things conspired so cleverly to put me directly in Ron's path while ensuring that he would find me. I remember so well how easily I could have chosen differently where one single change in what I felt that I needed to do would have meant me missing my other half at that point in time. I may well have met him another way at a later date but the situation of the restaurant provided us with the perfect setting which then allowed us the space to quickly get to know each other; given the way things were for both of us at that stage of our journey.

The important thing which comes to me now is that I remember feeling so strongly that I deserved better. Undoubtedly it was my acute anguish which initially got my attention but as a result of its presence I began listening to that quiet voice which then guided me forward; even though my choices seemed to be at odds with what I longed for. All I knew at that point on my pathway was that I just wanted to be much happier than I was then; and that life must have more to offer me in this respect. So I made my choices from listening to my heart and then following where it led me, the result of which was unbelievably more than I could have ever hoped for in my wildest of dreams.

You deserve to be happy too. It's your natural state of being but life allows us to experience other states of existence so that we can explore all of what being human has to offer. While you feel pain then you shut out the possibility of appreciating love. When learning lessons there is little advantage in protracting them as nothing of any value can be gained by not getting the message quickly. The answer will be nonetheless meaningful by living a life of lingering pain and suffering; but what do you think that this will achieve? If you pick up something which is hot then you put it down again and move away from it, so why not do the same thing in your life when it comes to the subject of pain and suffering. You choose not to be burned because you reason that you're not worthy of being treated in this way, so why not do the same thing with other aspects of your life. Be happy while giving unconditional love to yourself. You're worth it, but you need to make a conscious choice to do this as its no one else's responsibility but yours. Make this choice now, this very moment and stick to it!

#8 – Be aware that you are never alone

If your twin soul is presently in another dimension, not being in the physical with you in this incarnation or they have passed over, you can still reach them. Your twin flame energies are never truly separated in the way in which we view earthly separation. Twin souls transcend time and space while being eternal. As your awareness of your true self becomes more fully developed then your concept of time will change. As it does then it will become *easier to appreciate that 'aloneness' is simply a state of mind which you can choose to see differently.*

Aloneness is an illusion, albeit one which we perpetuate in order to learn more about ourselves. Through experiencing our feelings of isolation and being lost or abandoned we make choices which result in consequences. While dealing with all the emotional fallout which inevitably comes from this creative process we get to see what it is that we want and what we reject. In so doing we find our true self. It's like the sculptor who keeps chipping away at the rock while the form is revealed. Michelangelo once said that all he was doing was removing the surplus marble in order to get at the figure which he could already see inside.

We are no different except that we choose to extract ourselves from the rough hewn material which were sent here to fashion. This we do by the process of using our emotions as tools to chip away at what confines us until we are eventually freed. Escaping from our 'cell' in the process is one of the achievements which always gives us great pleasure. There's nothing like a good escape to stir the soul; go to watch any adventure movie so as to verify this assertion. We just love to see the good guy rescue the damsel in distress but really it's only a reflection of our deep seated need to rescue ourselves.

Good news! There's no need. You are already rescued and your twin soul is right there with you to share in the celebrations, so why not give them a big hug! On many occasions when I go to sleep, or I'm enjoying my dance classes, I feel Ron's presence so strongly that he takes me right out of the body. The freedom which I experience on these wonderful occasions is amazing as he lifts me up like Superman and whisks me off into the ether so that we can dance together in the clouds. Even though I appreciate that he is not here with me in the physical any more, I know without question that he is never truly apart from me; twin soul energies know nothing of distance.

We are eternally together in our energies and, at those precious times when he takes me 'flying', then I can see past the veil of this three dimensional existence and into the world which is our true home. The level of happiness that I am able to feel when I am with him, and the lightness of spirit which I experience, lifts my heart into a connection with a higher power that allows me a glimpse of the twin flame source. Always trust, like me, that you never ever walk this earthly pathway alone. In your quiet times allow yourself to let that special connective energy touch your heart while listening to what it guides you towards an appreciation of. Let your spirit soar like I do while trusting to a process which your mind has no concept of whatsoever.

#9 – Share yourself while always showing kindness

Keep your heart open for those around you also. Your love for others is also felt by your twin soul.

When you speak or act in love then you are also speaking to your twin soul. It doesn't matter whether they are with you on the physical plane or not, they can still 'hear' you. Speaking love is not just about saying the words but sincerely feeling that love at the deepest level within you. Light travels at 186 thousand miles per second but the speed of love is very much faster. It travels huge distances in an instant where absolutely nothing gets in its way while everything is affected by it.

At its circumference the earth is roughly 40,000 miles so if your twin soul is located somewhere on the planet they will feel your love the very same instant that you express it. This will be your way of influencing their compass needle in the same manner that they will influence yours. Even in the midst of a huge crowd, your twin soul will recognise the love which you give out. It will be your unique beacon which will be unmistakable to your other half and will be visible even if they are on the other side of the galaxy. Keep this beacon burning brightly so as to give your other half a constant star to steer by, just as they will be doing for you. Distance is no obstacle to the energy of love.

#10 – Accentuate the positive, eliminate the negative

Stay in joy, peace, and harmony. Negativity in you extends itself to your other half. To find the love you are looking for you must first find it in yourself. You have to know who you are before you can recognise your other half.

After following these steps, or even a few of them, you will be getting into the frame of mind which will be guiding your footsteps onto a different path. You will already be aware of when negative energies either affect you or are being created by you. Moving away from these is always beneficial. Always! Nothing is ever to be gained by remaining in or near them. Your ability to discriminate one from the other, while being conscious of their presence, will enable you to 'see' much more clearly. You will not be able to easily find your twin soul if you constantly bury their light in the darkness of negative emotions, thoughts, or deeds; whether they be of your own making or anyone else's.

Make a point of choosing to walk in peace and harmony every day of your life from now on. Even if you're not completely successful then just the intention of doing it will make the changes which you need. It doesn't matter where you start either. If you want to clear out your house then you can pick any room as eventually you will have done all that you needed to while making the necessary changes along the way. Always remember to throw away, or give away, what's not needed any longer so that new and more beneficial things can come to you. If you are to find your twin soul then there needs to be space in your life and your heart to accommodate them. Staying positive as much as humanly possible is a great way to achieve this. Or would you rather be miserable and stay locked up in the darkness? Hhhmmmm, it's what I've heard people aptly refer to as 'no-brainer'. Wouldn't you agree?

#11 – Be faithful to yourself

Work your way back as much as possible to the real you. The way it was in the garden of Eden before we were separated from our knowledge of the oneness with God and each other. This was before we judged each other.

As you put into practice what you have come to appreciate here then you will inevitably be drawn to an understanding of just how important you are to yourself. Words of timeless wisdom come out of the past to encourage you to make a sincere promise to yourself – *To Thine Own Self be True*. First and foremost you must, and I mean 'must', honour and respect yourself while being faithful to who you have come to appreciate yourself to be. Stand firmly in your truth while not allowing the opinions or judgements of others to undermine your new found sense of self.

You are a sovereign being who has been blessed with the gift of free choice where you can change the way in which you perceive things at any given stage on your journey. As this voyage of discovery leads you ever more into areas of yourself which you find increasingly pleasing then cultivate demonstrating the courage of your convictions by expressing who you consider yourself to be. Don't strive to achieve this by judging others or making yourself right through making others wrong. Simply state who you are at any appropriate opportunity while celebrating the fact that you have found the way into the deepest inner recesses of your wonderful heart. Then always be faithful to it. In this way you are actually being faithful to your twin soul as well.

#12 – Resist feeling separate

The more you tap into the oneness the more light you send out to your twin soul, others, and to God.

From all that you have read thus far, I hope now that you appreciate, or are at least willing to acknowledge, that you are most certainly not alone. You are in actuality One with everything there is but in your quiet times, or whenever you have a moment to get lost in yourself and your thoughts, then allow yourself to really feel the closeness of your twin flame. That energy is always waiting for you to acknowledge it, no matter where your other half may be in this world or the universe. Make a determined effort to move beyond the limitations of your mind which only ever sees everything in terms of physicality; individualness and apartness. You must be aware by now that to view things in this way is far too limited and only serves to restrict you in your quest to find your ultimate happiness; it does this through severely limiting your horizons. Expand your ability to achieve your intentions while fulfilling your dreams by letting yourself feel the intimate closeness of your other half. The very act of moving towards this awareness will take you ever closer to the point of achieving your greatest joy while banishing all thoughts of separation from that which you feel so abandoned by.

Move as quickly as you can beyond the conditioning of your mind which only wants to influence your emotions while in doing so it creates unfulfilling dramas that eventually you tire of. They achieve absolutely nothing while simply delaying your entry into the garden. Go play in the pasture. Why wait? There are many wonderful things to be discovered when you do. Be happy, be loved but most importantly of all remember to love yourself first.

With much love from me to you

- Janet -